Programmed Guide

to accompany

Calculus With Analytic Geometry

by Earl W. Swokowski

SECOND EDITION

ROY A. DOBYNS
Carson-Newman College

 Prindle, Weber & Schmidt
Boston, Massachusetts

Table
of
Contents

Introduction

This programmed guide is to be used in conjunction with the first ten chapters of *Calculus With Analytic Geometry,* Second Edition, by Earl W. Swokowski (Prindle, Weber & Schmidt, 1979). The emphasis throughout is on mastery of manipulative techniques. After the presentation of an idea, there is a question with several possible answers given. Select an answer and then go on to the frame associated with it. After you have selected a correct answer, go on to the next question. Starting in Section 5.5 (The Fundamental Theorem of Calculus), and continuing in certain later sections, a problem presented in one frame is followed by a detailed solution.

When you are using the guide you should have the text available for reference, and paper and pencil for working problems or taking notes. If you are asked a question that involves computation, do the work required before you select your answer. You might be able to select a correct answer by guessing, but this will not increase your understanding of the material. Read each frame to which you turn *completely* before going on to the next.

At the end of each chapter there are two tests, a review test and a sample test. Complete solutions are provided at the end of the book for the review tests, as well as answers for the sample tests. After completing a chapter, work through the review test and compare your solutions with those provided. This should help you to know if there are topics that you need to review. Once you feel you know the material, complete the sample test and check your answers.

CHAPTER 1

Prerequisites
for
Calculus

1.1 REAL NUMBERS

OBJECTIVES

You should know the definition of order, the properties of order, the notion of absolute value, and how to find the distance between two points on a coordinate line. You should also know how to solve inequalities and be able to express the solution in terms of intervals.

Q1 A brief description of the real numbers is presented on pages 1 and 2 of the text. Study the definitions of order and the four important rules concerning the symbols $>$ and $<$ presented on page 2 of the text.

If $x > 2$ and $2 > 1$, which one of the following is true?

$2 > x$ Frame **A** $1 > x$ Frame **B** $x > 1$ Frame **C**

A **YOUR ANSWER:** $2 > x$.
We are given $x > 2$; therefore, we cannot also have $2 > x$. Return to frame **Q1**, study the four rules, and then try again.

B **YOUR ANSWER:** $1 > x$.
Don't you have 1 and x reversed? From rule 1, we have if $a > b$ and $b > c$, then $a > c$. Now what follows from $x > 2$ and $2 > 1$? Return to frame **Q1** and select the correct answer.

C **YOUR ANSWER:** $x > 1$.
Right. From rule 1, we have if $a > b$ and $b > c$, then $a > c$. Therefore, if $x > 2$ and $2 > 1$, then $x > 1$.

Q2 The second rule says that if $a > b$, then $a + c > b + c$. This simply says that we can add the same real number to both sides of an inequality and the order of the inequality will remain the same.

Which one of the following is an example of this property of order?

If $4 > 2$, then $4 + (-1) > 2 + (-1)$.   Frame **A**
$5 > 2$, $5 = 2$, or $5 < 2$ Frame **B**
If $7 > 3$ and $3 > 1$, then $7 > 1$.   Frame **C**

A **YOUR ANSWER:** If $4 > 2$, then $4 + (-1) > 2 + (-1)$.

Right. Rule 2 says that we can add any real number to both sides of an inequality and not change the order of the inequality. In our case, we have added -1 to both sides of $4 > 2$. Therefore, if $4 > 2$, then $4 + (-1) > 2 + (-1)$ or $3 > 1$.

B **YOUR ANSWER:** $5 > 2$, $5 = 2$, or $5 < 2$.

No. This is an example of the property which says that for any two real numbers, say 5 and 2, one and only one of the following is true: $5 > 2$, $5 = 2$, or $5 < 2$. Now return to frame **Q2** and select an example of rule 2.

C **YOUR ANSWER:** If $7 > 3$ and $3 > 1$, then $7 > 1$.

No. This is an example of rule 1. Now return to frame **Q2** and select an example of rule 2.

Q3 Which one of the following is an example of rule 3, which states that if $a > b$ and $c > 0$, then $ac > bc$? (Notice $c > 0$ means that c is positive.)

If $5 > 3$, then $15 > 9$.	Frame **A**
If $6 > 3$, then $4 > 1$.	Frame **B**
If $4 > 1$, then $-8 > -2$.	Frame **C**

A **YOUR ANSWER:** If $5 > 3$, then $15 > 9$.

You are correct. If $5 > 3$, then $5 \cdot 3 > 3 \cdot 3$ or $15 > 9$. Remember, if we multiply both sides of an inequality by the same positive real number, the order of the inequality is not changed.

B **YOUR ANSWER:** If $6 > 3$, then $4 > 1$.

Look again. This is an example of rule 2 which says that if $a > b$, then $a + c > b + c$. In your answer, if $6 > 3$, then $6 + (-2) > 3 + (-2)$ or $4 > 1$. Return to frame **Q3**, study rule 3, and select the correct answer.

C **YOUR ANSWER:** If $4 > 1$, then $-8 > -2$.

What you have done here is not correct. You multiplied both sides of the inequality by the negative number -2. If you multiply both sides of an inequality by a negative number, then by rule 4 the order of the inequality is reversed. Now return to frame **Q3** and try again.

Q4 Now, which one of the following is an example of rule 4? Rule 4 says that if $a > b$ and $c < 0$, then $ac < bc$. That is, if we multiply both sides of an inequality by the same negative real number, then the order of the inequality is reversed.

If $2 > 1$, then $4 > 3$.	Frame **A**
If $6 > 3$, then $-2 < -1$.	Frame **B**
If $-2 > -3$, then $-4 > -6$.	Frame **C**

A **YOUR ANSWER:** If $2 > 1$, then $4 > 3$.

No. This is an example of rule 2 which says that if $a > b$, then $a + c > b + c$. In our case, if $2 > 1$, then $2 + 2 > 1 + 2$ or $4 > 3$. Return to frame **Q4** and try again.

B **YOUR ANSWER:** If $6 > 3$, then $-2 < -1$.

You are exactly right. Since $-1/3$ is negative, and $6 > 3$, then $6(-1/3) < 3(-1/3)$ or

$-2 < -1$ by rule 4. Remember, multiplying both sides of an inequality by the same negative number reverses the order of the inequality.

C   YOUR ANSWER: If $-2 > -3$, then $-4 > -6$.
No. This is an example of rule 3. You have simply multiplied both sides of the inequality $-2 > -3$ by the positive number 2. Now return to frame **Q4** and try again.

Q5   As a review of some of the other notions of inequalities, which one of the following expressions indicates that the real number a is between the real numbers $-1/3$ and π?

$\pi < a < -1/3$	Frame **A**
$-1/3 < a < \pi$	Frame **B**
$-1/3 < \pi$	Frame **C**

A   YOUR ANSWER: $\pi < a < -1/3$.
Don't you have the inequality reversed? The real number $-1/3$ is less than the real number π which is approximately 3.14. Return to frame **Q5** and select the correct answer.

B   YOUR ANSWER: $-1/3 < a < \pi$.
Certainly. The real number $-1/3$ is less than the real number π which is approximately 3.14. Therefore, if a is between $-1/3$ and π, we write $-1/3 < a < \pi$.

C   YOUR ANSWER: $-1/3 < \pi$.
This is true, but how do we express the fact that a is between $-1/3$ and π? Return to frame **Q5** and try again.

Q6   We can associate the set of real numbers with the points on a straight line l in such a way that for each real number x there corresponds one and only one point and, conversely, for each point P of l there corresponds precisely one real number. A method for accomplishing this is discussed on page 2 of the text. The number corresponding to a given point is called the *coordinate* of the point. Points will be designated by capital letters and their coordinates by small letters.
What is the coordinate of point P?

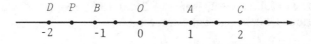

$-3/2$ Frame **A** $-1/2$ Frame **B** $3/2$ Frame **C**

A   YOUR ANSWER: $-3/2$.
Of course. The point P is midway between the points with coordinates -1 and -2; therefore, its coordinate is $-3/2$.

B   YOUR ANSWER: $-1/2$.
Be careful. Isn't the point P more than one unit distance to the left of the origin O? Now return to frame **Q6** and select the correct coordinate.

C **YOUR ANSWER:** 3/2.
No. The arrowhead indicates the positive direction. Notice that P is on the opposite side of the origin O from the positive direction. This indicates that the coordinate of P is negative. Return to frame **Q6** and try again.

Q7 Now let us investigate the notion of absolute value. The absolute value of x, denoted by $|x|$, indicates its size or magnitude without regard to its sign. For example, $|5| = 5$ or $|-5| = 5$.
What is $|-1/4|$?

1/4	Frame **A**	$-1/4$	Frame **B**	4	Frame **C**

A **YOUR ANSWER:** 1/4.
Right. $|-1/4| = 1/4$.

B **YOUR ANSWER:** $-1/4$.
Remember, the absolute value of a number indicates its size without regard to its sign. You have taken the sign into consideration. Return to frame **Q7** and select the correct answer.

C **YOUR ANSWER:** 4.
Where did you get 4? The absolute value of a number indicates its size without regard to its sign. For example, $|-2/3| = 2/3$. Now return to frame **Q7** and try again.

Q8 The following is a more formal definition for the *absolute value* of a real number:
$$|a| = \begin{cases} a \text{ if } a \geqslant 0; \\ -a \text{ if } a < 0. \end{cases}$$
This simply says that $|a|$ is a if a is positive or zero and $-a$ if a is negative. For example, $|-2| = 2$ because $-2 < 0$ and $|-2| = -(-2) = 2$.
What is $|x - 2|$ if $x < 2$?

$2 - x$	Frame **A**	$x - 2$	Frame **B**	2	Frame **C**

A **YOUR ANSWER:** $2 - x$.
You are correct. If $x < 2$, then $x - 2 < 0$; therefore, $|x - 2| = -(x - 2) = 2 - x$.

B **YOUR ANSWER:** $x - 2$.
Be careful. If $x < 2$, then $x - 2 < 0$; therefore, $|x - 2| = -(x - 2)$. Now return to frame **Q8** and select the correct answer.

C **YOUR ANSWER:** 2.
You are off base. If $x < 2$, then $x - 2 < 0$; therefore, $|x - 2| = -(x - 2)$. Now return to frame **Q8** and select the correct answer.

Q9 Let a and b be the coordinates of two points A and B, respectively, on a coordinate line l, and let AB denote the line segment from A to B. The length $d(A, B)$ of AB is defined by $d(A, B) = |b - a|$. The use of this definition is illustrated in Example 2 on page 4 of the text.
If A and B have coordinates -3 and 6, respectively, what is $d(A, B)$? That is,

what is the length of the segment AB?

   3   Frame **A** -9 Frame **B**   9   Frame **C**

A   **YOUR ANSWER:** 3.
Watch out. The coordinates of A and B are -3 and 6, respectively; therefore, $d(A, B) = |b - a| = |6 - (-3)|$. Now return to frame **Q9** and select the correct answer.

B   **YOUR ANSWER:** -9.
Be careful. Since $d(A, B) = |b - a|$, $d(A, B)$ cannot be negative. The coordinates of A and B are -3 and 6, respectively; therefore, $d(A, B) = |b - a| = |6 - (-3)|$. Now return to frame **Q9** and select the correct answer.

C   **YOUR ANSWER:** 9.
Correct. Since the coordinates of A and B are -3 and 6, respectively, $d(A, B) = |b - a| = |6 - (-3)| = |9| = 9$.

Q10   The notion of a *set* is basic in mathematics. A set is thought of as a collection of objects of some type—for example, the set of students in a college or the set of states in the United States. We will use capital letters to denote sets and lower-case letters to represent elements of sets. The symbol $a \in S$ denotes that a is an element of set S. The symbol $a \notin S$ denotes that a is not an element of set S.

   If A represents the set of states in the United States and b represents California, which one of the following is the correct notation?

   $b \notin A$ Frame **A** $b \in A$ Frame **B** $B \in a$ Frame **C**

A   **YOUR ANSWER:** $b \notin A$.
No. The symbol $b \notin A$ means that b is not an element of set A. Since A represents the set of states in the United States and b represents the state of California, isn't b an element of set A? How is this represented? Return to frame **Q10** and select the correct answer.

B   **YOUR ANSWER:** $b \in A$.
Right. If b represents California and A represents the set of states in the United States, then $b \in A$.

C   **YOUR ANSWER:** $B \in a$.
Don't you have the use of the capital letter and the lower-case letter reversed? We shall denote sets by capital letters and elements of a set by lower-case letters. Now return to frame **Q10** and try again.

Q11   If every element of a set A is also an element of a set B, then A is called a *subset* of B and is denoted by $A \subseteq B$. The symbol $A \nsubseteq B$ means that A is not a subset of B. We say that $A = B$ if and only if they have precisely the same elements.

   If $A = \{1, 3, 5\}$ and $B = \{1, 2, 3, 4, 5\}$, which one of the following is correct?

   $A \subseteq B$ Frame **A**
   $B \subseteq A$ Frame **B**
   $A = B$ Frame **C**

A **YOUR ANSWER:** $A \subseteq B$.
Certainly. Since $A = \{1, 3, 5\}$ and $B = \{1, 2, 3, 4, 5\}$, $A \subseteq B$. Every element of A is an element of B.

B **YOUR ANSWER:** $B \subseteq A$.
Don't you have this backwards? If $A = \{1, 3, 5\}$ and $B = \{1, 2, 3, 4, 5\}$, then $B \not\subseteq A$. Every element of B is not an element of A. For example, $2 \in B$, but $2 \notin A$. Return to frame **Q11** and try again.

C **YOUR ANSWER:** $A = B$.
No. We say that $A = B$ if and only if they contain precisely the same elements. Now since $A = \{1, 3, 5\}$ and $B = \{1, 2, 3, 4, 5\}$, they don't contain the same elements. Return to frame **Q11** and try again.

Q12 If the elements of a set S have a certain property, then we write $S = \{x: ...\}$ where the property describing the arbitrary element x is stated in the space after the colon. This is described on page 5 of the text.
     Which one of the following is a member of $A = \{x: x$ is one of the first five letters of the English alphabet$\}$?

a Frame **A** g Frame **B** x Frame **C**

A **YOUR ANSWER:** a.
You are correct. The letter a is one of the first five letters of the English alphabet. Therefore, $a \in A$ where $A = \{x: x$ is one of the first five letters of the English alphabet$\}$.

B **YOUR ANSWER:** g.
Watch out. The letter g is not one of the first five letters of the English alphabet. Therefore, $g \notin A$ where $A = \{x: x$ is one of the first five letters of the English alphabet$\}$. Now return to frame **Q12** and select the correct answer.

C **YOUR ANSWER:** x.
Wrong. You are confusing the x in the expression $\{x: x$ is one of the first five letters of the English alphabet$\}$ with an element of the set. The x in the expression is simply a symbol representing any object with the desired property. As a letter in the English alphabet, x is not one of the first five letters. Therefore, x does not belong to the set. Return to frame **Q12** and try again.

Q13 The *empty set* denoted by $\varnothing$ is the set that contains no elements. If A is any set, then $\varnothing \subseteq A$. That is, the empty set is a subset of every set.
     As a review, if $A = \{a, b, c\}$, $B = \{a, b, x, y\}$, and $C = \{a, b\}$, which one of the following groups has an error in it?

$\varnothing \subseteq A$ $C \subseteq B$
$a \in A$ Frame **A** $\{b\} \in B$ Frame **B**
$C \subseteq A$ $x \notin A$

$\{x, y\} \subseteq B$
$y \notin C$ Frame **C**
$c \in A$

A   YOUR ANSWER: $\emptyset \subseteq A$
$a \in A$
$C \subseteq A.$

All of these are correct. $A = \{a, b, c\}$ and $C = \{a, b\}$. The statement $\emptyset \subseteq A$ is correct because $\emptyset$ is a subset of every set. Since a is a member of set A, we have $a \in A$. Every element of C is an element of A; therefore, $C \subseteq A$. Now return to frame **Q13** and select the group that contains an error.

B   YOUR ANSWER: $C \subseteq B$
$\{b\} \in B$
$x \notin A.$

Right. One of these is incorrect.

C   YOUR ANSWER: $\{x, y\} \subseteq B$
$y \notin C$
$c \in A.$

All of these are correct. $A = \{a, b, c\}$, $B = \{a, b, x, y\}$, and $C = \{a, b\}$. Since x and y are elements of B, we have $\{x, y\} \subseteq B$. Since y is not an element of C, we have $y \notin C$ and since c is an element of A, we write $c \in A$. Now return to frame **Q13** and select the group that contains an error.

Q14 $A = \{a, b, c\}$, $B = \{a, b, x, y\}$, and $C = \{a, b\}$. Which one is incorrect?

   $C \subseteq B$ Frame **A** $\{b\} \in B$ Frame **B** $x \notin A$ Frame **C**

A   YOUR ANSWER: $C \subseteq B.$
There is nothing wrong with this. $B = \{a, b, x, y\}$ and $C = \{a, b\}$. Since every element of C is an element of B, we write $C \subseteq B$. Return to frame **Q14** and select the one that is incorrect.

B   YOUR ANSWER: $\{b\} \in B.$
Right. The notation here is wrong. The symbol $\in$ is used to denote that an element is a member of a set. The symbol $\{b\}$ denotes a set consisting of the single element b. Since b is an element of set B, we should write $b \in B$ or $\{b\} \subseteq B$.

C   YOUR ANSWER: $x \notin A.$
There is nothing wrong with this. $A = \{a, b, c\}$. Since x is not an element of A, we write $x \notin A$. Return to frame **Q14** and select the one that is incorrect.

Q15   Let us now state two definitions that have to do with combining sets.

   The *union* of two sets S and T, denoted by $S \cup T$, is the set $\{x: x \in S$ or $x \in T\}$.

   The *intersection* of two sets S and T, denoted by $S \cap T$, is the set $\{x: x \in S$ and $x \in T\}$.

These definitions are on page 5 of the text.

   If $X = \{1, 3, 5, 7\}$, $Y = \{2, 4, 6, 8\}$, and $Z = \{1, 2, 3\}$, which one of the following is $X \cup Z$?

   $\{1, 3\}$ Frame **A**
   $\{1, 3, 5, 7\}$ Frame **B**
   $\{1, 2, 3, 5, 7\}$ Frame **C**

A   **YOUR ANSWER:** {1, 3}.

Don't you have the intersection instead of the union of the two sets? $S \cup T = \{x: x \in S$ or $x \in T\}$. Return to frame **Q15** and try again.

B   **YOUR ANSWER:** {1, 3, 5, 7}.

Sorry, but you left out an element. $X = \{1, 3, 5, 7\}$ and $Z = \{1, 2, 3\}$. $X \cup Z = \{x: x \in X$ or $x \in Z\}$. Now return to frame **Q15** and select $X \cup Z$.

C   **YOUR ANSWER:** {1, 2, 3, 5, 7}.

Correct. $X = \{1, 3, 5, 7\}$, $Y = \{2, 4, 6, 8\}$, and $Z = \{1, 2, 3\}$. Therefore, $X \cup Z = \{1, 2, 3, 5, 7\}$ because 1, 2, 3, 5, and 7 belong to X or to Z or to both.

Q16 $X = \{1, 3, 5, 7\}$, $Y = \{2, 4, 6, 8\}$, $Z = \{1, 2, 3\}$, and we found $X \cup Z = \{1, 2, 3, 5, 7\}$. Now which one of the following is $(X \cup Z) \cap Y$?

     {2}   Frame **A**
     {1, 2, 3, 4, 5, 6, 7, 8}   Frame **B**
     {1, 3, 5, 7}   Frame **C**

A   **YOUR ANSWER:** {2}.

Of course. We know that $X \cup Z = \{1, 2, 3, 5, 7\}$ and $Y = \{2, 4, 6, 8\}$. Therefore, $(X \cup Z) \cap Y = \{2\}$ because 2 is the only element that belongs to $X \cup Z$ and to Y.

B   **YOUR ANSWER:** {1, 2, 3, 4, 5, 6, 7, 8}.

No. You found $(X \cup Z) \cup Y$. We want $(X \cup Z) \cap Y$. We know that $X \cup Z = \{1, 2, 3, 5, 7\}$ and $Y = \{2, 4, 6, 8\}$. Now what is $(X \cup Z) \cap Y$? Return to frame **Q16** and select the correct answer.

C   **YOUR ANSWER:** {1, 3, 5, 7}.

You are off base. We know that $X \cup Z = \{1, 2, 3, 5, 7\}$ and $Y = \{2, 4, 6, 8\}$, and we want $(X \cup Z) \cap Y$. $(X \cup Z) \cap Y = \{x: x \in (X \cup Z)$ and $x \in Y\}$. Now return to frame **Q16** and select the correct answer.

Q17   In our work, we will be working with subsets of real numbers called intervals. A notation for describing intervals and their graphs is presented on pages 5 and 6 of the text.

     Which one of the following intervals is the set of points with coordinates satisfying the inequality $2 \leqslant x < 15$?

     (2, 15)   Frame **A**   [2, 15)   Frame **B**   [2, 15]   Frame **C**

A   **YOUR ANSWER:** (2, 15).

Be careful. The left parenthesis indicates that 2 does not belong to the set. We want the set of points with coordinates satisfying the inequality $2 \leqslant x < 15$, which does include the real number 2, but not 15. Return to frame **Q17** and select the correct answer.

B   **YOUR ANSWER:** [2, 15).

Right. The set of points with coordinates satisfying the inequality $2 \leqslant x < 15$ is denoted by [2, 15). The left bracket indicates that 2 belongs to the set, and the right parenthesis indicates that 15 does not belong to the set. A sketch of the graph of the interval is as follows:

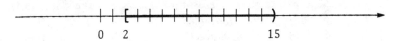

0   2   15

C   YOUR ANSWER: [2, 15].
Be careful. The brackets indicate that 2 and 15 belong to the set. We want the set of points with coordinates satisfying the inequality $2 \leqslant x < 15$, which does not include the real number 15, but does include 2. Return to frame **Q17** and select the correct answer.

Q18   Which one of the following sets is the interval $(-1, 8)$?

The set of points with coordinates satisfying the inequality $-1 \leqslant x \leqslant 8$.   **Frame A**

The set of points with coordinates satisfying the inequality $-1 < x < 8$.   **Frame B**

The set of points with coordinates satisfying the inequality $-1 < x \leqslant 8$.   **Frame C**

A   YOUR ANSWER: The set of points with coordinates satisfying the inequality $-1 \leqslant x \leqslant 8$.

Watch out. We use a bracket to indicate that the endpoint of the interval is included. Return to frame **Q18,** study the notation for intervals, and then select the correct answer.

B   YOUR ANSWER: The set of points with coordinates satisfying the inequality $-1 < x < 8$.

You are correct. The set of points with coordinates satisfying the inequality $-1 < x < 8$ is denoted by $(-1, 8)$.

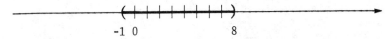

-1 0   8

C   YOUR ANSWER: The set of points with coordinates satisfying the inequality $-1 < x \leqslant 8$.

Watch out. We use a bracket to indicate that the endpoint of the interval is included. Return to frame **Q18,** study the notations for intervals, and then select the correct answer.

Q19   A statement of the form $p < q$ (or $p > q$), where p and q are algebraic expressions in a variable x, is called an inequality. If a true statement is obtained when x is replaced by a real number y, then y is called a solution of the inequality. To solve an inequality means to find all solutions. We say that two inequalities are equivalent if they have exactly the same solutions. As with equations, one method of solving an inequality is to replace it with a chain of equivalent inequalities for which the solutions of the last one are obvious. The following operations on inequalities will result in an equivalent inequality:

1. Adding the same expression to both sides of an inequality does not change the solutions.
2. Multiplying both sides of an inequality by the same positive expression does not change the solutions.
3. Multiplying both sides of an inequality by the same negative expression reverses the order of the inequality, but does not change the solutions.

Example 3 on page 7 of the text illustrates this technique.

Solve the inequality $5x + 4 > 7x - 10$.

$x < 7$ Frame **A** $x < 6$ Frame **B** $x > 7$ Frame **C**

A   **YOUR ANSWER:** $x < 7$.

You are correct.

$5x + 4 > 7x - 10$
$-2x > -14$ adding $-7x - 4$ to both expressions
$x < 7$ multiplying by $-1/2$

The solutions are the numbers in the interval $(-\infty, 7)$ and the graph is as follows:

B   **YOUR ANSWER:** $x < 6$.

Your calculations are off. Return to frame **Q19** and try again.

C   **YOUR ANSWER:** $x > 7$.

No. If you multiply by a negative real number, then the inequality is reversed.

$5x + 4 > 7x - 10$
$-2x > -14$ adding $-7x - 4$ to both expressions
$x < 7$ multiplying by $-1/2$

After thinking about this, return to frame **Q19** and select the correct answer.

Q20   Suppose we want to find the set of points with coordinates satisfying an inequality like $-4 \leqslant 3x + 7 \leqslant 3$. In order to find the solutions, we can work with both inequalities at the same time. For example,

$-4 \leqslant 3x + 7 \leqslant 3$
$-11 \leqslant 3x \leqslant -4$ by adding -7
$-11/3 \leqslant x \leqslant -4/3$ by multiplying by $1/3$

Therefore, the set of points with coordinates satisfying $-4 \leqslant 3x + 7 \leqslant 3$ is the interval $[-11/3, -4/3]$.

Find the set of points with coordinates satisfying $2 \leqslant 5 - 2x < 10$.

$[-3/2, 5/2)$ Frame **A**
$(-5/2, 3/2]$ Frame **B**
$[3/2, -5/2)$ Frame **C**

A   **YOUR ANSWER:** $[-3/2, 5/2)$.

Be careful with the signs. Return to frame **Q20,** carry out the calculations again, and then select the correct answer.

B   YOUR ANSWER: $(-5/2, 3/2]$.
Very good.

$$2 \leqslant 5 - 2x < 10$$
$$-3 \leqslant -2x < 5 \qquad \text{by adding } -5$$
$$3/2 \geqslant x < -5/2 \qquad \text{by multiplying by } -1/2 \text{ which reverses the order of the inequality}$$

The inequality $3/2 \geqslant x < -5/2$ is equivalent to $-5/2 < x \leqslant 3/2$, which is the interval $(-5/2, 3/2]$.

C   YOUR ANSWER: $[3/2, -5/2)$.
Watch out. The set $[3/2, -5/2)$ has no meaning because $3/2 > -5/2$. In an interval, the coordinate of the left endpoint must be less than the coordinate of the right endpoint. Let's take a look at the problem.

$$2 \leqslant 5 - 2x < 10$$
$$-3 \leqslant -2x < 5 \qquad \text{by adding } -5$$
$$3/2 \geqslant x > -5/2 \qquad \text{by multiplying by } -1/2 \text{ which reverses the order of the inequality}$$

The inequality $3/2 \geqslant x > -5/2$ is equivalent to $-5/2 < x \leqslant 3/2$. Think about this and then return to frame **Q20** and try again.

Q21   Suppose we want the solutions of the inequality $x^2 - 5x + 6 > 0$. Factoring the second-degree expression, we have $(x - 2)(x - 3) > 0$. Now $(x - 2)(x - 3) > 0$ means that $(x - 2)(x - 3)$ must be positive. The product of two factors is positive if both factors are positive or both factors are negative. In which interval are both of these factors positive?

   $(2, 3)$ Frame **A** $(3, \infty)$ Frame **B**

A   YOUR ANSWER: $(2, 3)$.
No. We want the interval where $x - 2 > 0$ and $x - 3 > 0$. The factor $x - 3$ is not positive in the interval $(2, 3)$. Now return to frame **Q21** and try again.

B   YOUR ANSWER: $(3, \infty)$.
Good. This is the set of numbers for which $x - 2$ and $x - 3$ are both positive. If $x - 2 > 0$, then $x > 2$; therefore, the factor $x - 2$ is positive in the interval $(2, \infty)$. If $x - 3 > 0$, then $x > 3$; therefore, the factor $x - 3$ is positive in the interval $(3, \infty)$. Now they are both positive in the interval $(3, \infty)$.

Q22   In order to find the solutions of $(x - 2)(x - 3) > 0$, we also need to include those numbers for which $x - 2 < 0$ and $x - 3 < 0$. What are these numbers?

   $(-\infty, 2)$ Frame **A** $(2, 3)$ Frame **B** $(2, \infty)$ Frame **C**

A   YOUR ANSWER: $(-\infty, 2)$.
Right. This is the interval for which $x - 2$ and $x - 3$ are both negative. If $x - 2 < 0$, then $x < 2$ and the factor $x - 2$ is negative in the interval $(-\infty, 2)$. If $x - 3 < 0$, then $x < 3$ and the factor $x - 3$ is negative in the interval $(-\infty, 3)$. Now both factors are negative in $(-\infty, 2)$ which is $(-\infty, 2) \cap (-\infty, 3)$.

We have already found that $(3, \infty)$ is the interval for which $x - 2$ and $x - 3$ are both positive. Therefore, the solutions of $(x - 2)(x - 3) > 0$ are the numbers in $(-\infty, 2) \cup (3, \infty)$.

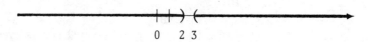

B   YOUR ANSWER: (2, 3).
No. We want the interval where both factors are negative. The factor $x - 2$ is not negative in the interval $(2, 3)$. Now return to frame **Q22** and try again.

C   YOUR ANSWER: $(2, \infty)$.
No. We want the interval where both factors are negative. The factor $x - 2$ is not negative in the interval $(2, \infty)$. Now return to frame **Q22** and try again.

Q23   Sometimes we need to solve inequalities containing absolute values. If d is a positive real number and p is an algebraic expression, then the inequality $|p| < d$ is equivalent to $-d < p < d$. Similarly, $|p| \leqslant d$ is equivalent to $-d \leqslant p \leqslant d$. For example, $|x + 1| \leqslant 2$ is equivalent to $-2 \leqslant x + 1 \leqslant 2$.

Using the above result, which one of the following is the solution of $|2x + 5| < 7$?

$(-6, 1)$	Frame **A**
$(-1, 6)$	Frame **B**
I don't know.	Frame **C**

A   YOUR ANSWER: $(-6, 1)$.
Right. The numbers satisfying $|2x + 5| < 7$ are the same as the numbers satisfying $-7 < 2x + 5 < 7$.

$$-7 < 2x + 5 < 7$$
$$-12 < 2x < 2 \qquad \text{adding} -5$$
$$-6 < x < 1 \qquad \text{multiplying by } 1/2$$

B   YOUR ANSWER: $(-1, 6)$.
You made a mistake in your calculations. The set of numbers satisfying $|2x + 5| < 7$ is the same as the set of numbers satisfying $-7 < 2x + 5 < 7$. Return to frame **Q23** and try again.

C   YOUR ANSWER: I don't know.
Let's try another example. Suppose we want the set of numbers satisfying $|x - 1| < 3$. The set of numbers satisfying $|x - 1| < 3$ is the same as the set of numbers satisfying $-3 < x - 1 < 3$.

$$-3 < x - 1 < 3$$
$$-2 < x \qquad < 4 \qquad \text{adding 1}$$

Therefore, the set of numbers satisfying $|x - 1| < 3$ is the interval $(-2, 4)$. Now return to frame **Q23** and try again.

Q24   Another important result involving absolute values and inequalities is the following. If d is a positive real number and if p is an algebraic expression in a variable x, then the solutions of $|p| > d$ consist of the solutions of $p > d$ and $p < -d$.
    Using this result, find the solutions of $|3x - 5| > 2$.

$(1, 7/3)$	Frame **A**
$(-\infty, 1) \cup (7/3, \infty)$	Frame **B**
$(7/3, \infty)$	Frame **C**

A   **YOUR ANSWER:** $(1, 7/3)$.
    Don't you have the solutions of $|3x - 5| < 2$ instead of $|3x - 5| > 2$? The solutions of $|3x - 5| > 2$ consist of the solutions of $3x - 5 > 2$ and $3x - 5 < -2$. Return to frame **Q24** and try again.

B   **YOUR ANSWER:** $(-\infty, 1) \cup (7/3, \infty)$.
    Very good. The solutions of $|3x - 5| > 2$ consist of the solutions of $3x - 5 > 2$ and $3x - 5 < -2$.

$3x - 5 > 2$	$3x - 5 < -2$
$3x > 7$	$3x < 3$
$x > 7/3$	$x < 1$

The solutions of $3x - 5 > 2$ are the real numbers in the interval $(7/3, \infty)$ and the solutions of $3x - 5 < -2$ are the real numbers in the interval $(-\infty, 1)$. Therefore, the solutions of $|3x - 5| > 2$ are the real numbers in the interval $(-\infty, 1) \cup (7/3, \infty)$.

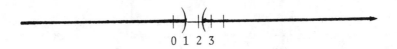

C   **YOUR ANSWER:** $(7/3, \infty)$.
    Almost, but you neglected part of the solutions. The solutions of $|3x - 5| > 2$ are the solutions of $3x - 5 > 2$ and $3x - 5 < -2$. You only have the solutions of $3x - 5 > 2$. Return to frame **Q24,** complete the problem, and select the correct answer.

1.2   COORDINATE SYSTEMS IN TWO DIMENSIONS

OBJECTIVES

You should be familiar with the rectangular coordinate system and how to find the coordinates of points in the plane. You should know the distance formula and the midpoint formula and how to use them in practical situations. You should also know how to sketch the graphs of certain types of equations.

Q25   Coordinate systems can also be introduced in planes. The *rectangular coordinate system* is discussed on page 10 of the text.
    Which one of the following points has coordinates $(-2, 3)$?

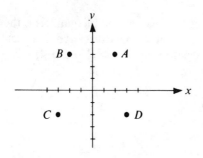

A	Frame **A**
B	Frame **B**
C	Frame **C**
D	Frame **D**

A   YOUR ANSWER: *A*.

Sorry, but *A* is in quadrant I and thus both the *x*-coordinate and the *y*-coordinate are positive. The coordinates of *A* are (2, 3). Return to frame **Q25,** locate the point with coordinates (− 2, 3), and select the correct answer.

B   YOUR ANSWER: *B*.

Right. Since the *x*-coordinate is − 2, we know that the point is 2 units to the left of the *y*-axis. Since the *y*-coordinate is 3, we know that the point is 3 units above the *x*-axis. Therefore, the point with coordinates (− 2, 3) is *B*.

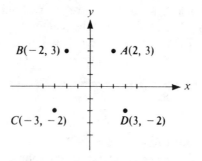

C   YOUR ANSWER: *C*.

Sorry, but *C* is in quadrant III and thus both the *x*-coordinate and the *y*-coordinate are negative. The coordinates of *C* are (− 3, − 2). Return to frame **Q25,** locate the point with coordinates (− 2, 3), and select the correct answer.

D   YOUR ANSWER: *D*.

Sorry, but *D* is in quadrant IV and thus the *x*-coordinate is positive and the *y*-coordinate is negative. The coordinates of *D* are (3, − 2). Return to frame **Q25,** locate the point with coordinates (− 2, 3), and select the correct answer.

Q26   Where in the coordinate plane are the points for which $y = -2$?

Two units to the left of the *y*-axis.	Frame **A**
Two units below the *x*-axis.	Frame **B**
On the *x*-axis.	Frame **C**
I don't know.	Frame **D**

A   YOUR ANSWER: Two units to the left of the *y*-axis.

No. The points two units to the left of the *y*-axis have an *x*-coordinate of − 2. The points for which $y = -2$ have a y-coordinate of -2. Now return to frame **Q26** and try again.

B   YOUR ANSWER: Two units below the x-axis.
Good. The points for which $y = -2$ are the points two units below the x-axis.

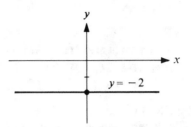

C   YOUR ANSWER: On the x-axis.
You are off base. The points on the x-axis have a y-coordinate of 0. Now return to frame **Q26** and try again.

D   YOUR ANSWER: I don't know.
The points for which $y = -2$ all have a y-coordinate of -2. Where are the points with a y-coordinate of -2? Return to frame **Q26** and describe their location.

Q27   Describe the points for which $x > 0$ and $y > 0$.

The set of points on the x-axis and y-axis.	Frame **A**
The set of points in the first quadrant.	Frame **B**
The set of points in the first or third quadrant.	Frame **C**

A   YOUR ANSWER: The set of points on the x-axis and y-axis.
The points on the x-axis have a y-coordinate of 0. The points on the y-axis have an x-coordinate of 0. We want the set of points for which the x and y-coordinates are both positive. Return to frame **Q27,** think about this, and then try again.

B   YOUR ANSWER: The set of points in the first quadrant.
You are correct. The graph of the set of points for which $x > 0$ and $y > 0$ is shown in the figure below.

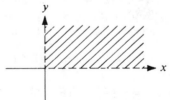

The dashes on the axes indicate that the points on the axes do not belong to the graph.

C   YOUR ANSWER: The set of points in the first or third quadrant.
We want the set of points for which both coordinates are positive. The point with coordinates $(-2, -5)$ is in the third quadrant, but the coordinates are not positive. Return to frame **Q27,** think about this, and then try again.

Q28   For all points $P_1(x_1, y_1)$ and $P_2(x_2, y_2)$ in a coordinate plane,

$$d(P_1, P_2) = \sqrt{(x_2 - x_1)^2 + (y_2 - y_1)^2}.$$

This is called the distance formula and is proved on page 12 of the text.
   Using this formula, what is the distance between $A(1, -5)$ and $B(-2, 6)$?

   $\sqrt{130}$ Frame **A** $\sqrt{2}$ Frame **B** $\sqrt{10}$ Frame **C**

A   **YOUR ANSWER:** $\sqrt{130}$.
   Certainly. The two points are $A(1, -5)$ and $B(-2, 6)$. Therefore,

$$\begin{aligned} d(A, B) &= \sqrt{(-2 - 1)^2 + (6 - (-5))^2} \\ &= \sqrt{(-3)^2 + 11^2} = \sqrt{9 + 121} = \sqrt{130}. \end{aligned}$$

B   **YOUR ANSWER:** $\sqrt{2}$.
   Be careful. The distance between $P_1(x_1, y_1)$ and $P_2(x_2, y_2)$ is

$$\sqrt{(x_2 - x_1)^2 + (y_2 - y_1)^2}.$$

You want the square root of the sum of the squares of the difference of the x-coordinates and y-coordinates of the given points. The two points are $A(1, -5)$ and $B(-2, 6)$. Therefore,

$$d(A, B) = \sqrt{(-2 - 1)^2 + (6 - (-5))^2}.$$

Now return to frame **Q28** and try again.

C   **YOUR ANSWER:** $\sqrt{10}$.
   Be careful. The distance between $P_1(x_1, y_1)$ and $P_2(x_2, y_2)$ is

$$\sqrt{(x_2 - x_1)^2 + (y_2 - y_1)^2}.$$

You want the square root of the sum of the squares of the difference of the x-coordinates and y-coordinates of the given points. The two points are $A(1, -5)$ and $B(-2, 6)$. Therefore,

$$d(A, B) = \sqrt{(-2 - 1)^2 + (6 - (-5))^2}.$$

Now return to frame **Q28** and try again.

Q29   Which one of the following triangles is isosceles? (A, B, and C are the vertices of the triangle.)

   $A(1, 3), B(-1, 4), C(2, 6)$ Frame **A**
   $A(-1, 3), B(3, 0), C(6, 4)$ Frame **B**
   What is an isosceles triangle?   Frame **C**

A   **YOUR ANSWER:** $A(1, 3), B(-1, 4), C(2, 6)$.
   Watch out.

$$\begin{aligned} d(A, B) &= \sqrt{(-1 - 1)^2 + (4 + 3)^2} = \sqrt{4 + 1} = \sqrt{5} \\ d(A, C) &= \sqrt{(2 - 1)^2 + (6 - 3)^2} = \sqrt{1 + 9} = \sqrt{10} \\ d(B, C) &= \sqrt{(2 - (-1)^2 + (6 - 4)^2} = \sqrt{9 + 4} = \sqrt{13} \end{aligned}$$

Since two sides are not equal, the triangle is not isosceles. Return to frame **Q29** and select the correct answer.

B   **YOUR ANSWER:** $A(-1, 3), B(3, 0), C(6, 4)$.
   Of course.

$$\begin{aligned} d(A, B) &= \sqrt{(3 - (-1))^2 + (0 - 3)^2} = \sqrt{16 + 9} = \sqrt{25} = 5 \\ d(B, C) &= \sqrt{(6 - 3)^2 + (4 - 0)^2} = \sqrt{9 + 16} = \sqrt{25} = 5 \end{aligned}$$

Since two sides are equal, the triangle is isosceles.

C   YOUR ANSWER: What is an isosceles triangle?
An isosceles triangle is a triangle with two equal sides. Return to frame **Q29**, calculate the length of the sides of the given triangle, and select the isosceles triangle.

Q30   The midpoint of the line segment from $P_1(x_1, y_1)$ to $P_2(x_2, y_2)$ is

$$\left(\frac{x_1 + x_2}{2} \, , \, \frac{y_1 + y_2}{2} \right) .$$

What is the midpoint of the line segment from $A(2, -5)$ to $B(6, 3)$?
$(8, -2)$ Frame **A**
$(4, 1)$ Frame **B**
$(4, -1)$ Frame **C**

A   YOUR ANSWER: $(8, -2)$.
You forgot to divide by 2. Return to **Q30**, study the midpoint formula, and try again.

B   YOUR ANSWER: $(4, 1)$.
Sorry, but you missed a sign. Be careful when you add a positive and a negative number. Return to frame **Q30** and try again.

C   YOUR ANSWER: $(4, -1)$.
Of course. The midpoint of the line segment from $A(2, -5)$ to $B(6, 3)$ is

$$\left(\frac{6 + 2}{2} \, , \, \frac{-5 + 3}{2} \right) = (4, -1).$$

Q31   Show that the distance between $A(8, 1)$ and the midpoint of the line joining $B(-2, -2)$ and $C(11, -9)$ is one-half the distance between B and C. How did it go?
Great   Frame **A**
Terrible   Frame **B**

A   YOUR ANSWER: Great.
Very good. The midpoint of the line joining $B(-2, -2)$ and $C(11, -9)$ is

$$\left(\frac{-2 + 11}{2} \, , \, \frac{-2 - 9}{2} \right) = (9/2, -11/2).$$

The distance between $A(8, 1)$ and the midpoint of the line joining B and C is
$$\sqrt{(8 - 9/2)^2 + (1 - (-11/2))^2} = \sqrt{(7/2)^2 + (13/2)^2}$$
$$= \sqrt{218/4}$$
$$= \sqrt{218}/2.$$

The distance between $B(-2, -2)$ and $C(11, -9)$ is
$$\sqrt{(11 - (-2))^2 + (-9 - (-2))^2} = \sqrt{(13)^2 + (-7)^2}$$
$$= \sqrt{218}.$$

Therefore, the distance between A and the midpoint of the line joining B and C is one-half the distance between B and C.

B   YOUR ANSWER: Terrible.
Nothing is that bad. The midpoint of the line joining $B(-2, -2)$ and $C(11, -9)$ is

$$\left(\frac{-2 + 11}{2} , \frac{-2 - 9}{2} \right) = (9/2, -11/2).$$

Now use the distance formula to find the distance between A and the midpoint and the distance between B and C. Complete the computations and then return to frame **Q31** and select the other alternative.

Q32   If W is a set of ordered pairs of real numbers, then the *graph* of W is defined as the set of all points in a coordinate plane which correspond to the ordered pairs in W.
    Can you find the graph of $W = \{(x, y): x \geqslant 0, |y| \leqslant 2\}$?

    Yes   Frame **A**   No   Frame **B**

A   YOUR ANSWER: Yes.
Very good. The graph of $W = \{(x, y): x \geqslant 0, |y| \leqslant 2\}$ is the set of points whose coordinates satisfy $x \geqslant 0$ and $|y| \leqslant 2$. Therefore, the graph of W is the shaded region below:

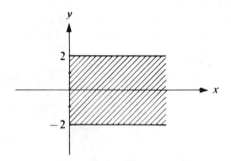

B   YOUR ANSWER: No.
Let's see if we can get you started. The graph of $W = \{(x, y): x \geqslant 0, |y| \leqslant 2\}$ is the set of points corresponding to ordered pairs of real numbers (x, y) such that $x \geqslant 0$ and $|y| \leqslant 2$. Won't these points have to be to the right of the y-axis in order to satisfy $x \geqslant 0$? Now where will these points have to be in order that the y-coordinate satisfies $|y| \leqslant 2$? Return to frame **Q32**, think about this, and then try again.

Q33   In order to sketch the graph of an equation in two variables, we plot a few points whose coordinates are solutions of the equation, and then draw a smooth curve through appropriate points. The graph of a linear equation, like the equation $y = 2x + 2$, is a straight line. Therefore, in order to sketch the graph, it is sufficient to plot two points.
    Which one of the following is the graph of $y = 2x + 2$?

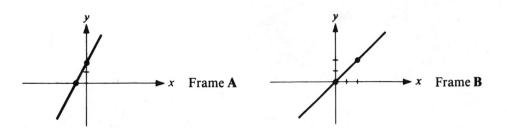

Frame A   Frame **B**

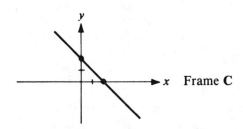

Frame C

A   YOUR ANSWER:

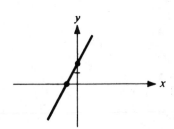

Right. Notice that the points with coordinates $(-1, 0)$ and $(0, 2)$ are on the graph. These are the points where the graph intersects the x- and y-axes and are usually the easiest to find.

B   YOUR ANSWER:

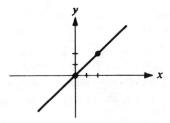

No. The graph of $y = 2x + 2$ is the graph of the solutions of $y = 2x + 2$. Your graph contains the point with coordinates $(0, 0)$, but $(0, 0)$ is not a solution of $y = 2x + 2$. Find two solutions, plot the corresponding points, and join the two points with a straight line. Now return to frame **Q33** and select the correct answer.

C   **YOUR ANSWER:**

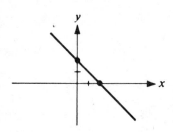

No. The graph of $y = 2x + 2$ is the graph of the solutions of $y = 2x + 2$. Your graph contains the point with coordinates $(2, 0)$, but $(2, 0)$ is not a solution of $y = 2x + 2$. Find two solutions, plot the corresponding points, and join the two points with a straight line. Now return to frame **Q33** and select the correct answer.

Q34   Sketch the graph of the equation $y = x^2 - x$. Were you successful?

     Yes   Frame **A**   No   Frame **B**

A   **YOUR ANSWER:**   Yes.

Very good. A few ordered pairs which are solutions of $y = x^2 - x$ are given in the table below. Plotting the corresponding points, we obtain the graph.

x	-2	-1	0	1	2
y	6	2	0	0	2

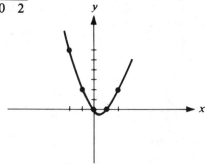

B   **YOUR ANSWER:**   No.

In order to sketch the graph of $y = x^2 - x$, we want to plot a few points whose coordinates are solutions, until some pattern emerges, and then draw a smooth curve through appropriate points. A few ordered pairs which are solutions of $y = x^2 - x$ are given in the table below.

x	-2	-1	0	1	2
y	6	2	0	0	2

Plot the corresponding points and hence approximate the graph. Now return to frame **Q34** and select the other alternative.

Q35   An equation of a line parallel to the y-axis is of the form $x = a$ because all of the points on a line parallel to the y-axis have the same x-coordinate. Similarly, an equation of a line parallel to the x-axis is of the form $y = b$ because all of the points on a line parallel to the x-axis have the same y-coordinate.

What is the equation of a line parallel to the x-axis and passing through the point $P(2, -3)$?

$y = -3$ Frame **A** $x = 2$ Frame **B** $y = 2$ Frame **C**

A   **YOUR ANSWER:** $y = -3$.
Certainly. Since all the points on a line parallel to the x-axis have the same y-coordinate, and the line must pass through $P(2, -3)$, we have $y = -3$.

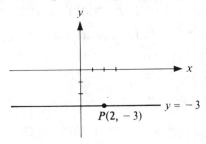

B   **YOUR ANSWER:** $x = 2$.
No. You have the equation of a line such that all of the points have an x-coordinate of 2. Doesn't that make the line parallel to the y-axis? Think about this and then return to frame **Q35** and try again.

C   **YOUR ANSWER:** $y = 2$.
Be careful. A line passing through the point $P(2, -3)$ and parallel to the x-axis cannot have any points with y-coordinate equal to 2. Return to frame **Q35** and try again.

Q36   The equation $(x - h)^2 + (y - k)^2 = r^2$ is an equation of a curve called a circle. The point with coordinates (h, k) is the center and r $(r > 0)$ is the radius. This is discussed on page 17 of the text.
   Which one of the following is the equation of a circle with center at the point with coordinates $(2, 1)$ and radius 3?

$(x - 2)^2 + (y - 1)^2 = 3$ Frame **A**
$(x - 2)^2 + (y - 1)^2 = 9$ Frame **B**
I don't know.   Frame **C**

A   **YOUR ANSWER:** $(x - 2)^2 + (y - 1)^2 = 3$.
You are wrong. The equation of a circle with center having coordinates (h, k) and radius r is $(x - h)^2 + (y - k)^2 = r^2$. You forgot to square the radius, didn't you? Return to frame **Q36** and select the correct answer.

B   **YOUR ANSWER:** $(x - 2)^2 + (y - 1)^2 = 9$.
You are correct. The equation for a circle with center having coordinates (h, k) and radius r is $(x - h)^2 + (y - k)^2 = r^2$. Since we want the equation of the circle with center having coordinates $(2, 1)$ and radius 3, we have $(x - 2)^2 + (y - 1)^2 = 9$.

C   **YOUR ANSWER:** I don't know.
The equation of a circle with center having coordinates (h, k) and radius r is $(x - h)^2 + (y - k)^2 = r^2$. Now in our problem, the center has coordinates $(2, 1)$ and the radius is 3. After substituting these values in the equation for a circle, return to frame **Q36** and select the correct answer.

Q37 Find the equation of a circle with center $C(-1, 3)$ and passing through $P(1, 2)$. (*Hint*: The radius is $d(C, P)$.) How did it go?

　　　Good　　　Frame **A**　　　Bad　　　Frame **B**

A　**YOUR ANSWER:**　Good.

That's great. The circle with center $C(-1, 3)$ and passing through $P(1, 2)$ has radius $r = d(C, P)$.

$$r = d(C, P) = \sqrt{(-1 - 1)^2 + (3 - 2)^2} = \sqrt{(-2)^2 + 1^2} = \sqrt{5}.$$

Therefore, the equation of the desired circle is

$$(x - (-1))^2 + (y - 3)^2 = (\sqrt{5})^2 \text{ or } (x + 1)^2 + (y - 3)^2 = 5.$$

B　**YOUR ANSWER:**　Bad.

We want the equation of a circle with center $C(-1, 3)$ and passing through $P(1, 2)$. Therefore,

$$r = d(C, P) = \sqrt{(-1 - 1)^2 + (3 - 2)^2} = \sqrt{(-2)^2 + 1^2} = \sqrt{5}.$$

Now we want the equation of a circle with center $C(-1, 3)$ and radius $\sqrt{5}$. Return to frame **Q37**, find the desired equation, and select the other alternative.

1.3　LINES

OBJECTIVES

You should know the definition of the slope of a line and how to find the slope of a line given the coordinates of two points on the line. You should know how to determine when two lines are parallel or perpendicular given the slopes of the lines, and be able to find the tangent of the angle between two lines if the slopes are given. You should know how to use the point-slope form and the slope-intercept form for the equation of a line. You should also know the general equation of a line.

Q38 DEFINITION: If $P_1(x_1, y_1)$ and $P_2(x_2, y_2)$ are two distinct points on a straight line which is not parallel to the y-axis, then the slope of the line is

$$m = \frac{y_2 - y_1}{x_2 - x_1}.$$

This definition is stated on page 20 of the text. Notice that if the line is parallel to the y-axis, then $x_1 = x_2$ and m would not be defined, since division by zero is not defined. This is why we stipulate that a line parallel to the y-axis has no slope.

　　Find the slope of the line passing through $A(2, 5)$ and $B(8, 5)$.

　　0　　Frame **A**　　The line has no slope.　　Frame **B**　　2/3　　Frame **C**

A　**YOUR ANSWER:**　0.

Right. The slope of a line passing through $P_1(x_1, y_1)$ and $P_2(x_2, y_2)$ is given by

$$m = \frac{y_2 - y_1}{x_2 - x_1}.$$

Therefore, the slope of the line passing through $A(2, 5)$ and $B(8, 5)$ is

$$\frac{5 - 5}{8 - 2} = \frac{0}{6} = 0.$$

Notice, the line passing through $A(2, 5)$ and $B(8, 5)$ is parallel to the x-axis. The slope of a line parallel to the x-axis is 0, and a line parallel to the y-axis has no slope.

B YOUR ANSWER: The line has no slope.
Be careful. The slope of a line passing through $P_1(x_1, y_1)$ and $P_2(x_2, y_2)$ is given by

$$m = \frac{y_2 - y_1}{x_2 - x_1} \; .$$

Therefore, the slope of the line passing through $A(2, 5)$ and $B(8, 5)$ is $(5 - 5)/(2 - 8)$. Now return to frame **Q38** and select the correct answer.

C YOUR ANSWER: 2/3.
Your calculations are off. The slope of a line passing through $P_1(x_1, y_1)$ and $P_2(x_2, y_2)$ is given by

$$m = \frac{y_2 - y_1}{x_2 - x_1} \; .$$

Now return to frame **Q38** and try again.

Q39   What is the slope of the line passing through $A(-4, 8)$ and $B(7, -3)$?

    1   Frame **A**   5/3   Frame **B** -1 Frame **C**

A YOUR ANSWER: 1.
Be careful. Didn't you miss a sign? Return to frame **Q39,** check your calculations, and then try again.

B YOUR ANSWER: 5/3.
No. The slope of the line passing through $A(-4, 8)$ and $B(7, -3)$ is the difference of the y-coordinates divided by the difference of the x-coordinates taken in the same order. Therefore, the slope is

$$\frac{8 - (-3)}{-4 - 7} \; .$$

Now return to frame **Q39** and select the correct answer.

C YOUR ANSWER: -1.
You are correct. The slope of the line passing through $A(-4, 8)$ and $B7, -3)$ is

$$\frac{8 - (-3)}{-4 - 7} = \frac{11}{-11} = -1.$$

Q40   Two lines are parallel if and only if the lines have equal slopes (or no slopes). This is Corollary (1.14) on page 23 of the text.

    Which one of the following pairs of points determines a line parallel to the line passing through $A(3, 6)$ and $B(-2, 8)$?

$C(1, 8), D(6, 10)$ Frame **A**
$C(-4, 9), D(1, 7)$ Frame **B**
$C(2, 6), D(3, 5)$ Frame **C**

A   **YOUR ANSWER:** $C(1, 8), D(6, 10)$.

Be careful. The slope of the line passing through $A(3, 6)$ and $B(-2, 8)$ is

$$\frac{8 - 6}{-2 - 3} = \frac{2}{-5} = -\frac{2}{5}.$$

The slope of the line passing through $C(1, 8)$ and $D(6, 10)$ is

$$\frac{10 - 8}{6 - 1} = \frac{2}{5}.$$

Now return to frame **Q40** and try again.

B   **YOUR ANSWER:** $C(-4, 9), D(1, 7)$.

Good. The slope of the line passing through $A(3, 6)$ and $B(-2, 8)$ is

$$\frac{8 - 6}{-2 - 3} = \frac{2}{-5} = -\frac{2}{5}.$$

The slope of the line passing through $C(-4, 9)$ and $D(1, 7)$ is

$$\frac{7 - 9}{1 - (-4)} = \frac{-2}{5} = -\frac{2}{5}.$$

Therefore, the line passing through A and B is parallel to the line passing through C and D.

C   **YOUR ANSWER:** $C(2, 6), D(3, 5)$.

Your calculations are off. The slope of the line passing through $A(3, 6)$ and $B(-2, 8)$ is

$$\frac{8 - 6}{-2 - 3} = \frac{2}{-5} = -\frac{2}{5}.$$

The slope of the line passing through $C(2, 6)$ and $D(3, 5)$ is

$$\frac{5 - 6}{3 - 2} = -1.$$

Return to frame **Q40** and find the pair C, D such that the slope is $-2/5$.

Q41   THEOREM: Two lines s_1 and s_2, not parallel to the coordinate axes, are perpendicular if and only if the product of their slopes is -1.

This theorem gives us a method for determining if two lines are perpendicular and is proved on page 24 of the text.

Which one of the following pairs of points determines a line perpendicular to a line with slope -3?

$A(2, 6), B(1, -3)$ Frame **A**
$A(1, 3), B(4, 4)$ Frame **B**
I don't understand.   Frame **C**

A   **YOUR ANSWER:** $A(2, 6), B(1, -3)$.

Watch out. The slope of the line passing through $A(2, 6)$ and $B(1, -3)$ is

$$\frac{6 - (-3)}{2 - 1} = 9.$$

Since $9(-3) \neq -1$, the lines are not perpendicular. Return to frame **Q41** and try again.

B   YOUR ANSWER: $A(1, 3)$, $B(4, 4)$.
Right. The slope of the line passing through $A(1, 3)$ and $B(4, 4)$ is

$$\frac{4 - 3}{4 - 1} = \frac{1}{3}.$$

Now since $(-3)(1/3) = -1$, the lines are perpendicular.

C   YOUR ANSWER: I don't understand.
Two lines, not parallel to the coordinate axes, are perpendicular if and only if the product of their slopes is -1. For example, the slope of the line passing through $A(3, 6)$ and $B(2, 8)$ is

$$\frac{8 - 6}{2 - 3} = \frac{2}{-1} = -2,$$

and the slope of the line passing through $C(5, 8)$ and $D(7, 9)$ is

$$\frac{9 - 8}{7 - 5} = \frac{1}{2}.$$

Since $(-2)(1/2) = -1$, the lines are perpendicular. Now return to frame **Q41** and try again.

Q42   Verify that the triangle with vertices $A(-1, 1)$, $B(3, -7)$, and $C(3, 3)$ is a right triangle. (*Hint*: Show that two sides are perpendicular.) Were you successful?

Yes   Frame **A**   No   Frame **B**

A   YOUR ANSWER: Yes.
Very good. The vertices are $A(-1, 1)$, $B(3, -7)$, and $C(3, 3)$. The slope of side AB is

$$\frac{-7 - 1}{3 - (-1)} = \frac{-8}{4} = -2$$

and the slope of side AC is

$$\frac{3 - 1}{3 - (-1)} = \frac{2}{4} = \frac{1}{2}.$$

Therefore, side AB is perpendicular to side AC because $(-2)(1/2) = -1$.

B   YOUR ANSWER: No.
Let's see if we can help. The vertices are $A(-1, 1)$, $B(3, -7)$, and $C(3, 3)$. The slope of side AB is

$$\frac{-7 - 1}{3 - (-1)} = \frac{-8}{4} = -2.$$

Now see if you can find a side whose slope is $1/2$. If you can, then two sides are perpendicular because $(-2)(1/2) = -1$. After completing the problem, return to frame **Q42**, and select the other alternative.

Q43   If a line is not parallel to the y-axis, then it can be completely determined by one of its points and its slope. If $P_1(x_1, y_1)$ is a point on a line and m is the slope, then

$$y - y_1 = m(x - x_1)$$

is an equation of the line. This is called the *point-slope form* of the equation of the line. The development of this equation is in the text.

Write the equation of a line passing through $P(-1, 4)$ with a slope 1/2.

$y - 4 = (1/2)(x + 1)$	Frame **A**	$y + 1 = (1/2)(x - 4)$	Frame **B**
$y - 4 = (1/2)(x - 1)$	Frame **C**	I don't understand.	Frame **D**

A   **YOUR ANSWER:** $y - 4 = (1/2)(x + 1)$.
Of course. An equation of a line passing through $P_1(x_1, y_1)$ with slope m is

$$y - y_1 = m(x - x_1).$$

Therefore, an equation of a line passing through $P(-1, 4)$ with slope 1/2 is $y - 4 = (1/2)(x + 1)$. Simplifying, we obtain

$$y - 4 = (1/2)(x + 1)$$
$$2y - 8 = x + 1$$
$$2y = x + 9$$
$$y = (1/2)x + 9/2.$$

B   **YOUR ANSWER:** $y + 1 = (1/2)(x - 4)$.
Sorry, but you interchanged x_1 and y_1 in the equation of the line. An equation of a line through $P_1(x_1, y_1)$ with slope m is

$$y - y_1 = m(x - x_1).$$

In our problem, $x_1 = -1$, $y_1 = 4$, and $m = 1/2$. Now return to frame **Q43**, substitute these values in the equation of the line, and then select the correct answer.

C   **YOUR ANSWER:** $y - 4 = (1/2)(x - 1)$.
Sorry, but you missed a sign. An equation of a line through $P_1(x_1, y_1)$ with slope m is

$$y - y_1 = m(x - x_1).$$

In our problem, $x_1 = -1$, $y_1 = 4$, and $m = 1/2$. Now return to frame **Q43**, substitute these values in the equation of the line, and then select the correct answer.

D   **YOUR ANSWER:** I don't understand.
Let's see if we can help. An equation of a line passing through $P_1(x_1, y_1)$ with slope m is

$$y - y_1 = m(x - x_1).$$

We want an equation of a line passing through $P(-1, 4)$ with slope 1/2. Therefore, in our problem, $x_1 = -1$, $y_1 = 4$, and $m = 1/2$. Now return to frame **Q43**, substitute these values in the equation of the line, and then select the correct answer.

Q44   Write an equation of a line passing through the points $A(2, -3)$ and $B(6, 8)$. (*Hint*: The slope of the line can be found using the two points.) Were you successful?

Yes   Frame **A**   No   Frame **B**

A   **YOUR ANSWER:** Yes.
Very good. We want an equation of the line passing through $A(2, -3)$ and $B(6, 8)$. The slope of the line passing through the two points is

$$m = \frac{8 - (-3)}{6 - 2} = \frac{11}{4} .$$

Now using $A(2, -3)$ and $m = 11/4$ in the point-slope form of the line, we obtain

$$y + 3 = (11/4)(x - 2)$$
$$4y + 12 = 11x - 22$$
$$4y = 11x - 34.$$

B YOUR ANSWER: No.

Let's see if we can get you started. The slope of the line passing through $A(2, -3)$ and $B(6, 8)$ is

$$m = \frac{8 - (-3)}{6 - 2} = \frac{11}{4} .$$

Now using $A(2, -3)$ and $m = 11/4$, write an equation of the given line. After completing the problem, return to frame **Q44** and select the other alternative.

Q45 What is an equation of a line passing through $P(0, b)$ with slope m?

$y = mx - mb$	Frame **A**
$y = mx + b$	Frame **B**
$y = x + b$	Frame **C**

A YOUR ANSWER: $y = mx - mb$.

Be careful. An equation of the line passing through $P(0, b)$ with slope m is $y - b = m(x - 0)$. Simplify this equation and then return to frame **Q45** and select the correct answer.

B YOUR ANSWER: $y = mx + b$.

Right. An equation of the line passing through $P(0, b)$ with slope m is

$$y - b = m(x - 0)$$
$$y - b = mx$$
$$y = mx + b.$$

This equation is called the *slope-intercept form* of the line. The number b is called the y-intercept because the point $P(0, b)$ is the point where the line intersects the y-axis.

C YOUR ANSWER: $y = x + b$.

Be careful. An equation of the line passing through $P(0, b)$ with slope m is $y - b = m(x - 0)$. Simplify this equation and then return to frame **Q45** and select the correct answer.

Q46 It can be shown that an equation of a straight line can be expressed in the form

$$ax + by + c = 0$$

where a, b, and c are constants, and a and b are not both zero. Conversely, an equation of the form $ax + by + c = 0$ is the equation of a straight line. Therefore, every straight line has an equation of the first degree in x and y, and every equation of the first degree in x and y represents a straight line. When we have the equation of a straight line in the form $ax + by + c = 0$, if $b \neq 0$, we can solve for y and thus determine the slope. For example,

$$2x + 3y - 4 = 0$$
$$3y = -2x + 4$$
$$y = (-2/3)x + 4/3.$$

We now have the equation in the form $y = mx + b$ and hence $-2/3$ is the slope.
What is the slope of a line with equation $3x - 2y + 7 = 0$?

2/3   Frame **A**   3/2   Frame **B** $-3/2$ Frame **C**

A   YOUR ANSWER: 2/3.
Sorry, but you made a mistake in your calculations.

$$3x - 2y + 7 = 0$$
$$2y = 3x + 7.$$

Return to frame **Q46** and select the correct answer.

B   YOUR ANSWER: 3/2.
You are correct.

$$3x - 2y + 7 = 0$$
$$2y = 3x + 7$$
$$y = (3/2)x + 7/2.$$

Therefore, the slope is 3/2.

C   YOUR ANSWER: $-3/2$.
Sorry, but you made a mistake in your calculations.

$$3x - 2y + 7 = 0$$
$$2y = 3x + 7.$$

Return to frame **Q46** and select the correct answer.

Q47 As a review, find an equation of a line passing through $P(6, -5)$ and perpendicular
to the line with equation $4x - 6y + 2 = 0$. How did it go?

Great   Frame **A**   Terrible   Frame **B**   I need help.   Frame **C**

A   YOUR ANSWER: Great.
Wonderful. We want an equation of a line passing through $P(6, -5)$ and perpendicular to the line with equation $4x - 6y + 2 = 0$. We have

$$4x - 6y + 2 = 0$$
$$6y = 4x + 2$$
$$y = (2/3)x + 1/3.$$

Therefore, the slope of $4x - 6y + 2 = 0$ is 2/3, and the slope of the desired line is
the negative reciprocal of 2/3, or $-3/2$. Now an equation of a line passing through
$P(6, -5)$ with slope $-3/2$ is

$$y + 5 = (-3/2)(x - 6)$$
$$2y + 10 = -3x + 18$$
$$3x + 2y - 8 = 0.$$

B   YOUR ANSWER: Terrible.
It can't be that bad. We want an equation of a line passing through $P(6, -5)$ and
perpendicular to the line with equation $4x - 6y + 2 = 0$. We have

$$4x - 6y + 2 = 0$$
$$6y = 4x + 2$$
$$y = (2/3)x + 1/3.$$

Therefore, the slope of the line $4x - 6y + 2 = 0$ is 2/3. Since we want our line to be perpendicular to $4x - 6y + 2 = 0$, we want the slope to be the negative reciprocal of 2/3, or $-3/2$. Now find an equation of a line passing through $P(6, -5)$ with slope $-3/2$. Return to frame **Q47** and try again.

C   **YOUR ANSWER:**   I need some help.
We want an equation of a line passing through $P(6, -5)$ and perpendicular to the line with equation $4x - 6y + 2 = 0$. Find the slope of the line $4x - 6y + 2 = 0$. The negative reciprocal of this slope will be the slope of the desired line since we want our line to be perpendicular to $4x - 6y + 2 = 0$. Now use the point $P(6, -5)$ in the point-slope form of the line. Return to frame **Q47** and try again.

1.4   FUNCTIONS

OBJECTIVES

You should know the definition of a function and the notation used for a function. You should know how to find the domain and range of a given function and be able to find the image of any element in the domain. You should know what is meant by the graph of a function and be able, by plotting points, to sketch the graph of a function. You should also know what is meant by a one-to-one function.

Q48   Now we are ready to look at the very important and useful concept of a function. A *function f* from a set X to a set Y is a correspondence that assigns to each element x of X a unique element y of Y. The element y is called the *image* of x under f and is denoted by $f(x)$. The set X is called the *domain* of the function. The *range* of the function is the set of all images of elements of X.

Remember, f is used to represent the function and is simply a rule which enables one to associate with elements of X certain elements of Y. However, $f(x)$ is an element of Y, namely, the image of x under f.

In order to describe a function f from X to Y, we need to specify the image $f(x)$ of each element x of X. This can be done in several ways:

1. We could give a verbal statement which determines each image. For example, if X is the set of states in the United States and Y is the set of state capitals, then let f associate with each state its state capital. This constitutes a function f from X to Y.
2. If the sets are finite, we can list all of the images.
3. We can use a formula to specify the image of each element. For example, $f(x) = x + 2$ describes a function from **R** to **R**. That is, each real number x is associated with the real number $x + 2$.

We will primarily be using the latter and we shall restrict ourselves to functions whose domain and ranges are subsets of **R**, the set of real numbers.

If f is defined by $f(x) = x^2 + 1$, what is $f(2)$?

2   Frame **A**   5   Frame **B**   What does this mean?   Frame **C**

A   **YOUR ANSWER:** 2.
No. The function f defined by $f(x) = x^2 + 1$ takes x into $x^2 + 1$. In other words, it takes a number into the square of the number plus one. For example, $f(3) = 3^2 + 1 = 10$. Return to frame **Q48** and determine $f(2)$.

B   **YOUR ANSWER:** 5.
You are correct. If $f(x) = x^2 + 1$, then $f(2) = 2^2 + 1 = 5$.

C   **YOUR ANSWER:**   What does this mean?
In the function f defined by $f(x) = x^2 + 1$, $f(2)$ is the image of 2 under f. Remember, the symbol $f(x)$ simply means the value of f at x. Now f takes x into $x^2 + 1$. That is, $x^2 + 1$ is the image of x. For example, $f(3) = 3^2 + 1 = 10$; therefore, the image of 3 is 10. Return to frame **Q48** and answer the question.

Q49   If $f(x) = 3x + 2$, what is $f(3)$?

9   Frame **A**   3   Frame **B**   11   Frame **C**

A   **YOUR ANSWER:** 9.
You apparently forgot to add 2. If $f(x) = 3x + 2$, $f(3) = 3 \cdot 3 + 2$. Now return to frame **Q49** and select the correct answer.

B   **YOUR ANSWER:** 3.
No. You want the value of f at $x = 3$ if $f(x) = 3x + 2$. Now return to frame **Q49** and select the correct answer.

C   **YOUR ANSWER:** 11.
Right. Since $f(x) = 3x + 2$, $f(3) = 3 \cdot 3 + 2 = 9 + 2 = 11$.

Q50   Other letters, such as u or v, may also represent elements of the domain with corresponding images $f(u)$ and $f(v)$.
Are f defined by $f(x) = 2x$ and f defined by $f(u) = 2u$ the same function?

Yes   Frame **A**   No   Frame **B**

A   **YOUR ANSWER:** Yes.
Of course. There is nothing special about the letter x. The functions defined by $f(x) = 2x$ and $f(u) = 2u$ say the same thing, namely, that f associates with each number in its domain that number which is two times the given number.

B   **YOUR ANSWER:** No.
Why not? We may use any letter we like to represent elements of the domain. The letter u is just as good as x. Return to frame **Q50** and select the other alternative.

Q51   There is also nothing special about the letter f for denoting a function. Other letters, such as g or h, may represent the function. That is $g(x) = 2x$ defines the same function as above.

If $g(x) = x^2 + 2x$, what is $g(a)$?

$a^2 + 2a$ Frame **A** a Frame **B**   I don't know.   Frame **C**

A **YOUR ANSWER:** $a^2 + 2a$.
Excellent. If $g(x) = x^2 + 2x$, then $g(a) = a^2 + 2a$. We simply substitute a for x. In other words, the value of g at $x = a$ is $a^2 + 2a$.

B **YOUR ANSWER:** a.
No. If $g(x) = x^2 + 2x$, then $g(a)$ is simply the value of $g(x)$ when $x = a$. We obtain $g(2) = 2^2 + 2 \cdot 2 = 4 + 4 = 8$ by replacing x in $g(x)$ by 2. Now to find $g(a)$, we replace x in $g(x)$ by a. Return to frame **Q51** and try again.

C **YOUR ANSWER:** I don't know.
If $g(x) = x^2 + 2x$, $g(x)$ is the value of g at x. Let us look at some of these values. By replacing x by 2, $g(2) = 2^2 + 2 \cdot 2 = 4 + 4 = 8$. By replacing x by 3, $g(3) = 3^2 + 2 \cdot 3 = 9 + 6 = 15$. By replacing x by -1, $g(-1) = (-1)^2 + 2(-1) = 1 - 2 = -1$. Now in order to find $g(a)$, we replace x by a. Return to frame **Q51** and try again.

Q52 We have been looking at functions defined by a formula. If, for some real number x, the formula is meaningless, we must exclude that x from the domain X of the function. We will assume the domain of a function is the set of real numbers for which the defining formula is meaningful.

Since we cannot divide by 0, the numbers that make the denominator 0 must be excluded from the domain. For example, consider f defined by $f(x) = 2/(3 - x)$. If $x = 3$, then $f(3) = 2/(3 - 3) = 2/0$, which is meaningless. Therefore, 3 must be excluded from the domain of f. The domain of f defined by $f(x) = 2/(3 - x)$ is the set of all real numbers except 3.

What value or values must be excluded from the domain of f defined by $f(x) = 2/(x^2 - 4)$?

2   Frame **A**   2 and -2 Frame **B**   4   Frame **C**

A **YOUR ANSWER:** 2.
We must exclude 2 from the domain of f defined by $f(x) = 2/(x^2 - 4)$ because $f(2) = 2/(2^2 - 4) = 2/0$, but that is not all. There is another number that we must exclude for the same reason. After thinking about this return to frame **Q52** and select the correct answer.

B **YOUR ANSWER:** 2 and -2.
Right. We must exclude 2 and -2 from the domain of f defined by $f(x) = 2/(x^2 - 4)$ because $2/(2^2 - 4) = 2/0$ and $2/[(-2)^2 - 4] = 2/0$. Thus the domain of f is the set of real numbers except 2 and -2.

C **YOUR ANSWER:** 4.
You didn't square 4, did you? Since $f(x) = 2/(x^2 - 4)$, $f(4) = 2/(4^2 - 4) = 2/(16 - 4) = 1/6$. There is nothing wrong with including 4, is there? Return to frame **Q52** and try again.

Q53 The square root of a negative number is not a real number. For example, $\sqrt{-3}$ is not a real number. Therefore, we must exclude from the domain all numbers that make the radicand of a square root negative. The radicand is the number under the radical.

What is the domain of f defined by $f(x) = \sqrt{x}$?

All positive real numbers	Frame **A**
All positive real numbers and zero	Frame **B**
All real numbers	Frame **C**

A **YOUR ANSWER:**   All positive real numbers.
You almost have it, but you left out one number that should be included in the domain. Can't 0 be included in the domain of f defined by $f(x) = \sqrt{x}$? Return to frame **Q53** and select the correct answer.

B **YOUR ANSWER:**   All positive real numbers and zero.
You are correct. The domain of f defined by $f(x) = \sqrt{x}$ consists of all positive real numbers and zero; that is, the domain is the set of real numbers greater than or equal to zero. We must exclude all negative real numbers because the square root of a negative number is not a real number.

C **YOUR ANSWER:**   All real numbers.
No. Remember, we must exclude all numbers from the domain that make the radicand of a square root negative. Therefore, we must exclude the negative real numbers from the domain of f defined by $f(x) = \sqrt{x}$. For example, the negative number -3 must be excluded because $\sqrt{-3}$ is not a real number. Now return to frame **Q53** and select the correct answer.

Q54 As a review, which one of the following is the domain of f defined by

$$f(x) = \frac{\sqrt{x - 1}}{2 - x} \ ?$$

All real numbers except 2	Frame **A**
All real numbers greater than or equal to 1	Frame **B**
All real numbers greater than or equal to 1 except 2	Frame **C**

A **YOUR ANSWER:**   All real numbers except 2.
Be careful. It is true that x cannot be equal to 2 because that would give $\sqrt{2 - 1}/(2 - 2) = 1/0$, which is undefined. However, what about $\sqrt{x - 1}$? The radicand of a square root must be greater than or equal to zero. Return to frame **Q54** and try again.

B **YOUR ANSWER:**   All real numbers greater than or equal to 1.
Be careful. It is true that $x \geqslant 1$ in order for $\sqrt{x - 1}$ to be defined since $x - 1 \geqslant 0$ implies $x \geqslant 1$, but what about the denominator of $\sqrt{x - 1}/(2 - x)$? The expression $2 - x$ must never be zero. Now return to frame **Q54** and select the correct answer.

C **YOUR ANSWER:**   All real numbers greater than or equal to 1 except 2.
Very good. If $\sqrt{x - 1}/(2 - x)$ is to be a real number, we must have $x - 1 \geqslant 0$ or $x \geqslant 1$, otherwise $\sqrt{x - 1}$ would be meaningless. Furthermore, we must also have $2 - x \neq 0$, since otherwise we would have to divide by zero; thus, $x \neq 2$. Consequently, the domain of f defined by $f(x) = \sqrt{x - 1}/(2 - x)$ is the set of real numbers greater than or equal to 1 except the number 2.

Q55 We have seen that different elements in the domain X of a function f may have the same image in Y. Now, if a function f from X to Y has the property that whenever $a \neq b$ in X, then $f(a) \neq f(b)$ in Y, we call the function a *one-to-one function* from X to Y.

Which one of the following functions f defined by the given expression is one-to-one?

$$f(x) = |x - 1| \quad \text{Frame } \mathbf{A}$$
$$f(x) = 1 + x^2 \quad \text{Frame } \mathbf{B}$$
$$f(x) = 2x + 1 \quad \text{Frame } \mathbf{C}$$

A   YOUR ANSWER: $f(x) = |x - 1|$.
Watch out. Since $f(2) = 1$ and $f(0) = 1$, f cannot be one-to-one. The function f is one-to-one if $a \neq b$ implies $f(a) \neq f(b)$. In this case, we have $2 \neq 0$, but $f(2) = f(0)$. Now return to frame **Q55,** study the definition of one-to-one, and try again.

B   YOUR ANSWER: $f(x) = 1 + x^2$.
Watch out. Since $f(1) = 2$ and $f(-1) = 2$, f cannot be one-to-one. The function f is one-to-one if $a \neq b$ implies $f(a) \neq f(b)$. In this case, we have $1 \neq -1$, but $f(1) = f(-1)$. Now return to frame **Q55,** study the definition of one-to-one, and try again.

C   YOUR ANSWER: $f(x) = 2x + 1$.
Good. Since $a \neq b$ implies $2a + 1 \neq 2b + 1$, f is a one-to-one function.

Q56 If X and Y are sets of real numbers, then a function f from X to Y determines a set S of ordered pairs (x, y), where $x \in X$ and $y \in Y$. That is, $S = \{(x, y): x \in X, y = f(x)\}$.

If f is defined by $f(x) = 3x + 2$, which one of the following ordered pairs belongs to the set S determined by f? That is, which one belongs to $S = \{(x, y): x \in \mathbf{R}, y = 3x + 2\}$?

(1, 5)	Frame **A**	(1, 2)	Frame **B**
(2, 3)	Frame **C**	I don't know.	Frame **D**

A   YOUR ANSWER: (1, 5).
Good. Since $5 = 3 \cdot 1 + 2$, $(1, 5) \in \{(x, y): x \in \mathbf{R}, y = 3x + 2\}$. That is, $(1, 5)$ is an ordered pair determined by $f(x) = 3x + 2$.

B   YOUR ANSWER: (1, 2).
No. If $(x, y) \in S$, then $y = 3x + 2$. Since $2 \neq 3 \cdot 1 + 2$, $(1, 2) \notin S = \{(x, y): x \in \mathbf{R}, y = 3x + 2\}$. Return to frame **Q56** and try again.

C   YOUR ANSWER: (2, 3).
No. If $(x, y) \in S$, then $y = 3x + 2$. Since $3 \neq 3 \cdot 2 + 2$, $(2, 3) \notin S = \{(x, y): x \in \mathbf{R}, y = 3x + 2\}$. Return to frame **Q56** and try again.

D   YOUR ANSWER: I don't know.
Let's see if we can help. The set $S = \{(x, y): x \in \mathbf{R}, y = 3x + 2\}$ is the set of ordered pairs (x, y) where the y-coordinate is 3 times the x-coordinate plus 2. If an ordered pair (x, y) has this property, then it belongs to S. Now return to frame **Q56** and determine which one belongs to S.

Q57   The graph of a function f is the graph of the set

$$\{(x, f(x)): x \text{ is in the domain of } f\}.$$

That is, the graph is the set of all points (x, y) in a coordinate plane such that $y = f(x)$. For example, the graph of f defined by $f(x) = 3x + 2$ is the graph of $S = \{(x, y): x \in \mathbf{R}, y = 3x + 2\}$. In order to visualize the graph of f, we plot a few points whose coordinates $(x, y) \in S$ and then draw a smooth curve through these points. Of course, this is simply an approximation.

Which one of the following is the graph of the function f defined by

$$f(x) = 3x + 2?$$

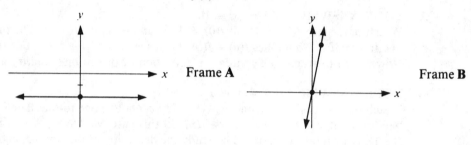

Frame **A**   Frame **B**

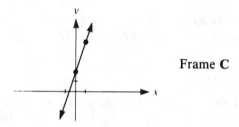

Frame **C**

A   YOUR ANSWER:

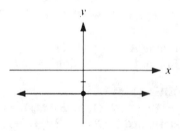

No. The function f is defined by $f(x) = 3x + 2$. Don't you have a sketch of f defined by $f(x) = -2$? Return to frame **Q57** and try again.

B   YOUR ANSWER:

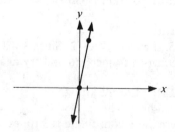

Sorry, but your graph passes through the point with coordinates $(0, 0)$. The ordered pair (0, 0) does not belong to the set determined by $f(x) = 3x + 2$ because $0 \neq 3 \cdot 0 + 2$. Now return to frame **Q57** and try again.

C   YOUR ANSWER:

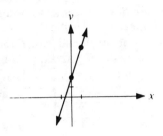

You are correct. We already found that (1, 5) belongs to the set determined by f defined by $f(x) = 3x + 2$. Similarly, (0, 2) and (−2/3, 0) also belong to this set. Therefore, we have a sketch of f defined by $y = 3x + 2$.

Q58   Sketch the graph of f defined by $f(x) = \sqrt{4 - 2x}$. Were you successful?

   Yes   Frame **A**   No   Frame **B**

A   YOUR ANSWER: Yes.
Very good.

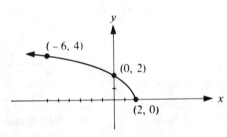

The domain of f defined by $f(x) = \sqrt{4 - 2x}$ is the set of real numbers x such that $4 - 2x \geqslant 0$ or $x \leqslant 2$. Therefore, the graph of f is the graph of the set of ordered pairs (x, y) such that $x \leqslant 2$ and $y = \sqrt{4 - 2x}$.

B   YOUR ANSWER: No.
We want the graph of f defined by $f(x) = \sqrt{4 - 2x}$. The domain of this function will consist of the real numbers x where $4 - 2x \geqslant 0$ or $x \leqslant 2$. Therefore, we want the *graph* of the set of ordered pairs (x, y) such that $x \leqslant 2$ and $y = \sqrt{4 - 2x}$. Return to frame **Q58**, plot some of the points with coordinates belonging to this set, and then sketch the graph.

1.5   COMBINATIONS OF FUNCTIONS

OBJECTIVES

You should know how to find the sum, difference, product, quotient, and composite of two functions.

Q59   If f and g are functions, then $h = f + g$ is the sum of f and g, and we write

$$h(x) = f(x) + g(x) \text{ or } (f + g)(x) = f(x) + g(x),$$

where the domain of h is the intersection of the domains of f and g. In other words, the image of x under $f + g$ is the sum of the images under f and g. The domain of h is the intersection of the domains of f and g because this is the set of elements that are in both the domain of f and the domain of g.

If $f(x) = x^2$ and $g(x) = \sqrt{x - 1}$, what is $(f + g)(x)$?

$(f + g)(x) = \sqrt{x^2 + x - 1}$ Frame **A**
$(f + g)(x) = x^2 + \sqrt{x - 1}$ Frame **B**
$(f + g)(x) = \sqrt{x^2 - 1}$ Frame **C**

A   YOUR ANSWER: $(f + g)(x) = \sqrt{x^2 + x - 1}$.
This is not the sum of $f(x)$ and $g(x)$. In order to determine $(f + g)(x)$, we simply add $f(x)$ and $g(x)$. Now return to frame **Q59** and try again.

B   YOUR ANSWER: $x^2 + \sqrt{x - 1}$.
Of course. If $f(x) = x^2$ and $g(x) = \sqrt{x - 1}$, then

$$(f + g)(x) = f(x) + g(x) = x^2 + \sqrt{x - 1}.$$

C   YOUR ANSWER: $(f + g)(x) = \sqrt{x^2 - 1}$.
Watch out. In order to determine $(f + g)(x)$, we simply add $f(x)$ and $g(x)$. Now return to frame **Q59** and try again.

Q60   We found that if $f(x) = x^2$ and $g(x) = \sqrt{x - 1}$, then $(f + g)(x) = x^2 + \sqrt{x - 1}$. Now what is the domain of $f + g$?

R   Frame **A** $[1, \infty)$ Frame **B**
$[0, \infty)$ Frame **C**   I don't understand.   Frame **D**

A   YOUR ANSWER: **R**.
Be careful. The domain of $f(x) = x^2$ is **R**, but the domain of $g(x) = \sqrt{x - 1}$ must be restricted. Remember, the domain of $f + g$ is the intersection of the domain of f and the domain of g. Now return to frame **Q60** and try again.

B   YOUR ANSWER: $[1, \infty)$.
Very good. The domain of $f(x) = x^2$ is **R** and the domain of $g(x) = \sqrt{x - 1}$ is $[1, \infty)$ because $x - 1 \geqslant 0$ or $x \geqslant 1$. Therefore, the domain of $f + g$ is $\mathbf{R} \cap [1, \infty) = [1, \infty)$. That is, the domain is the set of all real numbers x such that $x \geqslant 1$.

C   YOUR ANSWER: $[0, \infty)$.
You are on the right track, but you have miscalculated. The domain of $f(x) = x^2$ is **R** and the domain of $g(x) = \sqrt{x - 1}$ is $[1, \infty)$. Remember, the domain of $f + g$ is the intersection of the domain of f and the domain of g. Now return to frame **Q60** and select the correct answer.

D   YOUR ANSWER: I don't understand.
The domain of $f + g$ is the intersection of the domain of f and the domain of g. Now the domain of $f(x) = x^2$ is **R** and the domain of $g(x) = \sqrt{x - 1}$ is $[1, \infty)$ because $x - 1 \geqslant 0$ or $x \geqslant 1$. Return to frame **Q60**, think about this, and then try again.

Q61   The difference, product, and quotient are defined in a similar manner.

$$(f - g)(x) = f(x) - g(x)$$
$$(fg)(x) = f(x) \cdot g(x)$$
$$(f/g)(x) = f(x)/g(x)$$

The domain in each case is the intersection of the respective domains of f and g with the restriction, of course, in the case of f/g where $g(x) \neq 0$. If $f(x) = x^2$ and $g(x) = \sqrt{x - 1}$, we found

$$(f + g)(x) = x^2 + \sqrt{x - 1}, x \geqslant 1.$$

What is f/g?

$$(f/g)(x) = \frac{x^2}{\sqrt{x - 1}}, x \geqslant 1 \qquad \text{Frame } \mathbf{A}$$

$$(f/g)(x) = \sqrt{\frac{x^2}{x - 1}}, x \geqslant 1 \qquad \text{Frame } \mathbf{B}$$

$$(f/g)(x) = \frac{x^2}{\sqrt{x - 1}}, x > 1 \qquad \text{Frame } \mathbf{C}$$

A   **YOUR ANSWER:** $(f/g)(x) = \dfrac{x^2}{\sqrt{x - 1}}, x \geqslant 1.$

Almost, but you forgot that the denominator cannot be zero; therefore, $x = 1$ has to be deleted from the domain. Return to frame **Q61** and select the correct answer.

B   **YOUR ANSWER:** $(f/g)(x) = \sqrt{\dfrac{x^2}{x - 1}}, x \geqslant 1.$

By definition, $(f/g)(x) = f(x)/g(x)$. This is not what you have, is it? Return to frame **Q61** and try again.

C   **YOUR ANSWER:** $(f/g)(x) = \dfrac{x^2}{\sqrt{x - 1}}, x > 1.$

You are correct. Since $f(x) = x^2$ and $g(x) = \sqrt{x - 1}$,

$$(f/g)(x) = f(x)/g(x) = \frac{x^2}{\sqrt{x - 1}}, x > 1.$$

The intersection of the domains of f and g is the set of all x such that $x \geqslant 1$, but we must exclude 1 because if $x = 1$, then $\sqrt{x - 1} = 0$ and the denominator cannot be zero.

Q62   Suppose f is a function from X to Y and g is a function from Y to Z, then the composite function $g \circ f$ is the function from X to Z defined by

$$(g \circ f)(x) = g(f(x))$$

for every x in X. This idea can be illustrated pictorially in the following manner:

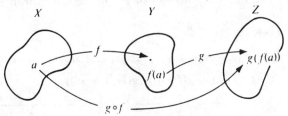

Notice that the domain of g must contain the range of f. That is, if a is in X and $f(a)$ does not belong in the domain of g, then we could not find $g(f(a))$. In other words, $f(a)$ would be stuck in set Y with no means of transportation to set Z.

Let's consider an example. If the functions f and g are defined by $g(x) = 2x$ and $f(x) = x^2 + 1$, we have

$$(g \circ f)(x) = g(f(x)) = g(x^2 + 1)$$
$$= 2(x^2 + 1) = 2x^2 + 2.$$

The domain of $g \circ f$ is the set of all real numbers. Now find $f \circ g$.

$(f \circ g)(x) = 2x^2 + 1$ Frame **A**
$(f \circ g)(x) = 4x^2 + 1$ Frame **B**
$(f \circ g)(x) = 2x + 1$ Frame **C**

A   **YOUR ANSWER:** $2x^2 + 1$.
Sorry, but you made a mistake. We have $f(x) = x^2 + 1$ and $g(x) = 2x$. Therefore,

$$(f \circ g)(x) = f(g(x)) = f(2x).$$

Now complete the calculation and then return to frame **Q62** and try again.

B   **YOUR ANSWER:** $4x^2 + 1$.
Right. We have $f(x) = x^2 + 1$ and $g(x) = 2x$. Therefore,

$$(f \circ g)(x) = f(g(x)) = f(2x)$$
$$= (2x)^2 + 1 = 4x^2 + 1.$$

C   **YOUR ANSWER:** $2x + 1$.
Sorry, but you made a mistake. We have $f(x) = x^2 + 1$ and $g(x) = 2x$. Therefore,

$$(f \circ g)(x) = f(g(x)) = f(2x).$$

Now complete the calculation and then return to frame **Q62** and try again.

Q63   Let's try another one. If functions f and g are defined by $f(x) = 1/(1 + x^2)$ and $g(x) = 3x + 5$, which one of the following is $g \circ f$?

$$\frac{1}{9x^2 + 30x + 26}$$ Frame **A**

$$\frac{8 + 5x^2}{1 + x^2}$$ Frame **B**

$$\frac{8}{1 + x^2}$$ Frame **C**

A   **YOUR ANSWER:** $\dfrac{1}{9x^2 + 30x + 26}$.
Didn't you find $f \circ g$ instead of $g \circ f$? Return to frame **Q63** and select $g \circ f$.

B   **YOUR ANSWER:** $\dfrac{8 + 5x^2}{1 + x^2}$.
Very good. Since $f(x) = 1/(1 + x^2)$ and $g(x) = 3x + 5$, we have

$$(g \circ f)(x) = g(f(x)) = g(1/(1 + x^2))$$
$$= 3\left(\frac{1}{1 + x^2}\right) + 5 = \frac{3 + 5(1 + x^2)}{1 + x^2} = \frac{8 + 5x^2}{1 + x^2}.$$

C YOUR ANSWER: $\dfrac{8}{1 + x^2}$.

Be careful. We have $f(x) = 1/(1 + x^2)$ and $g(x) = 3x + 5$. Therefore,

$$(g \circ f)(x) = g(f(x)) = g(1/(1 + x^2))$$
$$= 3\left(\frac{1}{1 + x^2}\right) + 5.$$

Now return to frame **Q63**, simplify this expression, and then select the correct answer.

Q64 We stated earlier that, for the composite function $g \circ f$, the domain of g must contain the range of f. If this is not true, then we may restrict the domain of $g \circ f$ to a subset of the domain of f so that $f(x)$ is in the domain of g. This technique is illustrated in Example 2 on page 41 of the text.

If f and g are defined by $f(x) = x + 2$ and $g(x) = x - \sqrt{x + 1}$, find $(g \circ f)(x)$ and determine the domain of $g \circ f$. How did it go?

Good   Frame **A**   Bad   Frame **B**

A YOUR ANSWER: Good.

Excellent. Since f and g are defined by $f(x) = x + 2$ and $g(x) = x - \sqrt{x + 1}$,

$$(g \circ f)(x) = g(f(x)) = g(x + 2)$$
$$= x + 2 - \sqrt{(x + 2) + 1} = x + 2 - \sqrt{x + 3}.$$

The domain of f is the set of all real numbers, but the domain of $g \circ f$ has to be restricted to $[-3, \infty)$ in order for $g \circ f$ to be defined. We must do this since $\sqrt{x + 3}$ is a real number only if $x + 3 \geqslant 0$.

B YOUR ANSWER: Bad.

It's not as bad as you think. Since f and g are defined by $f(x) = x + 2$ and $g(x) = x - \sqrt{x + 1}$,

$$(g \circ f)(x) = g(f(x)) = g(x + 2)$$
$$= x + 2 - \sqrt{(x + 2) + 1} = x + 2 - \sqrt{x + 3}.$$

Now the domain of f is the set of all real numbers, but we must restrict this domain in order for $f(x)$ to be in the domain of g, that is, in order for $(g \circ f)(x)$ to be defined. Think about this and then return to frame **Q64** and select the other alternative.

1.6 INVERSE FUNCTIONS

OBJECTIVES

You should know what is meant by the inverse of a function and how to find the inverse function when it exists.

Q65 Now suppose f is a one-to-one function with domain X and range Y. A function g with domain Y and range X is called the *inverse function* of f if

and
$$(f \circ g)(x) = x \text{ for every } x \text{ in } Y$$
$$(g \circ f)(x) = x \text{ for every } x \text{ in } X.$$

This is illustrated pictorially in the following manner:

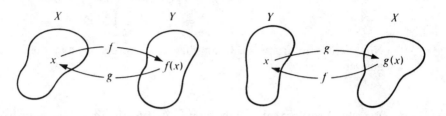

That is, if f carries x to $f(x)$, then g brings $f(x)$ back to x. Also, if g carries x to $g(x)$, then f brings $g(x)$ back to x.

Which one of the following is the inverse function of f defined by

$$f(x) = 2x + 1?$$

g defined by $g(x) = \dfrac{x + 1}{2}$ Frame **A**

h defined by $h(x) = \dfrac{x - 1}{2}$ Frame **B**

k defined by $k(x) = 2x - 1$ Frame **C**

A   **YOUR ANSWER:** g defined by $g(x) = \dfrac{x + 1}{2}$.

No. If g is the inverse function of f, then $(g \circ f)(x) = x$ and $(f \circ g)(x) = x$. Since f is defined by $f(x) = 2x + 1$, we have

$$(g \circ f)(x) = g(f(x)) = g(2x + 1)$$
$$= \frac{(2x + 1) + 1}{2} = x + 1.$$

Therefore, g is not the inverse function of f because $(g \circ f)(x) \neq x$. Return to frame **Q65** and try again.

B   **YOUR ANSWER:** h defined by $h(x) = \dfrac{x - 1}{2}$.

You are correct. Since f is defined by $f(x) = 2x + 1$, we have

$$(h \circ f)(x) = h(f(x)) = h(2x + 1)$$
$$= \frac{(2x + 1) - 1}{2} = \frac{2x}{2} = x$$

and

$$(f \circ h)(x) = f(h(x)) = f\left(\frac{x - 1}{2}\right)$$
$$= 2\left(\frac{x - 1}{2}\right) + 1 = (x - 1) + 1 = x.$$

Therefore, by definition h is the inverse function of f.

C   **YOUR ANSWER:** k defined by $k(x) = 2x - 1$.

No. If k is the inverse function of f, then $(k \circ f)(x)$ and $(f \circ k)(x) = x$. Since f is defined by $f(x) = 2x + 1$, we have

$$(k \circ f)(x) = k(f(x)) = k(2x + 1)$$
$$= 2(2x + 1) - 1 = 4x + 1.$$

Therefore, k is not the inverse function of f because $(k \circ f)(x) \neq x$. Return to frame **Q65** and try again.

Q66   We have discussed what has to be true in order for a function g to be the inverse function of f. Now given a function f, how do we find its inverse function? A technique for finding the inverse function is illustrated in Examples 1 and 2 on pages 44 and 45 of the text. Study these examples.

Now find the inverse function of f defined by $f(x) = 8x - 3$. How did it go?

Wonderful   Frame **A**   Bad   Frame **B**   Terrible   Frame **C**

A   YOUR ANSWER: Wonderful.
Great. We have f defined by $f(x) = 8x - 3$. Let $y = 8x - 3$ and then solve for x in terms of y.

$$y = 8x - 3$$
$$8x = y + 3$$
$$x = \frac{y + 3}{8}.$$

Now letting $g(y) = (y + 3)/8$, we have a function g from Y to X. Since the letter used for the independent variable is immaterial, we may replace y by x, obtaining

$$g(x) = \frac{x + 3}{8}.$$

Now, since

$$f(g(x)) = f\left(\frac{x + 3}{8}\right) = 8\left(\frac{x + 3}{8}\right) - 3 = (x + 3) - 3 = x$$

and

$$g(f(x)) = g(8x - 3) = \frac{(8x - 3) + 3}{8} = x,$$

g defined by $g(x) = (x + 3)/8$ is the inverse function of f.

B   YOUR ANSWER: Bad.
It really isn't too bad. We have f defined by $f(x) = 8x - 3$. Let $y = 8x - 3$ and then solve for x in terms of y and verify that the function obtained is in fact the inverse function of f. After completing the problem, return to frame **Q66** and select the wonderful response.

C   YOUR ANSWER: Terrible.
Nothing is that bad. Since f is defined by $f(x) = 8x - 3$, let $y = 8x - 3$ and then solve for x in terms of y.

$$y = 8x - 3$$
$$8x = y + 3$$
$$x = \frac{y + 3}{8}.$$

Now letting $g(y) = (y + 3)/8$, we have a function g from Y to X. Since the letter used for the independent variable is immaterial, we may replace y by x, obtaining

$$g(x) = \frac{x + 3}{8}.$$

Now verify that g is in fact the inverse function of f. After completing the problem, return to frame **Q66** and select the wonderful response.

Q67   Let's try one more. Can you find the inverse function of f if f is defined by $f(x) = 2x^2 + 1$ where the domain of f is restricted to $[0, \infty)$?

        Yes   Frame **A**   No   Frame **B**

A **YOUR ANSWER:** Yes.

Very good. Since f is defined by $f(x) = 2x^2 + 1$, let $y = 2x^2 + 1$ and then solve for x in terms of y.

$$y = 2x^2 + 1$$
$$2x^2 = y - 1$$
$$x^2 = \frac{y - 1}{2}$$
$$x = \pm\sqrt{\frac{y - 1}{2}}.$$

Now, letting $g(y) = \pm\sqrt{(y - 1)/2}$, and replacing y by x, we have

$$g(x) = \pm\sqrt{\frac{x - 1}{2}}.$$

It seems we have two possibilities for g, but only g defined by $g(x) = \sqrt{(x - 1)/2}$ works because we restricted the domain of f to be $[0, \infty)$. Therefore, the range of g cannot be negative.

$$f(g(x)) = f\left(\sqrt{\frac{x - 1}{2}}\right) = 2\left(\sqrt{\frac{x - 1}{2}}\right)^2 + 1$$
$$= 2\left(\frac{x - 1}{2}\right) + 1 = x$$

and

$$g(f(x)) = g(2x^2 + 1) = \sqrt{\frac{(2x^2 + 1) - 1}{2}} = \sqrt{x^2}$$
$$= x \text{ since } x \geqslant 0.$$

B **YOUR ANSWER:** No.

Sure you can. If f is defined by $f(x) = 2x^2 + 1$, let $y = 2x^2 + 1$ and then solve for x in terms of y.

$$y = 2x^2 + 1$$
$$2x^2 = y - 1$$
$$x^2 = \frac{y - 1}{2}$$
$$x = \pm\sqrt{\frac{y - 1}{2}}.$$

Now, letting $g(y) = \pm\sqrt{(y - 1)/2}$, and replacing y by x, we have

$$g(x) = \pm\sqrt{\frac{x - 1}{2}}.$$

It appears that we have two possibilities for $g(x)$: $g(x) = \sqrt{(x - 1)/2}$ and $g(x) = -\sqrt{(x - 1)/2}$. Which one is the inverse function of f? We restricted the domain of f to be the set $[0, \infty)$, that is, the set of positive real numbers. Therefore, the range of g must be nonnegative. Now return to frame **Q67**, think about this, and then select the other alternative.

REVIEW TEST

1 For each of the pairs of real numbers, determine which one is greater and express this relationship using the symbol $>$.

(a) $-28, -78$

(b) $(-1)(-8), (-7)(5)$

(c) $3 + (-8), (7)(-3)$

(d) $\dfrac{115}{4}, 28.63$

2 Simplify the following by removing the absolute value symbols.

(a) $|7 - 10|$ (b) $|-4| - |13|$ (c) $||-5| - |-8||$ (d) $\dfrac{5}{|-5|}$

3 If the coordinates of three points A, B, and C are -5, -3, and 6, respectively, show that $d(A, B) < d(B, C)$.

4 If $x < 3$, express $|x - 3|$ without using the absolute value symbol.

5 Express each of the following inequalities in interval notation and sketch a graph of the interval.

(a) $-1 < x \leqslant 5$ (b) $x \geqslant 6$

6 Express each of the following intervals as an inequality in the variable x.

(a) $(5, 25]$ (b) $(-\infty, 6)$

7 Solve the following inequalities and express the solutions in terms of intervals.

(a) $4x + 2 > 10$ (b) $6x + 3 \leqslant 5x - 7$ (c) $\dfrac{2}{3x - 6} > 0$

8 Solve the following inequalities.

(a) $|2 - 3x| < 8$ (b) $|x - 2| \geqslant 4$

9 Solve the inequalitity $x^2 - x - 2 > 0$.

10 Solve the inequality $\dfrac{x - 3}{x^2 - 4} < 0$.

11 Plot the following points on a rectangular coordinate system: $A(2, -1)$, $B(3, 5)$, $C(-1, -5)$, and $D(0, -2)$.

12 Describe the set of points $P(x, y)$ in a coordinate plane such that $x = -y$.

13 Find the distance between the given points A and B and the coordinates of the midpoint of the segment AB.

(a) $A(5, -2)$, $B(-4, 3)$ (b) $A(2, 8)$, $B(-1, -5)$

14 Prove that the triangle with vertices $A(-3, 1)$, $B(5, 4)$, and $C(0, -7)$ is a right triangle.

15 Find a formula which expresses the fact that $P(x, y)$ is equidistant from the points $A(2, 1)$ and $B(4, -1)$.

16   Sketch the graph of the set

$$W = \{(x, y): |x| > 1, |y - 1| < 1\}.$$

17   Sketch the graphs of the following equations.
(a) $y = 2x + 3$ (b) $y = 2x^2 - 3$ (c) $y = 1 + x^3$

18   Sketch the graphs of the following circles.
(a) $(x - 1)^2 + (y + 3)^2 = 9$ (b) $x^2 + (y - 4)^2 = 4$

19   Find the equation of a circle satisfying the stated conditions.
(a) Center $C(2, -3)$, radius 3   (b) Center $C(4, -2)$, passing through $P(2, -1)$

20   For each of the following, find the slope of the line through A and B.
(a) $A(2, 6)$, $B(-5, 10)$ (b) $A(-8, 7)$, $B(-7, 7)$
(c) $A\left(\dfrac{1}{2}, \dfrac{2}{3}\right)$, $B\left(-\dfrac{3}{4}, 2\dfrac{1}{3}\right)$

21   Find an equation for the line satisfying the given conditions.
(a) Through $A(4, -3)$, slope 1/2   (b) Through $A(-5, 2)$ and $B(4, -3)$
(c) Slope 1/3, y-intercept 2

22   Find an equation of the line passing through $A(2, -3)$ and parallel to the line

$$2x - 3y + 1 = 0.$$

23   If $f(x) = x^2 - 2x + 3$, find
(a) $f(1)$ (b) $f(-1)$ (c) $f(3)$ (d) $f(a)$

24   If $g(x) = \dfrac{x}{x^2 - 1}$, find

(a) $g(a)$ (b) $g(a + h)$ (c) $g\left(\dfrac{1}{a}\right)$ (d) $\dfrac{1}{g(a)}$

25   Assuming that the domain is the largest subset of **R** that can be used, find the domain of the following.

(a) $f(x) = \dfrac{x}{x - 1}$ (b) $g(x) = \sqrt{x - 5}$ (c) $h(x) = \dfrac{\sqrt{2x + 3}}{x - 5}$

26   Prove that $f(x) = -x + 3$ is a one-to-one function.

27   The fare for a certain taxi is 40 cents for the first half mile or any part thereof, and 25 cents for each additional half mile or part thereof. Find the function f that expresses the fare $f(x)$ for a trip of x miles where $0 \leqslant x \leqslant 2$.

28   Sketch the graph of

$$f(x) = \begin{cases} -1 & \text{if } x \leqslant -1 \\ x^2 - 2 & \text{if } -1 < x \leqslant 2 \\ -x + 4 & \text{if } x > 2 \end{cases}$$

29   For each of the following, find $(f \circ g)(x)$.
(a) $f(x) = 2x - 1$, $g(x) = x + 3$ (b) $f(x) = x^2 + 3$, $g(x) = 2x - 1$
(c) $f(x) = 1/x$, $g(x) = \sqrt{x + 1}$

30   Prove that $f(x) = x^2 - 4$, $x \leqslant 0$ and $g(x) = -\sqrt{x + 4}$, $x \geqslant -4$ are inverse functions of one another.

31   If $f(x) = 3x^2 + 2$, $x \geqslant 0$, find the inverse function of f.

SAMPLE TEST

1   For each of the pairs of real numbers, determine which one is greater and express this relationship using the symbol $>$.

(a) $-16, -20$ (b) $(-5) + (-3), (-5)(-2)$ (c) $\dfrac{7}{3}, \dfrac{9}{4}$ (d) $\dfrac{113}{3}, 37.2$

2   Simplify the following by removing the absolute value symbols.

(a) $|8 - 11|$ (b) $|-2 - (-5)|$ (c) $8 - |-6|$ (d) $\dfrac{-2}{|-2|}$

3   If the coordinates of three points A, B, and C are 10, -3, and -1, respectively, find $d(A, B)$, $d(B, C)$, and $d(A, C)$.

4   If $x < 4$, express $|4 - x|$ without using the absolute value symbols.

5   Express the following intervals as an inequality in the variable x.
(a) $[-2, 10]$ (b) $(-3, \infty)$

6   Solve the following inequalities.
(a) $-3x + 5 \leqslant 8$ (b) $2x - 8 > 5x + 10$

7   Solve the inequality $\dfrac{-3}{x - 3} > 0$.

8   Solve the following inequalities.
(a) $|x - 10| > 5$ (b) $|3x + 2| \leqslant 6$

9   Solve the inequality $x^2 - x - 6 < 0$.

10   Solve the inequality $\dfrac{x + 1}{x - 4} > 0$.

11   Plot the following points on a rectangular coordinate system: $A(5, -1)$, $B(0, 6)$, $C(3, 8)$, and $D(-2, -4)$.

12   Describe the set of points $P(x, y)$ in a coordinate plane such that $xy < 0$.

13   Find the distance between the given points A and B and the coordinates of the midpoint of the segment AB.
(a) $A(4, 3)$, $B(-2, 8)$ (b) $A(-5, 1)$, $B(0, -8)$

14   Prove that the triangle with vertices $A(0, 1)$, $B(4, 4)$, and $C(8, 1)$ is an isosceles triangle.

15   Find a formula which expresses the fact that $P(x, y)$ is twice as far from the point $A(1, 0)$ as from the point $B(-2, 0)$.

16   Sketch the graph of the set $W = \{(x, y): x \geqslant 0, |y| < 2\}$.

17   Sketch the graphs of the following equations.
(a) $y = -x + 3$ (b) $y^2 = 2x + 3$ (c) $y = \sqrt{x + 1}$

18   Sketch the graphs of the following circles.
(a) $(x + 2)^2 + (y - 1)^2 = 16$ (b) $(x - 2)^2 + y^2 = 9$

19   Find the equation of a circle satisfying the stated conditions.
(a) Center $C(-1, 4)$, radius 4   (b) Endpoints of a diameter $A(3, 5)$ and $B(-1, 7)$

20   For each of the following, find the slope of the line through A and B.

(a) $A(-1, 5)$, $B(0, -4)$ (b) $A(5, 8)$, $B(-6, -8)$ (c) $A\left(\dfrac{1}{2}, 2\dfrac{3}{4}\right)$, $B\left(-\dfrac{1}{3}, -\dfrac{3}{4}\right)$

21   Find an equation for the line satisfying the given conditions.
(a) Through $A(2, -1)$, slope -4 (b) Through $A(-3, -2)$ and $B(-5, 4)$
(c) x-intercept 2, y-intercept -3

22   Given the equation $3y - 4x = 12$, find the slope and y-intercept and sketch the graph.

23   If $f(x) = x^3 - 2x + 1$, find
(a) $f(0)$ (b) $f(1)$ (c) $f(-2)$ (d) $f(c)$

24   If $f(x) = x^2 - 1$, find
(a) $f(a)$ (b) $f(a + h)$ (c) $\dfrac{f(a + h) - f(a)}{h}$

25   Assuming that the domain is the largest subset of **R** that can be used, find the domain of the following.
(a) $f(x) = \sqrt{2x + 3}$ (b) $g(x) = \dfrac{\sqrt{x - 1}}{x - 2}$

26   Find the range of the function f where $f(x) = \sqrt{x - 2}$.

27   A store offers golf balls for \$1.25 per ball for 25 balls or less. If more than 25 are bought, the price per ball is reduced by one cent for each ball that is purchased over 25. The limit is 50 balls. Let C denote the total cost of the balls and x the number of balls purchased. Express C as a function of x for $0 \leqslant x \leqslant 50$.

28   Sketch the graph of
$$f(x) = \begin{cases} -x & \text{if } x \leqslant -3 \\ x + 6 & \text{if } -3 < x \leqslant 0 \\ -x^2 + 6 & \text{if } x > 0 \end{cases}$$

29   For each of the following find $(f \circ g)(x)$.
(a) $f(x) = x - 3$, $g(x) = 2x + 3$ (b) $f(x) = 3x - 2$, $g(x) = 2x^2 - 1$
(c) $f(x) = x^2$, $g(x) = \sqrt{x - 1}$

30   If $f(x) = 3x - 2$, find the inverse function of f.

31   If $f(x) = 16 - x^2$, $x \geqslant 0$, find the inverse function of f.

CHAPTER 2

Limits and
Continuity of
Functions

2.1 INTRODUCTION

OBJECTIVES

You should be familiar with the notion of the limit of a function and be able to find the limit of a function f(x) *as* x *approaches a constant in an intuitive manner.*

Q68 The concept of limit plays a fundamental role throughout the calculus. We want to say that the limit of $f(x)$ is L as x approaches a if $f(x)$ is near L when x is near a. Our problem, of course, is what we mean by "near." We will define what we mean later, but for now, let's take an intuitive look at the notion of limit.

What would you guess to be the limit of $f(x) = x^2 + 2$ as x approaches 1? That is, what number does $f(x)$ get close to as x gets closer and closer to 1?

2	Frame **A**	3	Frame **B**
1	Frame **C**	I don't have any idea.	Frame **D**

A   YOUR ANSWER: 2.
No. We want the limit of $f(x) = x^2 + 2$ as x approaches 1. That is, what number is $f(x)$ close to when x is close to 1? It is true that $f(0) = 2$, but try some numbers closer to 1 than 0 and you will find that $f(x)$ gets nearer something other than 2. Return to frame **Q68** and try again.

B   YOUR ANSWER: 3.
You are correct. We want the limit of $f(x) = x^2 + 2$ as x approaches 1. We have

$$f(0) = 0^2 + 2 = 2$$

$$f(1/2) = (1/2)^2 + 2 = 2\frac{1}{4}$$

$$f(3/4) = (3/4)^2 + 2 = 2\frac{9}{16}.$$

Intuitively, we see that $f(x)$ is getting near 3 as x gets near 1. Actually, $f(1) = 3$ in this case, but this does not have anything to do with the limit because we are not interested in what happens at $x = 1$, but only what happens to $f(x)$ when x is near 1.

C   YOUR ANSWER: 1.
No. We want the limit of $f(x) = x^2 + 2$ as x approaches 1. That is, what number is

$f(x)$ close to when x is close to 1? Find $f(x)$ for numbers close to 1 and see what you get. Now return to frame **Q68** and try again.

D   **YOUR ANSWER:**   I don't have any idea.
Well let's see. We want the limit of $f(x) = x^2 + 2$ as x approaches 1. That is, what number is $f(x)$ close to when x is close to 1? Let's try some numbers.

$$f(0) = 0^2 + 2 = 2$$
$$f(1/2) = (1/2)^2 + 2 = 2\frac{1}{4}$$
$$f(3/4) = (3/4)^2 + 2 = 2\frac{9}{16}.$$

Can you tell what number $f(x)$ is getting close to as we let x get closer to 1? Now return to frame **Q68** and try again.

Q69   We express the above notion by $\lim_{x \to 1} (x^2 + 2) = 3$. Let's try another one. Find $\lim_{x \to -2} (x^3)$.

    -8 Frame **A** 8 Frame **B** -2 Frame **C**

A   **YOUR ANSWER:** -8.
Very good. $\mathrm{Lim}_{x \to -2} (x^3) = -8$. Trying values of x near -2, we get

$$f(0) = 0^3 = 0$$
$$f(-1) = (-1)^3 = -1$$
$$f(-3/2) = (-3/2)^3 = -27/8 = -3\frac{3}{8}$$
$$f(-7/4) = (-7/4)^3 = -343/64 = -5\frac{23}{64}.$$

If we continue taking values of x near -2, we obtain values of $f(x)$ closer to -8. In fact, we have $f(-2) = -8$. However, this is not always the case.

B   **YOUR ANSWER:** 8.
Be careful. You want $\lim_{x \to -2} (x^3)$. Find the value of $f(x) = x^3$ for values of x near -2. Return to frame **Q69** and try again.

C   **YOUR ANSWER:** -2.
Be careful. You want $\lim_{x \to -2} (x^3)$. Find the value of $f(x) = x^3$ for values of x near -2. Return to frame **Q69** and try again.

Q70   It is not always true that the limit of $f(x)$ as x approaches a is equal to $f(a)$. For example, consider

$$\lim_{x \to 2} \left(\frac{x^2 - 4}{x - 2} \right).$$

Notice that $f(x) = (x^2 - 4)/(x - 2)$ is not defined when $x = 2$; therefore, $\lim_{x \to 2} f(x) \neq f(2)$. However, $f(x)$ does have a limit as x approaches 2. What do you suppose this limit is?

    2   Frame **A**   0   Frame **B**
    4   Frame **C**   I don't know.   Frame **D**

A **YOUR ANSWER:** 2.
Be careful. We want the limit of $f(x)$ as x approaches 2. This is not necessarily 2.
Find the value of $f(x)$ for some numbers that get closer and closer to 2 and see if $f(x)$
is getting near some number. Now return to frame **Q70** and try again.

B **YOUR ANSWER:** 0.
You are off base. We have $f(x) = (x^2 - 4)/(x - 2)$. If you try to find $f(2)$, you have
0/0 which is undefined. What you need to do is find $f(x)$ for numbers close to 2 and
see what you get. Now return to frame **Q70** and try again.

C **YOUR ANSWER:** 4.
Excellent. We want $\lim_{x\to 2} ((x^2 - 4)/(x - 2))$. Trying a few values of x near 2, we
obtain

$$f(0) = \frac{0 - 4}{0 - 2} = 2$$

$$f(1) = \frac{1 - 4}{1 - 2} = 3$$

$$f(3/2) = \frac{(3/2)^2 - 4}{(3/2) - 2} = 3\frac{1}{2}$$

$$f(7/4) = \frac{(7/4)^2 - 4}{(7/4) - 2} = 3\frac{3}{4}.$$

If we keep taking values of x closer to 2, $f(x)$ apparently gets near 4, which is expressed as

$$\lim_{x\to 2} \left(\frac{x^2 - 4}{x - 2}\right) = 4.$$

D **YOUR ANSWER:** I don't know.
Let's see if we can get you started. We have $f(x) = (x^2 - 4)/(x - 2)$. If you try to
find $f(2)$, you have 0/0 which is undefined. What you need to do is find the value
of $f(x)$ for some numbers that get closer and closer to 2 and see if $f(x)$ is getting
near some number as x gets closer to 2. Now return to frame **Q70** and try this approach.

2.2 DEFINITION OF LIMIT

OBJECTIVES

*You should know the definition of the limit of a function and how to find the limit
using this definition.*

Q71 We are now ready to give a more precise definition of limit.

DEFINITION: $\lim_{x \to a} f(x) = L$ means that, for each positive number ε, there is a positive number δ depending on ε such that

$$\text{if } 0 < |x - a| < \delta, \text{ then } |f(x) - L| < \varepsilon,$$

where f is defined on an open interval containing a, except possibly at a itself.

This is essentially the definition given on page 58 of the text. This definition still says that the limit of $f(x)$ as x approaches a is L if $f(x)$ is near L when x is near a, but we have defined precisely what we mean by near. We are saying that, given any ε distance from L, we can find a δ such that if x is within δ of a, $f(x)$ will be within ε of L. In other words, if this definition is satisfied, we can get as close to L as we want to if we get near enough to a.

Let's prove $\lim_{x \to 1} (2x + 3) = 5$ by using the above definition. Our task is to show that for each $\varepsilon > 0$, there exists a number $\delta > 0$, such that if $0 < |x - 1| < \delta$, then

$\|2x + 3\| < \varepsilon$	Frame **A**
$\|(2x + 3) - 5\| < \varepsilon$	Frame **B**
$\|(2x + 3) - 1\| < \varepsilon$	Frame **C**

A   **YOUR ANSWER:** $|2x + 3| < \varepsilon$.
Watch out. Look at the definition of limit on page 58 of the text and then return to frame **Q71** and try again.

B   **YOUR ANSWER:** $|(2x + 3) - 5| < \varepsilon$.
Right. By definition, $\lim_{x \to 1} (2x + 3) = 5$ if for each $\varepsilon > 0$ there exists a $\delta > 0$, such that if $0 < |x - 1| < \delta$, then $|(2x + 3) - 5| < \varepsilon$.

C   **YOUR ANSWER:** $|(2x + 3) - 1| < \varepsilon$.
Watch out. Look at the definition of limit on page 58 of the text and then return to frame **Q71** and try again.

Q72   By definition, $\lim_{x \to 1} (2x + 3) = 5$ if for each $\varepsilon > 0$ there exists a $\delta > 0$, such that if $0 < |x - 1| < \delta$, then $|(2x + 3) - 5| < \varepsilon$. Now, given $\varepsilon > 0$, the problem facing us is to find $\delta > 0$ such that if $0 < |x - 1| < \delta$, then $|(2x + 3) - 5| < \varepsilon$.

Which one of the following would be an appropriate value for δ?

    2ε Frame **A** $\varepsilon/2$ Frame **B**   I don't have any idea.   Frame **C**

A   **YOUR ANSWER:** 2ε.
Sorry, but 2ε won't work. We want to find δ such that if $0 < |x - 1| < \delta$, then $|(2x + 3) - 5| < \varepsilon$. Notice that $|(2x + 3) - 5| < \varepsilon$ is equivalent to $|2x - 2| < \varepsilon$ or $2|x - 1| < \varepsilon$. We would like to start with $0 < |x - 1| < \delta$ and arrive at $2|x - 1| < \varepsilon$. What must δ be in order to accomplish this task? Now return to frame **Q72** and select the correct answer.

B   **YOUR ANSWER:** $\varepsilon/2$.
Wonderful. $\lim_{x \to 1} (2x + 3) = 5$ if for any $\varepsilon > 0$, there exists a $\delta > 0$ such that if $0 < |x - 1| < \delta$, then $|(2x + 3) - 5| < \varepsilon$.

Given any $\varepsilon > 0$, let $\delta = \varepsilon/2$. Now if $0 < |x - 1| < \varepsilon/2$, then

$$2|x - 1| < \varepsilon$$
$$|2(x - 1)| < \varepsilon$$
$$|(2x + 3) - 5| < \varepsilon.$$

C   **YOUR ANSWER:**   I don't have any idea.

Let's see if we can help. Given any $\varepsilon > 0$, our task is to find a δ such that if $0 < |x - 1| < \delta$, then $|(2x + 3) - 5| < \varepsilon$. Notice that $|(2x + 3 - 5| < \varepsilon$ is equivalent to $|2x - 2| < \varepsilon$ or $2|x - 2| < \varepsilon$. Now we want to start with $0 < |x - 1| < \delta$ and obtain $2|x - 1| < \varepsilon$. What must δ be in order to accomplish this task? Return to frame **Q72** and try again.

Q73   As one might guess, it is not always easy to find the value of a limit using our definition. However, if the function is relatively simple, we are able to use the definition.

Using the definition, prove that $\lim_{x \to 2} (3x + 5) = 11$. How did it go?

Great   Frame **A**   Bad   Frame **B**   Terrible   Frame **C**

A   **YOUR ANSWER:**   Great.

Tremendous. In order to prove that $\lim_{x \to 2} (3x + 5) = 11$, we must show that for any $\varepsilon > 0$, there exists a $\delta > 0$ such that if $0 < |x - 2| < \delta$, then $|(3x + 5) - 11| < \varepsilon$.

Let $\delta = \varepsilon/3$. Now if $0 < |x - 2| < \varepsilon/3$, then

$$3|x - 2| < \varepsilon$$
$$|3(x - 2)| < \varepsilon$$
$$|(3x + 5) - 11| < \varepsilon.$$

B   **YOUR ANSWER:**   Bad.

Let's see if we can get you started. In order to prove that $\lim_{x \to 2} (3x + 5) = 11$, we must show that for any $\varepsilon > 0$, we can find a δ such that if $0 < |x - 2| < \delta$, then $|(3x + 5) - 11| < \varepsilon$. Analyze $|(3x + 5) - 11| < \varepsilon$ and see if you can find the necessary δ. Now return to frame **Q73** and try again.

C   **YOUR ANSWER:**   Terrible.

Nothing is that bad. In order to prove that $\lim_{x \to 2} (3x + 5) = 11$, we must show that for any $\varepsilon > 0$, we can find a $\delta > 0$ such that if $0 < |x - 2| < \delta$, then $|(3x + 5) - 11| < \varepsilon$. That is, for any $\varepsilon > 0$, our task is to find a $\delta > 0$ such that if $0 < |x - 2| < \delta$ is satisfied, then it will follow that $|(3x + 5) - 11| < \varepsilon$. Notice that $|(3x + 5) - 11| < \varepsilon$ is equivalent to $|3x - 6| < \varepsilon$ or $3|x - 2| < \varepsilon$. Now what does δ have to be so that if $|x - 2| < \delta$, then $3|x - 2| < \varepsilon$? Think about this and then return to frame **Q73** and try again.

Q74   Let's try one more. Prove that $\lim_{x \to 1} (2x^2 + 3) = 5$. Were you successful?

Yes   Frame **A**   No   Frame **B**

A   **YOUR ANSWER:**   Yes.

Very good. $\text{Lim}_{x \to 1} (2x^2 + 3) = 5$ if for each $\varepsilon > 0$, there exists a $\delta > 0$ such that if $0 < |x - 1| < \delta$, then $|(2x^2 + 3) - 5| < \varepsilon$.

First let's restrict x to the interval $(0, 2)$. This is permissible because we are only interested in what happens near 1. This means we are considering values of x which differ from 1 by less than 1 and hence $\delta < 1$. Notice that $|(2x^2 + 3) - 5| = 2|x + 1||x - 1|$ and, since x is restricted to the interval $(0, 2)$, we have $x < 2$ and hence $|x + 1| < 3$. Therefore, $|(2x^2 + 3) - 5| = 2|x + 1||x - 1| < 6|x - 1|$. Now let

$\delta = \varepsilon/6$ (or 1 if $1 < \varepsilon/6$). If $0 < |x - 1| < \delta \leqslant \varepsilon/6$, then $6|x - 1| < \varepsilon$. But since $|(2x^2 + 3) - 5| < 6|x - 1|$, we have $|(2x^2 + 3) - 5| < \varepsilon$.

B   **YOUR ANSWER:** No.

Let's see if we can help. $\text{Lim}_{x \to 1} (2x^2 + 3) = 5$ if for each $\varepsilon > 0$, there exists a $\delta > 0$ such that if $0 < |x - 1| < \delta$, then $|(2x^2 + 3) - 5| < \varepsilon$. Notice that $|(2x^2 + 3) - 5| < \varepsilon$ is equivalent to $2|x + 1||x - 1| < \varepsilon$. The trick here is to restrict x so that we can get a bound on $|x + 1|$. For example, if we restrict x to the interval $(0, 2)$, then $x < 2$ and $|x + 1| < 3$. We can restrict x to the interval $(0, 2)$ because we are only interested in what happens near $x = 1$. Since $|x + 1| < 3$, we have $2|x + 1||x - 1| < 6|x - 1|$. Now what value of δ do we need so that if $0 < |x - 1| < \delta$, then $6|x - 1| < \varepsilon$? Think about this and then return to frame **Q74** and select the other alternative.

2.3   THEOREMS ON LIMITS

OBJECTIVES

You should know the basic theorems concerning limits and how to use these theorems to find limits.

Q75   As we pointed out earlier, it is not very convenient to prove a limit by means of the definition. There are several limit theorems given in this section which you should become familiar with and which will help in finding certain limits. Theorem (2.8) on page 63 says that the limit of a constant is the constant. That is,

$$\lim_{x \to a} c = c,$$

and Theorem (2.9) says that

$$\lim_{x \to a} x = a.$$

Theorem (2.12) on page 65 says that the limit of a sum is the sum of the limits, the limit of a product is the product of the limits, and the limit of a quotient is the quotient of the limits, provided that the limit of the denominator is not zero.

     Using these limit theorems, prove

$$\lim_{x \to 2} (3x^2 + 5x) = 22.$$

Were you successful?

     Yes   Frame **A**   No   Frame **B**

A   **YOUR ANSWER:** Yes.

Excellent. We want $\lim_{x \to 2} (3x^2 + 5x)$. Using the limit theorems, we have

$\lim_{x \to 2} 3 = 3$	limit of a constant is the constant
$\lim_{x \to 2} x = 2$	$\lim_{x \to a} x = a$
$\lim_{x \to 2} 3x^2 = 3 \cdot 2 \cdot 2$	limit of a product is the product
$\qquad\quad = 12$	of the limits
$\lim_{x \to 2} 5 = 5$	limit of a constant is the constant
$\lim_{x \to 2} 5x = 5 \cdot 2 = 10$	limit of a product is the product
	of the limits
$\lim_{x \to 2} (3x^2 + 5x)$	limit of a sum is the sum of the
$\qquad = \lim_{x \to 2} 3x^2 + \lim_{x \to 2} 5x$	limits
$\qquad = 12 + 10 = 22$	

B   **YOUR ANSWER:**   No.

Let's see if we can get you started. We want $\lim_{x\to 2} (3x^2 + 5x)$.

$\lim_{x\to 2} 3 = 3$	limit of a constant is the constant
$\lim_{x\to 2} x = 2$	$\lim_{x\to a} x = a$
$\lim_{x\to 2} 3x^2 = 3 \cdot 2 \cdot 2$	limit of a product is the product
$\phantom{\lim_{x\to 2} 3x^2} = 12$	of the limits

Now find $\lim_{x\to 2} 5x$ in a similar manner and then find $\lim_{x\to 2} (3x^2 + 5x)$ using the fact that the limit of a sum is the sum of the limits. Return to frame **Q75**, finish the problem, and select the other alternative.

Q76   Theorems (2.18) and (2.19) on page 67 of the text are very useful. They simply say that if $f(x)$ is a polynomial function, then the limit of $f(x)$ as x approaches a is the value of the function at a. The same is true for a rational function $f(x)/h(x)$, provided $h(a) \neq 0$.

Using these theorems, what is $\lim_{x\to -1} \left(\dfrac{2x^2 + 3x - 1}{x^2 + 3} \right)$?

3/2	Frame **A**
-1	Frame **B**
$-1/2$	Frame **C**
I don't understand.	Frame **D**

A   **YOUR ANSWER:**   3/2.

Didn't you make a mistake with some signs? Evaluate

$$\frac{2x^2 + 3x - 1}{x^2 + 3}$$

for $x = -1$. Now return to frame **Q76** and try again.

B   **YOUR ANSWER:** -1.

No. The limit of a function as $x \to -1$ is not necessarily -1. Return to frame **Q76**, study the theorem, and try again.

C   **YOUR ANSWER:** $-1/2$.

You are correct.

$$\lim_{x\to -1} \left(\frac{2x^2 + 3x - 1}{x^2 + 3} \right) = \frac{2(-1)^2 + 3(-1) - 1}{(-1)^2 + 3} = -2/4 = -1/2.$$

D   **YOUR ANSWER:**   I don't understand.

In order fo find $\lim\limits_{x\to -1} \left(\dfrac{2x^2 + 3x - 1}{x^2 + 3} \right)$, evaluate $\dfrac{2x^2 + 3x - 1}{x^2 + 3}$ for $x = -1$. Now return to frame **Q76**, study the theorem, and then try again.

Q77   Let's try one more. Can you find $\lim\limits_{x\to 2} \left(\dfrac{x^2}{x - 2} - \dfrac{4}{x - 2} \right)$?

Yes   Frame **A**   No   Frame **B**

A   YOUR ANSWER: Yes.
Terrific.

$$\lim_{x \to 2} \left(\frac{x^2}{x-2} - \frac{4}{x-2} \right) = \lim_{x \to 2} \left(\frac{x^2 - 4}{x-2} \right)$$

We can divide by $x - 2$ because we are concerned not about what happens at 2 but about what happens as $x \to 2$.

$$= \lim_{x \to 2} (x + 2)$$

$$= 4.$$

B   YOUR ANSWER: No.
At first glance, there appears to be a problem. If you evaluate

$$\frac{x^2}{x-2} - \frac{4}{x-2}$$

for $x = -2$, the denominator is zero. However, simplify the expression first and the difficulty disappears. Now return to frame **Q77,** simplify the expression, and then find the limit.

2.4   ONE-SIDED LIMITS

OBJECTIVES

You should know what is meant by one-sided limits and how to find the value of one-sided limits. You should also know the theorem relating the notion of limit and one-sided limits.

Q78   Sometimes it is necessary to consider one-sided limits. One-sided limits are discussed and defined on page 72 of the text.
    If $f(x) = \sqrt{x^2 - 4}$, then the domain of f is $(-\infty, -2] \cup [2, \infty)$. If we want to know the limit of $\sqrt{x^2 - 4}$ as x approaches 2, then we can only approach from the right because only real numbers to the right of 2 are in the domain of f.
    What is $\lim_{x \to 2^+} \sqrt{x^2 - 4}$?

    2   Frame **A**   0   Frame **B**   1   Frame **C**

A   YOUR ANSWER: 2.
Be careful. $\lim_{x \to 2^+} \sqrt{x^2 - 4} = \sqrt{2^2 - 4}$. Now return to frame **Q78,** complete the calculations, and select the correct answer.

B   YOUR ANSWER: 0.
Of course. $\lim_{x \to 2^+} \sqrt{x^2 - 4} = \sqrt{2^2 - 4} = 0$.

C   **YOUR ANSWER:** 1.

You are off base. $\lim_{x\to 2^+} \sqrt{x^2 - 4} = \sqrt{2^2 - 4}$. Now return to frame **Q78,** complete the

calculations, and select the correct answer.

Q79   Consider the function f defined by

$$f(x) = \begin{cases} x^2 & \text{if } x \leqslant 1 \\ x + 1 & \text{if } x > 1. \end{cases}$$

What is $\lim_{x\to 1^+} f(x)$?

-1 Frame **A**   1   Frame **B**   2   Frame **C**

A   **YOUR ANSWER:** -1.

Something is wrong. If

$$f(x) = \begin{cases} x^2 & \text{if } x \leqslant 1 \\ x + 1 & \text{if } x > 1, \end{cases}$$

then $\lim_{x\to 1^+} f(x) = \lim_{x\to 1} (x + 1)$ because $f(x) = x + 1$ when x is to the right of 1. Now return to frame **Q79** and select the correct answer.

B   **YOUR ANSWER:** 1.

Don't you have $\lim_{x\to 1^-} f(x)$ instead of $\lim_{x\to 1^+} f(x)$? Now return to frame **Q79** and try again.

C   **YOUR ANSWER:** 2.

Right. Since

$$f(x) = \begin{cases} x^2 & \text{if } x \leqslant 1 \\ x + 1 & \text{if } x > 1, \end{cases}$$

$\lim_{x\to 1^+} f(x) = \lim_{x\to 1} (x + 1) = 1 + 1 = 2.$

Q80   If

$$f(x) = \begin{cases} x^2 & \text{if } x \leqslant 1 \\ x + 1 & \text{if } x > 1, \end{cases}$$

we found that $\lim_{x\to 1^+} f(x) = 2$. We can also find the limit from the left.

$$\lim_{x\to 1^-} f(x) = \lim_{x\to 1} x^2 = 1.$$

In this case does $\lim_{x\to 1} f(x)$ exist?

Yes   Frame **A**   No   Frame **B**

A   **YOUR ANSWER:** Yes.

Watch out. Since $\lim_{x\to 1^+} f(x) = 2$ and $\lim_{x\to 1^-} f(x) = 1$, $\lim_{x\to 1} f(x)$ does not exist. This is expressed in Theorem (2.26) on page 73 of the text. Study this theorem and then return to frame **Q80** and select the other alternative.

B   **YOUR ANSWER:** No.

Great. Since $\lim_{x\to 1^+} f(x) = 2$ and $\lim_{x\to 1^-} f(x) = 1$, $\lim_{x\to 1} f(x)$ does not exist. The right-hand and left-hand limits must be the same in order for the limit to exist. If they are the same, then the common value is the value of the limit. In this case, they are not the same; therefore, the limit does not exist.

2.5   CONTINUOUS FUNCTIONS

OBJECTIVES

You should know the definition of a continuous function. You should be able to determine when a function is continuous using the definition or some of the basic theorems concerning continuity. You should also know the Intermediate Value Theorem and how to use it.

Q81   We now turn to the important notion of *continuity*.

DEFINITION: A function *f* is said to be continuous at *a* if
1) $f(x)$ is defined on an open interval containing *a*.
2) $\lim_{x \to a} f(x)$ exists.
3) $\lim_{x \to a} f(x) = f(a)$.

Notice that in order for a function to be continuous at *a* it must satisfy three conditions. Roughly, these three conditions guarantee that there are no breaks in the graph of the function.
   Consider the following functions:

$$f(x) = \begin{cases} \dfrac{x^2 - 4}{x - 2} & \text{if } x \neq 2 \\ 5 & \text{if } x = 2; \end{cases}$$

$$g(x) = \frac{x^2 + 3}{x - 2} \; ;$$

$$h(x) = \begin{cases} 4 & \text{if } x < 2 \\ 5 & \text{if } x = 2 \\ x + 1 & \text{if } x > 2. \end{cases}$$

A function is discontinuous if it fails to meet one of the three conditions of continuity. Each of the above functions is discontinuous at $x = 2$. Which one is discontinuous at 2 because $f(2)$ is not defined?

   f   Frame **A**   *g*   Frame **B**   *h*   Frame **C**

A   **YOUR ANSWER:** *f*.
The function *f* is defined at 2, isn't it? We have

$$f(x) = \begin{cases} \dfrac{x^2 - 4}{x - 2} & \text{if } x \neq 2 \\ 5 & \text{if } x = 2. \end{cases}$$

The rule for finding $f(x)$ for any *x* is simply to use $(x^2 - 4)/(x - 2)$ if $x \neq 2$ and to use 5 if $x = 2$. Therefore, $f(2) = 5$. Return to frame **Q81** and select the function that is not defined at 2.

B   **YOUR ANSWER:** *g*.
You are correct. The function $g(x) = (x^2 + 3)/(x - 2)$ is not defined at $x = 2$ since we cannot divide by zero. Therefore, *g* is not continuous at $x = 2$.

C   **YOUR ANSWER:** *h*.
The function *h* is defined at 2, isn't it? We have

$$h(x) = \begin{cases} 4 & \text{if } x < 2 \\ 5 & \text{if } x = 2 \\ x + 1 & \text{if } x > 2. \end{cases}$$

The rule for finding $f(x)$ for any x is simply to use 4 if $x < 2$, use 5 if $x = 2$, and use $x + 1$ if $x > 2$. Therefore, $f(2) = 5$. Return to frame **Q81** and select the function that is not defined at 2.

Q82 The other functions are:

$$f(x) = \begin{cases} \dfrac{x^2 - 4}{x - 2} & \text{if } x \neq 2 \\ 5 & \text{if } x = 2; \end{cases}$$

$$h(x) = \begin{cases} 4 & \text{if } x < 2 \\ 5 & \text{if } x = 2 \\ x + 1 & \text{if } x > 2. \end{cases}$$

Which one is discontinuous at $x = 2$ because the limit does not exist?

    f Frame **A** h Frame **B**

A **YOUR ANSWER:** f.
Sorry, but $\lim_{x \to 2} (x^2 - 4)/(x - 2) = 4$. Since $x \neq 2$, $(x^2 - 4)/(x - 2) = x + 2$ and $\lim_{x \to 2} (x + 2) = 4$. Think about this and then return to frame **Q82** and select the other alternative.

B **YOUR ANSWER:** h.
Right. The limit of the function

$$h(x) = \begin{cases} 4 & \text{if } x < 2 \\ 5 & \text{if } x = 2 \\ x + 1 & \text{if } x > 2 \end{cases}$$

does not exist as x approaches 2. The graph of h is as follows:

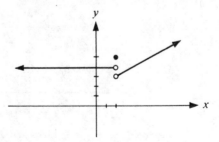

Notice the break in the graph at $x = 2$. The limit as x approaches 2 from the left is 4, and the limit as x approaches 2 from the right is 3. Therefore, the limit does not exist.

    The other function

$$f(x) = \begin{cases} \dfrac{x^2 - 4}{x - 2} & \text{if } x \neq 2 \\ 5 & \text{if } x = 2 \end{cases}$$

is not continuous at $x = 2$ because $\lim_{x \to 2} f(x) \neq f(2)$. $\text{Lim}_{x \to 2} f(x) = 4$, but $f(2) = 5$. The graph of f is as follows:

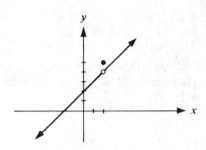

Notice the difference between the functions h and f. The function h has a break, but you can't fill in the hole; whereas, in f, if we made $f(2) = 4$, we could fill in the hole and thus make it continuous.

Q83   Which one of the following functions has a point of discontinuity?

$f(x) = 2x^2 + 3x + 5$ Frame **A**

$g(x) = \begin{cases} x + 3 & \text{if } x \leqslant 2 \\ 4x - 3 & \text{if } x > 2 \end{cases}$ Frame **B**

$h(x) = \dfrac{x^2 + 2x - 3}{x + 4}$ Frame **C**

A   **YOUR ANSWER:** $f(x) = 2x^2 + 3x + 5$.
No. This is a polynomial and it can be shown that all polynomials are continuous everywhere. Return to frame **Q83** and try again.

B   **YOUR ANSWER:** $g(x) = \begin{cases} x + 3 & \text{if } x \leqslant 2 \\ 4x - 3 & \text{if } x > 2 \end{cases}$.
Watch out. This function is continuous.

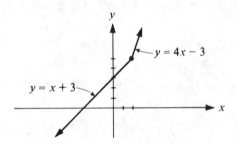

Notice that there are no breaks in the graph. Return to frame **Q83** and try again.

C   **YOUR ANSWER:** $h(x) = \dfrac{x^2 + 2x - 3}{x + 4}$.
Right. This function is discontinuous at $x = -4$ because h is not defined at -4 since division by zero is impossible.

Q84   There are certain functions that are continuous everywhere. For example, $f(x) = 2x^2 + 3x + 5$ is continuous everywhere. In general, all polynomials are continuous everywhere. Now if a function is continuous at $x = a$, then its limit at $x = a$ must equal $f(a)$. For example, since $2x^2 + 3x + 5$ is continuous,

$$\lim_{x \to 2} (2x^2 + 3x + 5) = 2(2)^2 + 3(2) + 5 = 19.$$

Do you remember in our previous work with limits that sometimes the limit was equal to the functional value? This occurred when the function was continuous. What is $\lim_{x \to 3} (4x^3 + 2x^2 - 5x - 4)$?

   107   Frame **A**   23   Frame **B**   145   Frame **C**

A **YOUR ANSWER:** 107.
Correct. Since polynomials are continuous,

$$\lim_{x \to 3} (4x^3 + 2x^2 - 5x - 4) = 4(3)^3 + 2(3)^2 - 5(3) - 4 = 107.$$

B **YOUR ANSWER:** 23.
Sorry, but your calculations are off. Since polynomials are continuous, in order to find $\lim_{x \to 3} (4x^3 + 2x^2 - 5x - 4)$, we simply evaluate the polynomial $4x^3 + 2x^2 - 5x - 4$ at $x = 3$. Now return to frame **Q84** and select the correct answer.

C **YOUR ANSWER:** 145.
Sorry, but your calculations are off. Since polynomials are continuous, in order to find $\lim_{x \to 3} (4x^3 + 2x^2 - 5x - 4)$, we simply evaluate the polynomial $4x^3 + 2x^2 - 5x - 4$ at $x = 3$. Now return to frame **Q84** and select the correct answer.

Q85 Rational functions are continuous everywhere except for those numbers for which the denominator is zero. For example,

$$f(x) = \frac{x^3 + 2x^2 + 3x - 5}{x^2 - 3x + 2}$$

is continuous everywhere except when $x = 1$ and $x = 2$. The function f is discontinuous at $x = 1$ and $x = 2$ because the denominator $x^2 - 3x + 2$ is zero when $x = 1$ or $x = 2$.

Find $\lim_{x \to 2} \left(\dfrac{x^2 + 3x + 5}{x - 5} \right)$.

   -5 Frame **A** -4 Frame **B**   1   Frame **C**

A **YOUR ANSWER:** -5.
Good.

$$\lim_{x \to 2} \left(\frac{x^2 + 3x + 5}{x - 5} \right) = \frac{\lim_{x \to 2} (x^2 + 3x + 5)}{\lim_{x \to 2} (x - 5)}$$

$$= \frac{2^2 + 3(2) + 5}{2 - 5} = -5.$$

B **YOUR ANSWER:** -4.
Your calculations are off.

$$\lim_{x \to 2} \left(\frac{x^2 + 3x + 5}{x - 5} \right) = \frac{\lim_{x \to 2} (x^2 + 3x + 5)}{\lim_{x \to 2} (x - 5)}.$$

Now use the fact that $x^2 + 3x + 5$ and $x - 5$ are continuous and then return to frame **Q85** and select the correct answer.

C   YOUR ANSWER: 1.
Your calculations are off.

$$\lim_{x \to 2} \left(\frac{x^2 + 3x + 5}{x - 5} \right) = \frac{\lim_{x \to 2} (x^2 + 3x + 5)}{\lim_{x \to 2} (x - 5)} .$$

Now use the fact that $x^2 + 3x + 5$ and $x - 5$ are continuous and then return to frame **Q85** and select the correct answer.

Q86   The *Intermediate Value Theorem* states that if f is a continuous function on a closed interval $[a, b]$, and if $f(a) \neq f(b)$, then f takes on every value between $f(a)$ and $f(b)$. That is, if w is a real number between $f(a)$ and $f(b)$, then there exists a number c in $[a, b]$ such that $f(c) = w$.

   $f(x) = 2x^2 - 1$ is continuous in the interval $[0, 5]$. $f(0) = -1$ and $f(5) = 49$. Now 17 is between -1 and 49. Therefore, by the Intermediate Value Theorem, there should be a number in $[0, 5]$ that has a functional value of 17. What is this number?

   9   Frame **A**   3   Frame **B** ± 3 Frame **C**   17   Frame **D**

A   YOUR ANSWER: 9.
You didn't complete the problem. We want a number c such that $f(c) = 17$ where $f(x) = 2x^2 - 1$.

$$2c^2 - 1 = 17$$
$$2c^2 = 18$$
$$c^2 = 9$$

Now what is the required value of c? Return to frame **Q86** and try again.

B   YOUR ANSWER: 3.
You are correct. The given function is $f(x) = 2x^2 - 1$ in the interval $[0, 5]$. If c is a number such that $f(c) = 17$, we have

$$2c^2 - 1 = 17$$
$$2c^2 = 18$$
$$c^2 = 9.$$

Therefore, $c = 3$ because $3 \in [0, 5]$. We could find a number c for any number between $f(0) = -1$ and $f(5) = 49$ in a similar manner.

C   YOUR ANSWER: ± 3.
You missed one important point. We are looking for a number in the interval $[0, 5]$. Return to frame **Q86** and select the correct answer.

D   YOUR ANSWER: 17.
You missed the point of the Intermediate Value Theorem. We want a number c such that $f(c) = 17$. This is not necessarily 17. Return to frame **Q86** and try again.

REVIEW TEST

1   In an intuitive manner, find $\lim_{x \to -3} \dfrac{x^2 - 9}{x + 3}$.

2   Find an equation of the tangent line to $y = 2x^2 + 1$ at the point $P(2, 9)$.

3   By means of the definition of limit, prove each of the following.
   (a) $\lim_{x \to -1} (3x + 5) = 2$ (b) $\lim_{x \to 2} (x^2 + 3) = 7$

4 Show that $\lim_{x \to 1} \left(\dfrac{1}{x - 1} \right)$ does not exist.

5 Find the following limits if they exist.

   (a) $\lim_{x \to 2} (2x_2 + 3x - 1)$ (b) $\lim_{x \to -1} \left(\dfrac{x^2 - 3x + 1}{x - 5} \right)$ (c) $\lim_{x \to 5} \sqrt{\dfrac{x + 4}{x - 1}}$

6 Use the Sandwich Theorem to prove that

$$\lim_{x \to 0} \left(\frac{|x|}{\sqrt{x^2 + 1}} \right) = 0.$$

7 Find each of the following limits.

   (a) $\lim_{x \to 3^+} (\sqrt{x - 3} + x)$ (b) $\lim_{x \to -2^-} \left(\dfrac{|x + 2|}{x + 2} \right)$

8 If $f(x) = \begin{cases} x & \text{if } x \leqslant 0 \\ x + 1 & \text{if } 0 < x \leqslant 1 \\ x^2 + 3 & \text{if } x > 1 \end{cases}$, find $\lim_{x \to 1^-} f(x)$.

9 Prove $\lim_{x \to 4} \left(\dfrac{\sqrt{(x - 4)^2}}{x - 4} \right)$ does not exist.

10 Show that $f(x) = \dfrac{x + 1}{x^2}$ is continuous at $a = 2$.

11 Show that $f(x) = \dfrac{x^2}{x - 2}$ is continuous on the interval $(2, 4]$.

12 Find all real numbers for which $f(x) = \dfrac{2x}{x^2 - 4}$ is not continuous.

13 Prove $f(x) = \begin{cases} x & \text{if } x \leqslant 1 \\ x^2 & \text{if } 1 < x \leqslant 5 \\ 2x + 3 & \text{if } x > 5 \end{cases}$ is not continuous at $x = 5$.

14 Verify the Intermediate Value Theorem for $f(x) = x^2 + 3$ on the interval $[0, 3]$.

SAMPLE TEST

1 In an intuitive manner, find $\lim_{x \to 2} \left(\dfrac{x^2 + x - 6}{x - 2} \right)$.

2 Find an equation of the tangent line to $y = x^3 + 5$ at $P(1, 6)$.

3 By means of the definition, prove each of the following.

   (a) $\lim_{x \to 3} (2x - 5) = 1$ (b) $\lim_{x \to 2} \left(x - \dfrac{1}{x} \right) = \dfrac{3}{2}$

4 Show that $\lim_{x \to -1} \left(\dfrac{|x + 1|}{x + 1} \right)$ does not exist.

5 Find the following limits if they exist.

   (a) $\lim_{x \to -1} (3x^3 - x^2 + 4)$ (b) $\lim_{x \to 4} \left(\dfrac{\sqrt{x + 5}}{x^2 + 3} \right)$ (c) $\lim_{x \to 3} (\sqrt[3]{x^2 - 1})$

6 Find $\lim\limits_{x\to 2}\left[\dfrac{x^2}{x-2}-\dfrac{4}{x-2}\right]$.

7 Find each of the following limits.

   (a) $\lim\limits_{x\to -2^+}(\sqrt{x+2}+x^2)$ (b) $\lim\limits_{x\to 3^-}\left(\dfrac{x-3}{|x-3|}\right)$

8 If $f(x)=\begin{cases}x^2 & \text{if } x\leqslant 0 \\ x+1 & \text{if } x>0\end{cases}$, find $\lim\limits_{x\to 0}f(x)$.

9 Show that $\lim\limits_{x\to 0}f(x)$ does not exist where f is the function in Problem 8.

10 Show that $f(x)=\dfrac{\sqrt{x-5}}{x-5}$ is continuous at $a=6$.

11 Show that $f(x)=\dfrac{2x+3}{x^2-1}$ is continuous on the interval $(-1,0]$.

12 Find all real numbers for which $f(x)=\begin{cases}x-1 & \text{if } x\leqslant 0 \\ x^2-1 & \text{if } 0<x\leqslant 1 \\ x^3 & \text{if } x>1\end{cases}$ is not continuous.

13 Prove $f(x)=\dfrac{|x-1|}{x-1}$ is not continuous at $x=1$.

14 Verify the Intermediate Value Theorem for $f(x)=2x^2-1$ on the interval $[-1,2]$.

CHAPTER 3

The Derivative

3.1 INTRODUCTION

OBJECTIVES

You should know how to find the slope m *of the tangent line to the graph of a function at a given point and how to find the velocity of a point moving on a coordinate line at a given time.*

Q87 Consider a curve with equation $y = f(x)$ and a point P on the curve with coordinates $(a, f(a))$. Suppose we increment the x-coordinate by h, obtaining $a + h$. Now the point Q on the curve with x-coordinate $a + h$ will have coordinates $(a + h, f(a + h))$.

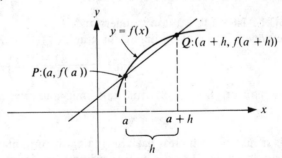

You may remember from Chapter One that the slope of the line joining P and Q is the ratio of the difference of the y-coordinates and the difference of the x-coordinates. Therefore, the slope is

$$\frac{f(a + h) - f(a)}{h} .$$

The slope of the tangent line to the graph of f at the point $P(a, f(a))$ is

$$\lim_{h \to 0} \left(\frac{f(a + h) - f(a)}{h} \right) .$$

This is Definition (3.1) on page 88 of the text.

If $f(x) = 2x^2 + 1$, find the slope of the tangent line to the graph of f at the point $P(1, 3)$.

4	Frame **A**
3	Frame **B**
0	Frame **C**
I don't understand.	Frame **D**

A   YOUR ANSWER: 4.

Right. The slope of the tangent line to the graph of $f(x) = 2x^2 + 1$ at the point $P(1, 3)$ is

$$\lim_{h \to 0} \left(\frac{f(1 + h) - f(1)}{h} \right) = \lim_{h \to 0} \left(\frac{2(1 + h)^2 + 1 - 3}{h} \right)$$

$$= \lim_{h \to 0} \left(\frac{2 + 4h + 2h^2 + 1 - 3}{h} \right)$$

$$= \lim_{h \to 0} \left(\frac{4h + 2h^2}{h} \right) = \lim_{h \to 0} (4 + 2h) = 4.$$

B   YOUR ANSWER: 3.

No. $f(1) = 3$, but we want

$$\lim_{h \to 0} \left(\frac{f(1 + h) - f(1)}{h} \right).$$

Now return to frame **Q87** and try again.

C   YOUR ANSWER: 0.

Be careful. We want

$$\lim_{h \to 0} \left(\frac{f(1 + h) - f(1)}{h} \right).$$

Now return to frame **Q87** and try again.

D   YOUR ANSWER: I don't understand.

The slope of the tangent line to the graph of $f(x) = 2x^2 + 1$ at the point $P(1, 3)$ is

$$\lim_{h \to 0} \left(\frac{f(1 + h) - f(1)}{h} \right).$$

Now return to frame **Q87**, find this limit, and select the correct answer.

Q88   This same type of limit is used in finding the instantaneous velocity of a point P at time a. If a point P moves on a coordinate line l such that its coordinate at time t is $f(t)$, then the velocity of P at time a is

$$\lim_{h \to 0} \left(\frac{f(a + h) - f(a)}{h} \right)$$

provided this limit exists.

   If the position of a point P moving on a coordinate line l is given by $f(t) = 3t^2 + 2t - 1$, what is the velocity of P at $t = 2$?

12 ft/sec	Frame **A**	14 ft/sec	Frame **B**	15 ft/sec	Frame **C**

A   YOUR ANSWER: 12 ft/sec.

Your calculations are off. The velocity of P at $t = 2$ is given by

$$\lim_{h \to 0} \left(\frac{f(2 + h) - f(2)}{h} \right).$$

Now return to frame **Q88** and try again.

B   YOUR ANSWER: 14 ft/sec.
You are correct. If $f(t) = 3t^2 + 2t - 1$, then the velocity of P at $t = 2$ is

$$\lim_{h\to 0}\left(\frac{f(2 + h) - f(2)}{h}\right) = \lim_{h\to 0}\left(\frac{3(2 + h)^2 + 2(2 + h) - 1 - 15}{h}\right)$$

$$= \lim_{h\to 0}\left(\frac{14h + 3h^2}{h}\right) = \lim_{h\to 0}(14 + 3h) = 14.$$

C   YOUR ANSWER: 15 ft/sec.
Sorry, $f(2) = 15$, but we want

$$\lim_{h\to 0}\left(\frac{f(2 + h) - f(2)}{h}\right).$$

Return to frame **Q88** and try again.

3.2   DEFINITION OF DERIVATIVE

OBJECTIVES

You should know the definition of the derivative of a function at a given point and how to find the derivative using the definition.

Q89   Two applications of

$$\lim_{h\to 0}\left(\frac{f(a + h) - f(a)}{h}\right)$$

were discussed in the last section. Since this limit is so important, we give it a special name.

If a function f is defined on an open interval containing a, then the *derivative* $f'(a)$ of f at a is given by

$$f'(a) = \lim_{h\to 0}\left(\frac{f(a + h) - f(a)}{h}\right)$$

provided the limit exists.

In order to find the derivative of f at $x = a$, we must find

$$\lim_{h\to 0}\left(\frac{f(a + h) - f(a)}{h}\right).$$

What is the derivative of $f(x) = 3x + 1$ at $x = a$?

$3a$	Frame **A**	3	Frame **B**
0	Frame **C**	I don't know.	Frame **D**

A   YOUR ANSWER: $3a$.
Your calculations must be off. The derivative of f at $x = a$ is

$$\lim_{h\to 0}\left(\frac{f(a + h) - f(a)}{h}\right).$$

Since $f(x) = 3x + 1$, we want

$$\lim_{h \to 0} \left(\frac{3(a + h) + 1 - (3a + 1)}{h} \right).$$

After evaluating this limit, return to frame **Q89** and select the correct answer.

B   YOUR ANSWER: 3.
You are correct. The derivative of f at $x = a$ is

$$\lim_{h \to 0} \left(\frac{f(a + h) - f(a)}{h} \right).$$

Since $f(x) = 3x + 1$, we have

$$\lim_{h \to 0} \left(\frac{3(a + h) + 1 - (3a + 1)}{h} \right) = \lim_{h \to 0} \left(\frac{3h}{h} \right) = \lim_{h \to 0} (3) = 3.$$

$\text{Lim}_{h \to 0} (3h/h) = \lim_{h \to 0} (3)$ because we can divide numerator and denominator by the factor h since we are interested in h near zero and not at zero.

C   YOUR ANSWER: 0.
Your calculations must be off. The derivative of f at $x = a$ is

$$\lim_{h \to 0} \left(\frac{f(a + h) - f(a)}{h} \right).$$

Since $f(x) = 3x + 1$, we want

$$\lim_{h \to 0} \left(\frac{3(a + h) + 1 - (3a + 1)}{h} \right).$$

After evaluating this limit, return to frame **Q89** and select the correct answer.

D   YOUR ANSWER: I don't know.
Let's get you started. The derivative of f at $x = a$ is

$$\lim_{h \to 0} \left(\frac{f(a + h) - f(a)}{h} \right).$$

Since $f(x) = 3x + 1$, we want

$$\lim_{h \to 0} \left(\frac{3(a + h) + 1 - (3a + 1)}{h} \right).$$

Now evaluate this limit and then return to frame **Q89** and select the correct answer.

Q90   We have been discussing the derivative of a function f at $x = a$. If the derivative exists for every number x in the domain of f, then the derivative itself becomes a function of x which we denote by f'.

DEFINITION: The derivative f' of a function f is a new function defined by

$$f'(x) = \lim_{h \to 0} \left(\frac{f(x + h) - f(x)}{h} \right)$$

if the limit exists.

What is $f'(x)$ if $f(x) = 2x^2 + 1$?

$4x$ Frame **A**   2   Frame **B**   4   Frame **C**

A   YOUR ANSWER: 4x.

Wonderful. If $f(x) = 2x^2 + 1$, then

$$f'(x) = \lim_{h \to 0} \left(\frac{f(x + h) - f(x)}{h} \right) = \lim_{h \to 0} \left(\frac{2(x + h)^2 + 1 - (2x^2 + 1)}{h} \right)$$

$$= \lim_{h \to 0} \left(\frac{2x^2 + 4xh + 2h^2 + 1 - 2x^2 - 1}{h} \right)$$

$$= \lim_{h \to 0} \left(\frac{h(4x + 2h)}{h} \right) = \lim_{h \to 0} (4x + 2h)$$

$$= \lim_{h \to 0} 4x + \lim_{h \to 0} 2h = 4x + 0 = 4x.$$

$\text{Lim}_{h \to 0} \, 4x = 4x$ because $4x$ is a constant with respect to h.

B   YOUR ANSWER: 2.

Are you having trouble with the limit? If $f(x) = 2x^2 + 1$, then

$$f'(x) = \lim_{h \to 0} \left(\frac{f(x + h) - f(x)}{h} \right) = \lim_{h \to 0} \left(\frac{2(x + h)^2 + 1 - (2x^2 + 1)}{h} \right).$$

Evaluate this limit and then return to frame **Q90** and try again.

C   YOUR ANSWER: 4.

Are you having trouble with the limit? If $f(x) = 2x^2 + 1$, then

$$f'(x) = \lim_{h \to 0} \left(\frac{f(x + h) - f(x)}{h} \right) = \lim_{h \to 0} \left(\frac{2(x + h)^2 + 1 - (2x^2 + 1)}{h} \right).$$

Evaluate this limit and then return to frame **Q90** and try again.

Q91 Let's try one more. Can you find the derivative of $f(x) = 1/2x$?

      Yes   Frame **A**   No   Frame **B**

A   YOUR ANSWER: Yes.

Very good. If $f(x) = 1/2x$, then

$$f'(x) = \lim_{h \to 0} \left(\frac{\dfrac{1}{2(x + h)} - \dfrac{1}{2x}}{h} \right) = \lim_{h \to 0} \left(\frac{x - (x + h)}{2hx(x + h)} \right)$$

$$= \lim_{h \to 0} \left(\frac{-h}{2hx(x + h)} \right) = \lim_{h \to 0} \left(\frac{-1}{2x(x + h)} \right) = -\frac{1}{2x^2} \, .$$

B   YOUR ANSWER: No.

Sure you can. If $f(x) = 1/2x$, then

$$f'(x) = \lim_{h \to 0} \left(\frac{\dfrac{1}{2(x + h)} - \dfrac{1}{2x}}{h} \right) = \lim_{h \to 0} \left(\frac{x - (x + h)}{2hx(x + h)} \right)$$

$$= \lim_{h \to 0} \left(\frac{-h}{2hx(x + h)} \right) = \lim_{h \to 0} \left(\frac{-1}{2x(x + h)} \right).$$

Now what happens to $-1/2x(x + h)$ as h approaches 0? Think about this and then return to frame **Q91** and select the other alternative.

Q92   If the derivative of a function f exists at $x = a$, then f is continuous at $x = a$. This is
discussed and proved on page 97 of the text. If a function is continuous at $x = a$,
does it necessarily have a derivative at $x = a$?

     Yes   Frame **A**   No   Frame **B**

A   **YOUR ANSWER:** Yes.
Sorry, but you are wrong. An example of a function that is continuous but not differentiable is given at the bottom of page 95 of the text. After studying this example,
return to frame **Q92** and select the other alternative.

B   **YOUR ANSWER:** No.
You are correct. A function may be continuous at $x = a$ without having a derivative
at $x = a$. This is discussed at the top of page 98 of the text. Remember, if a function
is differentiable, then it must be continuous, but if it is continuous, then it need not
be differentiable.

3.3   RULES FOR FINDING DERIVATIVES

OBJECTIVES

*You should know the rules for finding derivatives, such as the power rule,
derivatives of sums, the product rule, and the quotient rule.*

Q93   We have found a few derivatives using the definition. However, we are not going to
have to use this definition every time we want the derivative of a function. We are
going to develop formulas or rules for finding the derivatives of certain functions.
Of course, these formulas will be developed using the definition, but we can then use
the formulas instead of having to go back and use the definition. Let's consider a
few of these now.

    (3.9)   If $f(x) = c$, then $f'(x) = 0$.
    (3.10)   If $f(x) = x$, then $f'(x) = 1$.
    (3.12)   If $f(x) = x^n$, then $f'(x) = nx^{n-1}$ where n is a positive integer.
    (3.14)   If $g(x) = cf(x)$ where c is a real number, then $g'(x) = cf'(x)$.

These rules or formulas are derived in the text on pages 99-101. The last rule, (3.14),
says that the derivative of a constant times a function is the constant times the
derivative of the function. You should learn these formulas.
    If $f(x) = 3x^2$, what is $f'(x)$?

    3   Frame **A** $2x$ Frame **B** $6x$ Frame **C**

A   **YOUR ANSWER:** 3.
Be careful. If $f(x) = 3x^2$, then by rule (3.14), $f'(x)$ is 3 times the derivative of x^2.
What is the derivative of x^2? Now return to frame **Q93** and select the correct answer.

B   **YOUR ANSWER:** $2x$.
Be careful. If $f(x) = 3x^2$, then by rule (3.14), $f'(x)$ is 3 times the derivative of x^2.
What is the derivative of x^2? Now return to frame **Q93** and select the correct answer.

C   YOUR ANSWER: $6x$.
Correct. By rule (3.14), the derivative of $3x^2$ is 3 times the derivative of x^2, and by rule (3.12), the derivative of x^2 is $2x$. Therefore, if $f(x) = 3x^2$, then $f'(x) = 3(2x) = 6x$.

Q94   Using (3.12) and (3.14), we have if $f(x) = cx^n$, then $f'(x) = cnx^{n-1}$. If $f(x) = 5x^6$, what is $f'(x)$?

  $30x^5$ Frame **A** x^5 Frame **B** $5x$ Frame **C**

A   YOUR ANSWER: $30x^5$.
Certainly. If $f(x) = x^n$, then $f'(x) = nx^{n-1}$. Therefore, if $f(x) = 5x^6$, then $f'(x) = 5(6x^5) = 30x^5$.

B   YOUR ANSWER: x^5.
Watch out. If $f(x) = x^n$, then $f'(x) = nx^{n-1}$. The derivative of $5x^6$ is 5 times the derivative of x^6. What is the derivative of x^6 using the formula above? Now return to frame **Q94** and try again.

C   YOUR ANSWER: $5x$.
Watch out. If $f(x) = x^n$, then $f'(x) = nx^{n-1}$. The derivative of $5x^6$ is 5 times the derivative of x^6. What is the derivative of x^6 using the formula above? Now return to frame **Q94** and try again.

Q95   We also have the following rule:

  If f and g are differentiable, and if $k(x) = f(x) + g(x)$, then $k'(x) = f'(x) + g'(x)$.

That is, the derivative of the sum or difference is the sum or difference of the derivatives. This is developed on page 102 of the text. Since polynomials are sums and differences of terms of the form cx^n where n is a nonnegative integer, we have the tools to find the derivative of any polynomial.
  What is the derivative of $f(x) = 3x^5 + 4x^4 - 3x^3 + 2x^2 - 8$?

  $15x^4 + 16x^3 + 9x^2 + 4x$ Frame **A**
  $5x^4 + 4x^3 - 3x^2 + 2x$ Frame **B**
  $15x^4 + 16x^3 - 9x^2 + 4x$ Frame **C**

A   YOUR ANSWER: $15x^4 + 16x^3 + 9x^2 + 4x$.
Sorry, but you missed a sign. Return to frame **Q95**, look at $f(x)$ again, and then select the correct answer.

B   YOUR ANSWER: $5x^4 + 4x^3 - 3x^2 + 2x$.
Didn't you overlook all of the coefficients? For example, the derivative of $3x^5$ is $3(5x^4) = 15x^4$ and not simply $5x^4$. Now return to frame **Q95** and select the correct answer.

C   YOUR ANSWER: $15x^4 + 16x^3 - 9x^2 + 4x$.
Right. If $f(x) = 3x^5 + 4x^4 - 3x^3 + 2x^2 - 8$, then $f'(x) = 3(5x^4) + 4(4x^3) - 3(3x^2) + 2(2x) - 0 = 15x^4 + 16x^3 - 9x^2 + 4x$.

Q96 If the letter y is used to represent the number $f(x)$, then the derivative is written as y' or dy/dx. If $y = 2x^2 - 3x + 5$, what is y'?

$2x - 3$	Frame **A**
$4x - 3$	Frame **B**
$4x - 3 + 5$	Frame **C**

A YOUR ANSWER: $2x - 3$.
You aren't using the rules properly. Study the rules on pages 99-102 of the text and then return to frame **Q96** and try again.

B YOUR ANSWER: $4x - 3$.
Right. If $y = 2x^2 - 3x + 5$, then $y' = 2(2x) - 3(1) + 0 = 4x - 3$.

C YOUR ANSWER: $4x - 3 + 5$.
You aren't using the rule properly. Study the rules on pages 99-102 of the text and then return to frame **Q96** and try again.

Q97 We are now ready to look at the derivative of the product of two functions. Would you guess that the derivative of the product is the product of the derivatives?

Yes   Frame **A**   No   Frame **B**

A YOUR ANSWER: Yes.
Sorry, that would be a good guess, but the derivative of the product is not the product of the derivatives. Return to frame **Q97,** read page 103 of the text, and then select the other alternative.

B YOUR ANSWER: No.
Right. The derivative of the product is not the product of the derivatives.

Q98 If f and g are differentiable and if $k(x) = f(x)g(x)$, then
$$k'(x) = f(x)g'(x) + g(x)f'(x).$$
That is, the derivative of the product of two functions is the first times the derivative of the second plus the second times the derivative of the first. The product formula is developed on page 103 of the text.

Using the product rule, find the derivative of $(3x + 1)(x^2 + 3x - 5)$. Were you successful?

Yes   Frame **A**   No   Frame **B**

A YOUR ANSWER: Yes.
Very good. The derivative of $(3x + 1)(x^2 + 3x - 5)$ is $(3x + 1)(2x + 3) + (x^2 + 3x - 5)(3)$ which is $3x + 1$ times the derivative of $x^2 + 3x - 5$ plus $x^2 + 3x - 5$ times the derivative of $3x + 1$. Simplifying this, we obtain
$$(3x + 1)(2x + 3) + (x^2 + 3x - 5)(3) = 6x^2 + 11x + 3 + 3x^2 + 9x - 15$$
$$= 9x^2 + 20x - 12.$$

B YOUR ANSWER: No.
Let's see if we can get you started. The product rule states that if $k(x) = f(x)g(x)$, then $k'(x) = f(x)g'(x) + g(x)f'(x)$. Therefore, the derivative of $(3x + 1)(x^2 + 3x - 5)$

is $3x + 1$ times the derivative of $x^2 + 3x - 5$ plus $x^2 + 3x - 5$ times the derivative of $3x + 1$. After calculating this, return to frame **Q98** and select the other alternative.

Q99 Now let's consider the quotient rule:

If $k(x) = \dfrac{f(x)}{g(x)}$, $(g(x) \neq 0)$, then $k'(x) = \dfrac{g(x)f'(x) - f(x)g'(x)}{[g(x)]^2}$.

The quotient rule states that the derivative of a quotient is the denominator times the derivative of the numerator minus the numerator times the derivative of the denominator divided by the square of the denominator. This formula is developed on page 104 of the text.

Using the quotient rule, find $f'(x)$ if $f(x) = \dfrac{3x + 2}{x^2 + 1}$.

$\dfrac{3}{2x}$ Frame **A**

$\dfrac{-3x^2 - 4x + 3}{(x^2 + 1)^2}$ Frame **B**

$\dfrac{x^2 - 3x - 1}{(x^2 + 1)^2}$ Frame **C**

A   **YOUR ANSWER:** $3/2x$.
No. The derivative of the quotient is not the quotient of the derivatives. Return to frame **Q99,** use the quotient rule, and then select the correct answer.

B   **YOUR ANSWER:** $\dfrac{-3x^2 - 4x + 3}{(x^2 + 1)^2}$.

You are correct. The quotient rule states that if $k(x) = \dfrac{f(x)}{g(x)}$, then $k'(x)$

$= \dfrac{g(x)f'(x) - f(x)g'(x)}{[g(x)]^2}$. Therefore,

$$\text{if } f(x) = \frac{3x + 2}{x^2 + 1} \text{ , then } f'(x) = \frac{(x^2 + 1)3 - (3x + 2)2x}{(x^2 + 1)^2}$$

$$= \frac{3x^2 + 3 - 6x^2 - 4x}{(x^2 + 1)^2}$$

$$= \frac{-3x^2 - 4x + 3}{(x^2 + 1)^2} \ .$$

C   **YOUR ANSWER:** $\dfrac{x^2 - 3x - 1}{(x^2 + 1)^2}$.
Your calculations are off. Using the quotient rule,

$$\text{if } f(x) = \frac{3x + 2}{x^2 + 1} \text{ , then } f'(x) = \frac{(x^2 + 1)3 - (3x + 2)2x}{(x^2 + 1)^2} \ .$$

Return to frame **Q99,** study the quotient rule, and then try again.

Q100 We have already shown that if n is a natural number, and if $f(x) = x^n$, then $f'(x) = nx^{n-1}$. Now using the quotient rule, it can be shown that this formula is also valid if n

is a negative integer. For example,

$$\text{if } f(x) = x^{-3}, \text{ then } f'(x) = -3x^{-3-1} = -3x^{-4} = \frac{-3}{x^4} \ .$$

What is the derivative of x^{-5}?

$\dfrac{-5}{x^6}$ Frame **A** $\dfrac{-5}{x^4}$ Frame **B** $\dfrac{1}{x^5}$ Frame **C**

A   **YOUR ANSWER:** $-5/x^6$.
Right. If $f(x) = x^{-5}$, then $f'(x) = -5x^{-5-1} = -5x^{-6} = -5/x^6$.

B   **YOUR ANSWER:** $-5/x^4$.
Be careful. If $f(x) = x^n$, then $f'(x) = nx^{n-1}$. In our case $n = -5$; therefore, $f'(x) = -5x^{-5-1}$. Now return to frame **Q100**, simplify $f'(x)$, and select the correct answer.

C   **YOUR ANSWER:** $1/x^5$.
Don't you simply have $x^{-5} = 1/x^5$? Return to frame **Q100** and find the derivative of x^{-5}.

Q101   If $g(x) = 3/x^4$, what is $g'(x)$?

$\dfrac{-4}{x^5}$ Frame **A** $\dfrac{-12}{x^3}$ Frame **B**

$12x^3$ Frame **C** $\dfrac{-12}{x^5}$ Frame **D**

A   **YOUR ANSWER:** $-4/x^5$.
Be careful. If $g(x) = 3/x^4 = 3x^{-4}$, then $g'(x) = 3(-4)x^{-4-1}$. Now return to frame **Q101** and select the correct answer.

B   **YOUR ANSWER:** $-12/x^3$.
Be careful. If $g(x) = 3/x^4 = 3x^{-4}$, then $g'(x) = 3(-4)x^{-4-1}$. Now return to frame **Q101** and select the correct answer.

C   **YOUR ANSWER:** $12x^3$.
Didn't you find the derivative of $3x^4$ instead of $3/x^4$? Return to frame **Q101** and try again.

D   **YOUR ANSWER:** $-12/x^5$.
Good. If $g(x) = 3/x^4 = 3x^{-4}$, then $g'(x) = 3(-4)x^{-4-1} = -12x^{-5} = -12/x^5$.

Q102   We have discussed the basic rules for differentiation. As a review, find the derivative of

$$f(x) = \frac{(2x + 1)(3x^2 + 2x - 4)}{x^4 + 1} \ .$$

Were you successful?

    Yes   Frame **A**
    No   Frame **B**

A YOUR ANSWER: Yes.

Very good. If $f(x) = \dfrac{(2x + 1)(3x^2 + 2x - 4)}{x^4 + 1}$, then

$$f'(x) = \frac{(x^4 + 1)[(2x + 1)(6x + 2) + (3x^2 + 2x - 4)2] - (2x + 1)(3x^2 + 2x - 4)4x^3}{(x^4 + 1)^2}$$

$$= \frac{-6x^6 - 14x^5 + 18x^4 + 16x^3 + 18x^2 + 14x - 6}{(x^4 + 1)^2} .$$

B YOUR ANSWER: No.

Don't panic. When faced with finding the derivative of a more complicated function, simply take it a step at a time using our rules for differentiation. We have

$$f(x) = \frac{(2x + 1)(3x^2 + 2x - 4)}{x^4 + 1} .$$

Since this is a quotient, we want to use the quotient rule. However, the numerator is a product and thus when we need the derivative of the numerator, we must use the product rule. Therefore,

$$f'(x) = \frac{(x^4 + 1)[(2x + 1)(6x + 2) + (3x^2 + 2x - 4)2] - (2x + 1)(3x^2 + 2x - 4)4x^3}{(x^4 + 1)^2}$$

The quantity $[(2x + 1)(6x + 2) + (3x^2 + 2x - 4)2]$ is the derivative of $(2x + 1) \cdot$ $(3x^2 + 2x - 4)$ using the product rule. Simplify $f'(x)$ and then return to frame **Q102** and select the other alternative.

Q103 Let's state the two applications mentioned at the beginning of this chapter in terms of derivative.

The *slope* of the graph of $y = f(x)$ at the point $P(x, f(x))$ is the derivative $f'(x)$.

If the position at time t of an object moving on a straight line is $s = f(t)$, then the *velocity* at time t is the derivative $f'(t)$.

What is the slope of $y = 3x^2 + 1$ at the point $P(2, 13)$?

12	Frame **A**	2	Frame **B**
6	Frame **C**	I don't understand.	Frame **D**

A YOUR ANSWER: 12.

Right. The slope of $y = 3x^2 + 1$ at the point $P(2, 13)$ is the derivative of $y = 3x^2 + 1$ evaluated at $x = 2$. We have $y' = 6x$ which is 12 when $x = 2$.

B YOUR ANSWER: 2.

Be careful. The slope of $y = 3x^2 + 1$ at the point $P(2, 13)$ is the derivative of $y = 3x^2 + 1$ at $x = 2$. Find the derivative and then evaluate at $x = 2$. Now return to frame **Q103** and try again.

C YOUR ANSWER: 6.

Be careful. The slope of $y = 3x^2 + 1$ at the point $P(2, 13)$ is the derivative of $y = 3x^2 + 1$ at $x = 2$. Find the derivative and then evaluate at $x = 2$. Now return to frame **Q103** and try again.

D YOUR ANSWER: I don't understand.

The slope of the graph of $y = f(x)$ at the point $P(x, f(x))$ is the derivative $f'(x)$. We want the slope of $y = 3x^2 + 1$ at the point $P(2, 13)$. Therefore, we want the derivative of $y = 3x^2 + 1$ evaluated at $x = 2$. Notice that 2 is the x-coordinate of the point $P(2, 13)$ which is on the graph of $y = 3x^2 + 1$. Now return to frame **Q103** and try again.

Q104 We have the point $P(2, 13)$ on the graph of $y = 3x^2 + 1$ with slope 12 at P. Can you find the equation of the line tangent to $y = 3x^2 + 1$ at the point P?

      Yes   Frame **A**
      No   Frame **B**

A **YOUR ANSWER:** Yes.
Very good. We want the equation of the line passing through $P(2, 13)$ with slope 12. In Chapter One, we found that the equation of a line passing through $P(x_1, y_1)$ with slope m is

$$y - y_1 = m(x - x_1).$$

Therefore, the required equation is

$$y - 13 = 12(x - 2) \quad \text{or} \quad y = 12x - 11.$$

B **YOUR ANSWER:** No.
Let's see if we can help. We want the equation of the line tangent to $y = 3x^2 + 1$ at $P(2, 13)$. Since the slope of $y = 3x^2 + 1$ at P is 12, we want the equation of the line passing through $P(2, 13)$ with slope 12.

    In Chapter One, we discovered that the equation of a line passing through $P(x_1, y_1)$ with slope m is

$$y - y_1 = m(x - x_1).$$

Using $x_1 = 2$, $y_1 = 13$, and $m = 12$, find the necessary equation and then return to frame **Q104** and select the other alternative.

Q105 If the position at time t of an object moving on a straight line is $s = 2t^2 + 5t - 3$, what is its velocity at time $t = 3$?

      12   Frame **A**
      17   Frame **B**
      I don't understand.   Frame **C**

A **YOUR ANSWER:** 12.
Sorry, but you made a mistake. If $s = 2t^2 + 5t - 3$, then $s' = 4t + 5$. Now evaluate s' when $t = 3$ and then return to frame **Q105** and select the correct answer.

B **YOUR ANSWER:** 17.
Right. If $s = 2t^2 + 5t - 3$, then $s' = 4t + 5$. Therefore, the velocity at $t = 3$ is $4(3) + 5 = 17$.

C **YOUR ANSWER:** I don't understand.
If the position at time t of an object moving on a straight line is $s = f(t)$, then the velocity at time t is the derivative $f'(t)$. Therefore, the velocity at $t = 3$ is the derivative of $s = 2t^2 + 5t - 3$ evaluated at $t = 3$. Now return to frame **Q105** and try again.

3.4 INCREMENTS AND DIFFERENTIALS

OBJECTIVES

You should know how to find the exact change in a function given a change in the independent variable. You should also know what is meant by the differential of a function and how to use the differential to approximate the exact change in a function given a change in the independent variable.

Q106 The exact change in y corresponding to a change of Δx in x is
$$\Delta y = f(x + \Delta x) - f(x).$$
If $y = 3x^2$, what is Δy when x changes from $x = 2$ to $x = 2.5$?

6	Frame **A**	6.75	Frame **B**
5.5	Frame **C**	I don't know.	Frame **D**

A **YOUR ANSWER:** 6.
If x changes from 2 to 2.5, then $\Delta y = f(2.5) - f(2)$. Return to frame **Q106** and find Δy.

B **YOUR ANSWER:** 6.75.
Correct. If x changes from $x = 2$ to $x = 2.5$, and $f(x) = 3x^2$, then $\Delta y = f(2.5) - f(2) = 18.75 - 12 = 6.75$.

C **YOUR ANSWER:** 5.5.
Your calculations are off. We have $f(x) = 3x^2$. If x changes from 2 to 2.5, then $\Delta y = f(2.5) - f(2)$. Now return to frame **Q106** and try again.

D **YOUR ANSWER:** I don't know.
Let's see if we can help. We have $f(x) = 3x^2$. We want Δy, the exact change in y, when x changes from 2 to 2.5. Therefore, $\Delta y = f(2.5) - f(2)$. Now return to frame **Q106** and try again.

Q107 If $y = f(x)$ is a differentiable function and Δx is an increment of x, then we define dy, the *differential* of y, in the following manner:
$$dy = f'(x)\Delta x.$$
Notice that dy depends on $f'(x)$ and Δx.
If $y = 4x^2$, what is dy?

$8x\,\Delta x$	Frame **A**	$4x^2\,\Delta x$	Frame **B**	$2x\,\Delta x$	Frame **C**

A **YOUR ANSWER:** $8x\,\Delta x$.
Right. If $f(x) = 4x^2$, then $dy = f'(x)\Delta x = 8x\,\Delta x$. We also define $\Delta x = dx$. Therefore, $dy = f'(x)dx$. In our problem, $dy = 8x\,dx$.

B **YOUR ANSWER:** $4x^2\,\Delta x$.
Didn't you use $f(x)$ instead of $f'(x)$? We have $dy = f'(x)\Delta x$. If $f(x) = 4x^2$, find $f'(x)$ and thus dy. Now return to frame **Q107** and select the correct answer.

C   YOUR ANSWER: $2x\,\Delta x$.
Didn't you make an error in determining $f'(x)$? We have $dy = f'(x)\Delta x$. If $f(x) =$ $4x^2$, find $f'(x)$ and thus dy. Now return to frame **Q107** and select the correct answer.

Q108 A geometrical interpretation of Δy and dy is discussed on page 110 of the text. The differential of y, dy, is an approximate change in y corresponding to a change Δx in x, whereas, Δy is the exact change in y.

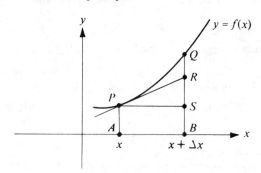

In the above figure, which segment represents dy?

AP Frame **A** SQ Frame **B** SR Frame **C**

A   YOUR ANSWER: AP.
No. The segment AP is simply $f(x)$. Return to frame **Q108**, study the discussion on page 110 of the text, and then try again.

B   YOUR ANSWER: SQ.
No. The segment SQ is Δy, the exact change in y; that is, $\Delta y = f(x + \Delta x) - f(x)$. Return to frame **Q108**, study the discussion on page 110 of the text, and then try again.

C   YOUR ANSWER: SR.
Right. The segment SR is the approximate change in y as discussed on page 110 of the text.

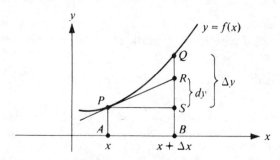

Q109 In many cases dy is easier to evaluate than Δy and we simply use dy to approximate Δy corresponding to a small change Δx in x. What is the approximate change in the area of a circle if the radius changes from 5 to 5.2 inches?

2π square inches	Frame **A**
0.04π square inches	Frame **B**
1.08 square inches	Frame **C**
I need some help.	Frame **D**

A   **YOUR ANSWER:** 2π square inches.
Good. If $A = \pi r^2$, then $dA = 2\pi r\, dr$. If r changes from 5 to 5.2, $r = 5$ and $dr = 0.2$. Therefore, $dA = 2\pi r\, dr$ and we have $dA = 2\pi(5)(0.2) = 2\pi$.

B   **YOUR ANSWER:** 0.04π square inches.
You are off base. If $A = \pi r^2$, then $dA = 2\pi r\, dr$. We want dA when $r = 5$ and $dr = 0.2$. Now return to frame **Q109** and try again.

C   **YOUR ANSWER:** 1.08π square inches.
You are off base. If $A = \pi r^2$, then $dA = 2\pi r\, dr$. We want dA when $r = 5$ and $dr = 0.2$. Now return to frame **Q109** and try again.

D   **YOUR ANSWER:**   I need some help.
Let's see if we can help. The area of a circle is $A = \pi r^2$. We want the change in A when r changes from 5 to 5.2; that is, we want dA when $r = 5$ and $dr = 0.2$. Now return to frame **Q109** and try again.

3.5   THE CHAIN RULE

OBJECTIVES

You should know the chain rule and the power rule for functions and how to use them to find the derivatives of functions.

Q110   Now let's consider the concept of a *function of a function*. We say y is a function of a function of x if $y = f(u)$ and $u = g(x)$; that is, $y = f[g(x)]$. In general, we have y a function of u where u in turn is a function of x; therefore, y is basically a function of x. For example, if $y = u^4$ where $u = 2x^2 + 1$, then we have $y = (2x^2 + 1)^4$.

Now we would like to find the derivative of a function of a function. In the example above, we could expand $(2x^2 + 1)^4$ and use the methods we already have available. However, it would be desirable to be able to find the derivative without having to do this.

If the derivatives $f'(u)$ and $g'(x)$ exist for the values of u and x under consideration, if f' is continuous, and if $y = f[g(x)]$, then

$$\frac{dy}{dx} = \frac{dy}{du} \cdot \frac{du}{dx}$$

with $u = g(x)$. This is referred to as the Chain Rule and is discussed on page 115 of the text. In our example above, if $y = u^4$ where $u = 2x^2 + 1$ or $y = (2x^2 + 1)^4$, then

$$\frac{dy}{dx} = \frac{dy}{du} \cdot \frac{du}{dx}$$
$$= (4u^3)(4x) = 16x(2x^2 + 1)^3, \text{ since } u = 2x^2 + 1.$$

If $y = (2x^3 + 5)^5$, find dy/dx.

$5(2x^3 + 5)^4$	Frame **A**
$30x^2(2x + 5)^4$	Frame **B**
$5(6x^2)^4$	Frame **C**
I don't know.	Frame **D**

A **YOUR ANSWER:** $5(2x^3 + 5)^4$.
You are off base. If $y = (2x^3 + 5)^5$, let $u = 2x^3 + 5$. Now we have $y = u^5$ where $u = 2x^3 + 5$. Therefore,

$$\frac{dy}{dx} = \frac{dy}{du} \cdot \frac{du}{dx} = (5u^4)(6x^2).$$

Now return to frame **Q110** and try again.

B **YOUR ANSWER:** $30x^2(2x^3 + 5)^4$.
Very good. If $y = (2x^3 + 5)^5$, let $u = 2x^3 + 5$. Now we have $y = u^5$ where $u = 2x^3 + 5$. Therefore,

$$\frac{dy}{dx} = \frac{dy}{du} \cdot \frac{du}{dx}$$
$$= (5u^4)(6x^2) = 30x^2u^4 = 30x^2(2x^3 + 5)^4.$$

Notice that we can find dy/dx directly by simply taking $5(2x^3 + 5)^{5-1}$ times the derivative of the expression $2x^3 + 5$, which is $5(2x^3 + 5)^4(6x^2) = 30x^2(2x^3 + 5)^4$.

C **YOUR ANSWER:** $5(6x^2)^4$.
You are off base. If $y = (2x^3 + 5)^5$, let $u = 2x^3 + 5$. Now we have $y = u^5$ where $u = 2x^3 + 5$. Therefore,

$$\frac{dy}{dx} = \frac{dy}{du} \cdot \frac{du}{dx} = (5u^4)(6x^2).$$

Now return to frame **Q110** and try again.

D **YOUR ANSWER:**   I don't know.
Let's see if we can get you started. If $y = (2x^3 + 5)^5$, let $u = 2x^3 + 5$. Now we have $y = u^5$ where $u = 2x^3 + 5$. Therefore,

$$\frac{dy}{dx} = \frac{dy}{du} \cdot \frac{du}{dx} .$$

Evaluate this derivative and then simplify. Now return to frame **Q110** and try again.

Q111   Using the Chain Rule, we obtain a general power rule for functions.

If $k(x) = [g(x)]^n$, then
$$k'(x) = n[g(x)]^{n-1}g'(x).$$

This is (3.38) on page 117 of the text. Examples 2, 3, and 4 on page 118 illustrate the use of this rule.

If $f(x) = (2x^2 + x - 3)^4$, what is $f'(x)$?

$4(2x^2 + x - 3)^3$	Frame **A**
$4(2x^2 + x - 3)^3(4x + 1)$	Frame **B**
$4(4x + 1)^3$	Frame **C**

A **YOUR ANSWER:** $4(2x^2 + x - 3)^3$.

You are on the right track, but you forgot to multiply by the derivative of the expression $2x^2 + x - 3$. Return to frame **Q111** and select the correct answer.

B **YOUR ANSWER:** $4(2x^2 + x - 3)^3(4x + 1)$.

Correct. If $f(x) = (2x^2 + x - 3)^4$, then $f'(x)$ is $4(2x^2 + x - 3)^{4-1}$ time the derivative of the expression $2x^2 + x - 3$. Therefore,

$$f'(x) = 4(2x^2 + x - 3)^{4-1}(4x + 1)$$
$$= 4(2x^2 + x - 3)^3(4x + 1).$$

C **YOUR ANSWER:** $4(4x + 1)^3$.

Be careful. If $f(x) = (2x^2 + x - 3)^4$, then $f'(x)$ is $4(2x^2 + x - 3)^{4-1}$ times the derivative of the expression $2x^2 + x - 3$. Now return to frame **Q111** and try again.

Q112 If $f(x) = \dfrac{(3x + 1)^2}{(x^2 - 3)^4}$, find $f'(x)$. How did it go?

      Great   Frame **A**   Miserable   Frame **B**

A **YOUR ANSWER:** Great.

Very good. If $f(x) = \dfrac{(3x + 1)^2}{(x^2 - 3)^4}$, then by the quotient rule, we have

$$f'(x) = \frac{(x^2 - 3)^4 D_x[(3x + 1)^2] - (3x + 1)^2 D_x[(x^2 - 3)^4]}{(x^2 - 3)^8}$$

$$= \frac{(x^2 - 3)^4(2)(3x + 1)(3) - (3x + 1)^2(4)(x^2 - 3)^3(2x)}{(x^2 - 3)^8}$$

$$= \frac{6(x^2 - 3)^4(3x + 1) - 8x(x^2 - 3)^3(3x + 1)^2}{(x^2 - 3)^8}$$

$$= \frac{6(x^2 - 3)(3x + 1) - 8x(3x + 1)^2}{(x^2 - 3)^5} .$$

Notice that

$$D_x[(3x + 1)^2] = 2(3x + 1)(3) = 6(3x + 1)$$

and

$$D_x[(x^2 - 3)^4] = 4(x^2 - 3)^3(2x) = 8x(x^2 - 3)^3.$$

B **YOUR ANSWER:** Miserable.

Let's see if we can cheer you up. If $f(x) = \dfrac{(3x + 1)^2}{(x^2 - 3)^4}$, then using the quotient rule, we have

$$f'(x) = \frac{(x^2 - 3)^4 D_x[(3x + 1)^2] - (3x + 1)^2 D_x[(x^2 - 3)^4]}{(x^2 - 3)^8} .$$

Now find $D_x[(3x + 1)^2]$ and $D_x[(x^2 - 3)^4]$ and simplify. Return to frame **Q112** and select the other alternative.

Q113 If $f(x) = (x^2 + 3)^4$, what is dy?

$$8x(x^2 + 3)^3 \, dx \qquad \text{Frame } \mathbf{A}$$
$$4(x^2 + 3)^3 \, dx \qquad \text{Frame } \mathbf{B}$$
$$(2x)^4 \, dx \qquad \text{Frame } \mathbf{C}$$

A   **YOUR ANSWER:** $8x(x^2 + 3)^3 \, dx.$
Correct. If $f(x) = (x^2 + 3)^4$, then $dy = 4(x^2 + 3)^3(2x) \, dx = 8x(x^2 + 3)^3 \, dx.$

B   **YOUR ANSWER:** $4(x^2 + 3)^3 \, dx.$
Didn't you overlook the derivative of $x^2 + 3$? If $f(x) = (x^2 + 3)^4$, then $f'(x)$ is $4(x^2 + 3)^3$ times the derivative of $x^2 + 3$. Now return to frame **Q113** and try again.

C   **YOUR ANSWER:** $(2x)^4 \, dx.$
You are off base. If $f(x) = (x^2 + 3)^4$, then $f'(x)$ is $4(x^2 + 3)^3$ times the derivative of $x^2 + 3$. Now return to frame **Q113** and try again.

Q114   If $y = (x^2 + 3)^4$, we found that $dy = 8x(x^2 + 3)^3 \, dx$. If $x = 2$ and $dx = 0.1$, what is dy?

548.8	Frame **A**	78.4	Frame **B**
274.4	Frame **C**	I don't know.	Frame **D**

A   **YOUR ANSWER:**   548.8.
You are correct. We have $dy = 8x(x^2 + 3)^3 \, dx$. If $x = 2$ and $dx = 0.1$, then $dy = 8(2)(7)^3(0.1) = 548.8.$

B   **YOUR ANSWER:**   78.4.
Your calculations are off. We have $dy = 8x(x^2 + 3)^3 \, dx$. If $x = 2$ and $dx = 0.1$, then $dy = 8(2)(7)^3(0.1)$. Now return to frame **Q114** and select the correct answer.

C   **YOUR ANSWER:**   274.4.
Your calculations are off. We have $dy = 8x(x^2 + 3)^3 \, dx$. If $x = 2$ and $dx = 0.1$, then $dy = 8(2)(7)^3(0.1)$. Now return to frame **Q114** and select the correct answer.

D   **YOUR ANSWER:**   I don't know.
We have $dy = 8x(x^2 + 3)^3 \, dx$. We want to evaluate dy when $x = 2$ and $dx = 0.1$. Now return to frame **Q114,** substitute these values in the expression for dy, and then try again.

3.6   IMPLICIT DIFFERENTIATION

OBJECTIVES

You should know what is meant by an implicit function. You should also be able to use the technique of implicit differentiation to find the derivative of a function.

Q115   We have been considering functions in which y is expressed explicitly in terms of x. However, it may be that y and x are connected by an equation expressed in the form $F(x, y) = 0$. For example, $x^2 + 2xy + y^3 + 2 = 0$. If the equation $F(x, y) = 0$ determines y as a function of x, we say that $F(x, y) = 0$ determines y as a function of x *implicitly* or that y is an implied function of x. For example, in the expression $2x + 3y = 4$, y is an implied function of x. If we solve for y, we have $y = -2x/3 + 4/3$ where y is an explicit function of x.

Sometimes it may be difficult to solve for y explicitly, but we might still want the derivative. Assuming that y is a differentiable function of x, we can find $y'(dy/dx)$ if $F(x, y)$ is sufficiently simple by differentiating $F(x, y) = 0$ term by term and then solving for y'. For example, suppose we want y' when $xy + x^2 = 0$. Differentiating term by term, we obtain $(xy' + y) + 2x = 0$ or $y' = -(y + 2x)/x$. Notice that $xy' + y$ is the derivative of xy using the product rule.

Study the examples on pages 122-124 of the text and then find y' if $3xy + 2y = 0$.

$$\dfrac{-3y}{3x + 2} \quad \text{Frame A} \qquad \dfrac{-3(x + y)}{2} \quad \text{Frame B} \qquad \dfrac{-3x}{2} \quad \text{Frame C}$$

A **YOUR ANSWER:** $\dfrac{-3y}{3x + 2}$.

Very good. If $3xy + 2y = 0$, then we have

$$3(xy' + y) + 2y' = 0$$
$$(3x + 2)y' + 3y = 0$$
$$y' = \frac{-3y}{3x + 2}.$$

B **YOUR ANSWER:** $\dfrac{-3(x + y)}{2}$.

You are off base. If $3xy + 2y = 0$, then differentiating term by term we obtain $3(xy' + y) + 2y' = 0$. Now solve for y' and then return to frame **Q115** and select the correct answer.

C **YOUR ANSWER:** $\dfrac{-3x}{2}$.

You are off base. If $3xy + 2y = 0$, then differentiating term by term we obtain $3(xy' + y) + 2y' = 0$. Now solve for y' and then return to frame **Q115** and select the correct answer.

Q116 What is the slope of the curve $4x^2 + 9y^2 = 25$ at the point $P(2, -1)$?

$-4/9$	Frame **A**	$8/9$	Frame **B**
$-8/9$	Frame **C**	I don't know.	Frame **D**

A **YOUR ANSWER:** $-4/9$.

Be careful. If $4x^2 + 9y^2 = 25$, then differentiating term by term we obtain

$$8x + 18yy' = 0$$
$$y' = \frac{-8x}{18y}.$$

Isn't the slope of the curve $4x^2 + 9y^2 = 25$ obtained by evaluating the derivative at $P(2, -1)$? Return to frame **Q116** and try again.

B **YOUR ANSWER:** $8/9$.

Correct. If $4x^2 + 9y^2 = 25$, then we obtain

$$8x + 18yy' = 0$$
$$y' = \frac{-8x}{18y}.$$

Evaluating at $P(2, -1)$, we have

$$y' = \frac{(-8)(2)}{18(-1)} = 8/9.$$

C   YOUR ANSWER: $-8/9$.
Sorry, but you missed a sign. If $4x^2 + 9y^2 = 25$, then differentiating term by term we obtain

$$8x + 18yy' = 0$$
$$y' = \frac{-8x}{18y}.$$

Now return to frame **Q116**, evaluate y' at $P(2, -1)$, and select the correct answer.

D   YOUR ANSWER: I don't know.
Let's see if we can help. The slope of the curve $4x^2 + 9y^2 = 25$ at the point $P(2, -1)$ is the derivative evaluated at P. Differentiating term by term, we obtain

$$8x + 18yy' = 0$$
$$y' = \frac{-8x}{18y}.$$

Now return to frame **Q116** and try again.

3.7   DERIVATIVES OF ALGEBRAIC FUNCTIONS

OBJECTIVES

You should be able to find the derivatives of algebraic functions.

Q117   With the aid of the formula for the derivative of a function, we can show that

$$\text{if } f(x) = x^n \ (n \text{ rational}), \text{ then } f'(x) = nx^{n-1}$$

whenever nx^{n-1} exists. For example, if $f(x) = x^{1/2}$, then $f'(x) = (1/2)x^{(1/2)-1} = (1/2)x^{-1/2} = 1/2x^{1/2}$. Notice that this is the same formula we had for n an integer. This formula is developed on page 126 of the text.
    If $y = x^{2/3}$, what is y'?

$\dfrac{2}{3}x^{1/3}$ Frame **A** $\dfrac{1}{x^{1/3}}$ Frame **B** $\dfrac{2}{3x^{1/3}}$ Frame **C**

A   YOUR ANSWER: $(2/3)x^{1/3}$.
Be careful. If $y = x^{2/3}$ then $y' = (2/3)x^{(2/3)-1}$. Return to frame **Q117** and try again.

B   YOUR ANSWER: $\dfrac{1}{x^{1/3}}$.
Be careful. If $y = x^{2/3}$, then $y' = (2/3)x^{(2/3)-1}$. Return to frame **Q117** and try again.

C   YOUR ANSWER: $\dfrac{2}{3x^{1/3}}$.

Right. If $y = x^{2/3}$, then $y' = (2/3)x^{(2/3)-1} = (2/3)x^{-1/3} = 2/(3x^{1/3})$.

Q118   In conjunction with the Chain Rule, we can now find the derivative of the radical of any rational function.

What is the derivative of $\sqrt{3x^2 + 2x + 1}$? (*Hint*: Let $\sqrt{3x^2 + 2x + 1} = (3x^2 + 2x + 1)^{1/2}$.)

$\dfrac{3x + 1}{\sqrt{3x^2 + 2x + 1}}$ Frame **A**

$(3x + 1)\sqrt{3x^2 + 2x + 1}$ Frame **B**

$\dfrac{6x + 2}{\sqrt{3x^2 + 2x + 1}}$ Frame **C**

A   YOUR ANSWER: $\dfrac{3x + 1}{\sqrt{3x^2 + 2x + 1}}$.

Correct. If $y = \sqrt{3x^2 + 2x + 1} = (3x^2 + 2x + 1)^{1/2}$, then

$$y' = (1/2)(3x^2 + 2x + 1)^{-1/2}(6x + 2) = \dfrac{3x + 1}{\sqrt{3x^2 + 2x + 1}} \ .$$

B   YOUR ANSWER: $(3x + 1)\sqrt{3x^2 + 2x + 1}$.

Almost, but you have the sign wrong on the exponent of the factor $3x^2 + 2x + 1$. If $y = \sqrt{3x^2 + 2x + 1} = (3x^2 + 2x + 1)^{1/2}$, then $y' = (1/2)(3x^2 + 2x + 1)^{-1/2}(6x + 2)$. Return to frame **Q118** and select the correct answer.

C   YOUR ANSWER: $\dfrac{6x + 2}{\sqrt{3x^2 + 2x + 1}}$.

Almost, but you forgot to multiply by 1/2. If $y = \sqrt{3x^2 + 2x + 1} = (3x^2 + 2x + 1)^{1/2}$, then $y' = (1/2)(3x^2 + 2x + 1)^{-1/2}(6x + 2)$. Return to frame **Q118** and select the correct answer.

Q119   If $f(x) = \dfrac{2}{\sqrt[3]{2x + 1}}$, find $f'(x)$.

$\dfrac{-2}{3(2x + 1)^{4/3}}$ Frame **A**

$\dfrac{-4}{3(2x + 1)^{4/3}}$ Frame **B**

$\dfrac{-4}{3(2x + 1)^{2/3}}$ Frame **C**

I need some help.   Frame **D**

A   YOUR ANSWER: $\dfrac{-2}{3(2x + 1)^{4/3}}$.

Almost, but you forgot to multiply by the derivative of the expression $2x + 1$. If $f(x) = 2/\sqrt[3]{2x + 1} = 2(2x + 1)^{-1/3}$, then $f'(x) = 2(-1/3)(2x + 1)^{(-1/3)-1}(2)$. Now return to frame **Q119** and select the correct answer.

B   YOUR ANSWER: $\dfrac{-4}{3(2x\ +\ 1)^{4/3}}$.

Excellent. If $f(x)\ =\ 2/\sqrt[3]{2x\ +\ 1}\ =\ 2(2x\ +\ 1)^{-1/3}$, then

$$f'(x)\ =\ 2(-1/3)(2x\ +\ 1)^{(-1/3)-1}(2)$$

$$=\ (-4/3)(2x\ +\ 1)^{-4/3}\ =\ \dfrac{-4}{3(2x\ +\ 1)^{4/3}}\ .$$

C   YOUR ANSWER: $\dfrac{-4}{3(2x\ +\ 1)^{2/3}}$.

Sorry, but you made a mistake on the exponent. If $f(x)\ =\ 2/\sqrt[3]{2x\ +\ 1}\ =\ 2(2x\ +\ 1)^{-1/3}$, then $f'(x)\ =\ 2(-1/3)(2x\ +\ 1)^{(-1/3)-1}(2)$. Now return to frame **Q119** and select the correct answer.

D   YOUR ANSWER: I need some help.

Let's see if we can give you some help. Express $2/\sqrt[3]{2x\ +\ 1}$ as $2(2x\ +\ 1)^{-1/3}$. Now find the derivative using the function of a function rule and the rule if $f(x)\ =\ x^n$, then $f'(x)\ =\ nx^{n-1}$. Return to frame **Q119** and try again.

Q120   Find the derivative of $y\ =\ (2x^2\ +\ 1)/\sqrt{3x\ +\ 2}$. (*Hint*: Use the quotient rule.) How did it go?

Great   Frame **A**   Bad   Frame **B**

A   YOUR ANSWER: Great.

Very good. If $y\ =\ (2x^2\ +\ 1)/\sqrt{3x\ +\ 2}$, then using the quotient rule

$$y'\ =\ \dfrac{\sqrt{3x\ +\ 2}\,(\text{derivative of }2x^2\ +\ 1)\ -\ (2x^2\ +\ 1)\,(\text{derivative of }\sqrt{3x\ +\ 2})}{(\sqrt{3x\ +\ 2})^2}$$

$$=\ \dfrac{\sqrt{3x\ +\ 2}(4x)\ -\ (2x^2\ +\ 1)[(1/2)(3x\ +\ 2)^{-1/2}(3)]}{3x\ +\ 2}$$

$$=\ \dfrac{(3x\ +\ 2)^{1/2}(4x)\ -\ \dfrac{3(2x^2\ +\ 1)}{2(3x\ +\ 2)^{1/2}}}{3x\ +\ 2}\ =\ \dfrac{18x^2\ +\ 16x\ -\ 3}{2(3x\ +\ 2)^{3/2}}\ .$$

B   YOUR ANSWER: Bad.

It really isn't as bad as it looks. We have $y\ =\ (2x^2\ +\ 1)/\sqrt{3x\ +\ 2}$. Using the quotient rule, we obtain

$$y'\ =\ \dfrac{\sqrt{3x\ +\ 2}\,(\text{derivative of }2x^2\ +\ 1)\ -\ (2x^2\ +\ 1)\,(\text{derivative of }\sqrt{3x\ +\ 2})}{(\sqrt{3x\ +\ 2})^2}\ .$$

Supply the missing derivatives and simplify. Now return to frame **Q120** and select the other alternative.

Q121   Let's try one more. Can you find the derivative of $(\sqrt{2x\ +\ 1}\ +\ x^2)^3$?

Yes   Frame **A**   No   Frame **B**

A   YOUR ANSWER: Yes.

Wonderful.

If $y = (\sqrt{2x + 1} + x^2)^3$, then
$$y' = 3(\sqrt{2x + 1} + x^2)^2[(1/2)(2x + 1)^{-1/2}(2) + 2x]$$
$$= 3(\sqrt{2x + 1} + x^2)^2[(2x + 1)^{-1/2} + 2x].$$

B   YOUR ANSWER: No.
Sure you can. If $y = (\sqrt{2x + 1} + x^2)^3$, then y' is $3(\sqrt{2x + 1} + x^2)^2$ times the derivative of $\sqrt{2x + 1} + x^2$. Now return to frame **Q121**, find the derivative, and select the other alternative.

Q122   What is the slope of the curve $y = \sqrt{2x + 1}$ at the point $P(4, 3)$?

1/3	Frame **A**	1/9	Frame **B**
3/2	Frame **C**	I don't understand.	Frame **D**

A   YOUR ANSWER: 1/3.
Right. If $y = \sqrt{2x + 1} = (2x + 1)^{1/2}$, then $y' = (1/2)(2x + 1)^{-1/2}(2) = 1/\sqrt{2x + 1}$. Therefore, the slope of $y = \sqrt{2x + 1}$ at $P(4, 3)$ is $1/\sqrt{2 \cdot 4 + 1} = 1/\sqrt{9} = 1/3$. Since the slope is 1/3, the tangent line to the curve at $P(4, 3)$ is $y - 3 = (1/3)(x - 4)$ or $3y = x + 5$.

B   YOUR ANSWER: 1/9.
Be careful. The slope of the curve $y = \sqrt{2x + 1}$ at $P(4, 3)$ is the derivative evaluated at $x = 4$. Since $y = \sqrt{2x + 1} = (2x + 1)^{1/2}$,
$$y' = \frac{1}{2}(2x + 1)^{-1/2}(2) = \frac{1}{(2x + 1)^{1/2}} = \frac{1}{\sqrt{2x + 1}} \ .$$
After evaluating y' at $x = 4$, return to frame **Q122** and select the correct answer.

C   YOUR ANSWER: 3/2.
Be careful. The slope of the curve $y = \sqrt{2x + 1}$ at $P(4, 3)$ is the derivative evaluated at $x = 4$. Since $y = \sqrt{2x + 1} = (2x + 1)^{1/2}$,
$$y' = \frac{1}{2}(2x + 1)^{-1/2}(2) = \frac{1}{(2x + 1)^{1/2}} = \frac{1}{\sqrt{2x + 1}} \ .$$
After evaluating y' at $x = 4$, return to frame **Q122** and select the correct answer.

D   YOUR ANSWER: I don't understand.
The slope of the curve $y = \sqrt{2x + 1}$ at $P(4, 3)$ is the value of y' at $x = 4$. Return to frame **Q122** and try again.

Q123   Using differentials, approximate $\sqrt{65}$.

1/16	Frame **A**
1/8	Frame **B**
I need some help.	Frame **C**

A   YOUR ANSWER: 1/16.
Excellent. In order to approximate $\sqrt{65}$, let $y = \sqrt{x}$; therefore, $dy = dx/2\sqrt{x}$. Now if $x = 64$ and $dx = 1$, we have $dy = 1/2\sqrt{64} = 1/16$.

B   **YOUR ANSWER:**   1/8.
You have an error somewhere. In order to approximate $\sqrt{65}$, let $y = \sqrt{x}$ where $x = 64$ and $dx = 1$. Now return to frame **Q123** and try again.

C   **YOUR ANSWER:**   I need some help.
All right. In order to approximate $\sqrt{65}$, let $y = \sqrt{x}$ where $x = 64$ and $dx = 1$. Now find dy using these values of x and dx. We let $x = 64$ because $\sqrt{64}$ is exact. Now return to frame **Q123** and try again.

3.8   HIGHER ORDER DERIVATIVES

OBJECTIVES

You should know what is meant by higher order derivatives and how to find higher order derivatives.

Q124   The notion of higher order derivatives is discussed on page 129 of the text.
If $f(x) = 2x^3 + 6x^2 - x + 5$, what is $f''(x)$?

$6x^2 + 12x - 1$	Frame **A**	$12x$	Frame **B**
$12x + 12$	Frame **C**	0	Frame **D**

A   **YOUR ANSWER:** $6x^2 + 12x - 1$.
Not exactly. If $f(x) = 2x^3 + 6x^2 - x + 5$, then $f'(x) = 6x^2 + 12x - 1$. Now find the derivative of $f'(x)$ and return to frame **Q124** and select the correct answer.

B   **YOUR ANSWER:** $12x$.
Be careful. You left off a term. If $f(x) = 2x^3 + 6x^2 - x + 5$, then $f'(x) = 6x^2 + 12x - 1$. Now find the derivative of $f'(x)$ and return to frame **Q124** and select the correct answer.

C   **YOUR ANSWER:** $12x + 12$.
Of course.

$$f(x) = 2x^3 + 6x^2 - x + 5$$
$$f'(x) = 6x^2 + 12x - 1$$
$$f''(x) = 12x + 12.$$

D   **YOUR ANSWER:**   0.
Where did you get this? You need to differentiate successively twice in order to obtain $f''(x)$. Now return to frame **Q124** and try again.

Q125   If $y = \sqrt{x + 3}$, find $D_x^2 y$.

$$\frac{1}{2\sqrt{x + 3}} \qquad \text{Frame } \mathbf{A}$$

$$\frac{1}{(x + 3)^{3/2}} \qquad \text{Frame } \mathbf{B}$$

$$\frac{-1}{4(x + 3)^{3/2}} \qquad \text{Frame } \mathbf{C}$$

A   YOUR ANSWER: $1/(2\sqrt{x + 3})$.
Don't you have $D_x y$ instead of $D_x^2 y$? Find the derivative of your answer. Now return to frame **Q125** and try again.

B   YOUR ANSWER: $1/(x + 3)^{3/2}$.
Almost, but you don't have the correct coefficient.

$$y = \sqrt{x + 3} = (x + 3)^{1/2}$$
$$D_x y = (1/2)(x + 3)^{-1/2}$$

Now find the derivative of $D_x y$, return to frame **Q125,** and select the correct answer.

C   YOUR ANSWER: $-1/4(x + 3)^{3/2}$.
Very good.

$$y = \sqrt{x + 3} = (x + 3)^{1/2}$$
$$D_x y = (1/2)(x + 3)^{-1/2}$$
$$D_x^2 y = (-1/4)(x + 3)^{-3/2}$$
$$= \frac{-1}{4(x + 3)^{3/2}}$$

Q126   Study Example 2 on page 130 of the text which illustrates how to find higher derivatives of implicit functions. Let's try one. If $xy + x^2 - y = 0$, find y''. Were you successful?

Yes   Frame **A**   No   Frame **B**

A   YOUR ANSWER: Yes.
Excellent.

$$xy + x^2 - y = 0$$
$$xy' + y + 2x - y' = 0$$

Therefore, $y' = (y + 2x)/(1 - x)$. Now

$$y'' = \frac{(1 - x)(y' + 2) - (y + 2x)(-1)}{(1 - x)^2}$$

Substituting the value of y', we have

$$y'' = \frac{(1 - x)\left(\dfrac{y + 2x}{1 - x} + 2\right) + (y + 2x)}{(1 - x)^2}$$

$$= \frac{y + 2x + 2(1 - x) + y + 2x}{(1 - x)^2} = \frac{2y + 2x + 2}{(1 - x)^2}.$$

B   YOUR ANSWER: No.
Let's see if we can get you started.

$$xy + x^2 - y = 0$$
$$(xy' + y) + 2x - y' = 0$$

Solving for y', we have

$$y' = \frac{y + 2x}{1 - x}.$$

Now find y'' by using the quotient rule and substituting the value of y' in the result. Return to frame **Q126**, complete the problem, and select the other response.

Q127 In this chapter we have developed several differentiation formulas. As a review of these formulas, which one of the following groups contains an error?

If $y = x^5 + 5x^4 - 10x^2 + 6$, then $dy/dx = 5x^4 + 20x^3 - 20x$.
If $y = 3x^{1/2} - x^{3/2} + 2x^{-1/2}$, then $y' = 3/2x^{1/2} - 3x^{1/2}/2 - 1/x^{3/2}$.   Frame **A**
If $y = (1 - 5x)^6$, then $y' = -30(1 - 5x)^5$.

If $f(x) = (3x - x^3 + 1)^4$, then $f'(x) = 12(1 - x^2)(3x - x^3 + 1)^3$.
If $y = (3 + 4x - x^2)^{1/2}$, then $y' = (2 - x)/(3 + 4x - x^2)^{1/2}$.   Frame **B**
If $r = (3s + 2)/(2s + 3)$, then $dr/ds = 5/(2s + 3)^2$.

If $y = \left(\dfrac{x}{1 + x}\right)^5$, then $y' = \dfrac{5x^2}{(1 + x)^6}$.

If $f(x) = (x - 1)\sqrt{x^2 - 2x + 2}$, then $f'(x) = \dfrac{2x^2 - 4x + 3}{\sqrt{x^2 - 2x + 2}}$ Frame **C**

If $xy + x - 2y - 1 = 0$, then $y' = (1 + y)/(2 - x)$.

A   YOUR ANSWER:

If $y = x^5 + 5x^4 - 10x^2 + 6$, then $dy/dx = 5x^4 + 20x^3 - 20x$.
If $y = 3x^{1/2} - x^{3/2} + 2x^{-1/2}$, then $y' = 3/2x^{1/2} - 3x^{1/2}/2 - 1/x^{3/2}$.
If $y = (1 - 5x)^6$, then $y' = -30(1 - 5x)^5$.

All of these are correct. The first two use the rule that the derivative of the sum is the sum of the derivatives and the theorem that states if $f(x) = x^n$, then $f'(x) = nx^{n-1}$. In the last one, we need the Chain Rule. If $y = (1 - 5x)^6$, then $y' = 6(1 - 5x)(-5)$ where -5 is the derivative of the expression $1 - 5x$. Now return to frame **Q127** and select the group that contains an error.

B   YOUR ANSWER:

If $f(x) = (3x - x^3 + 1)^4$, then $f'(x) = 12(1 - x^2)(3x - x^3 + 1)^3$.
If $y = (3 + 4x - x^2)^{1/2}$, then $y' = (2 - x)/(3 + 4x - x^2)^{1/2}$.
If $r = (3s + 2)/(2s + 3)$, then $dr/ds = 5/(2s + 3)^2$.

All of these are correct. In the first two, we need the Chain Rule. If $f(x) = (3x - x^3 + 1)^4$, then $f'(x) = 4(3x - x^3 + 1)^3(3 - 3x^2)$ where $3 - 3x^2$ is the derivative of the expression $3x - x^3 + 1$. Therefore, $f'(x) = 12(1 - x^2)(3x - x^3 + 1)^3$. If $y = (3 + 4x - x^2)^{1/2}$, then $y' = (1/2)(3 + 4x - x^2)^{-1/2}(4 - 2x)$ where $4 - 2x$ is the derivative of the expression $3 + 4x - x^2$. Therefore, $y' = (2 - x)(3 + 4x - x^2)^{-1/2}$, or

$$y' = \frac{2 - x}{(3 + 4x - x^2)^{1/2}}.$$

In the last one, we need the quotient rule. If $r = (3s + 2)/(2s + 3)$, then

$$\frac{dr}{ds} = \frac{(2s + 3)(\text{derivative of } 3s + 2) - (3s + 2)(\text{derivative of } 2s + 3)}{(2s + 3)^2}$$

$$= \frac{(2s + 3)(3) - (3s + 2)(2)}{(2s + 3)^2} = \frac{5}{(2s + 3)^2} \ .$$

Now return to frame **Q127** and select the group that contains an error.

C   YOUR ANSWER:

If $y = \left(\dfrac{x}{1 + x}\right)^5$, then $y' = \dfrac{5x^2}{(1 + x)^6}$.

If $f(x) = (x - 1)\sqrt{x^2 - 2x + 2}$, then $f'(x) = \dfrac{2x^2 - 4x + 3}{\sqrt{x^2 - 2x + 2}}$.

If $xy + x - 2y - 1 = 0$, then $y' = (1 + y)/(2 - x)$.

Right. One of these is not correct.

$5\left(\dfrac{x}{1+x}\right)^4\Big($

Q128   Which one of the following is not correct?

If $y = \left(\dfrac{x}{1 + x}\right)^5$, then $y' = \dfrac{5x^2}{(1 + x)^6}$.   Frame **A**

If $f(x) = (x - 1)\sqrt{x^2 - 2x + 2}$, then $f'(x) = \dfrac{2x^2 - 4x + 3}{\sqrt{x^2 - 2x + 2}}$.   Frame **B**

If $xy + x - 2y - 1 = 0$, then $y' = (1 + y)/(2 - x)$.   Frame **C**

A   YOUR ANSWER: If $y = \left(\dfrac{x}{1 + x}\right)^5$, then $y' = \dfrac{5x^2}{(1 + x)^6}$.

Right. If $y = \left(\dfrac{x}{1 + x}\right)^5$, then

$$y' = 5\left(\frac{x}{1 + x}\right)^4 \left(\text{derivative of } \frac{x}{1 + x}\right)$$

$$= 5\left(\frac{x}{1 + x}\right)^4 \left(\frac{1 + x - x}{(1 + x)^2}\right) = \frac{5x^4}{(1 + x)^6} \ .$$

B   YOUR ANSWER: If $f(x) = (x - 1)\sqrt{x^2 - 2x + 2}$, then $f'(x) = \dfrac{2x^2 - 4x + 3}{\sqrt{x^2 - 2x + 2}}$.

There is nothing wrong with this. Using the product rule, if $f(x) = (x - 1) \cdot \sqrt{x^2 - 2x + 2}$, then

$$f'(x) = (x - 1)(\text{derivative of } \sqrt{x^2 - 2x + 2}) + \sqrt{x^2 - 2x + 2}\,(\text{derivative of } x - 1)$$
$$= (x - 1)[(1/2)(x^2 - 2x + 2)^{-1/2}(2x - 2)] + \sqrt{x^2 - 2x + 2}$$
$$= \frac{(x - 1)^2}{\sqrt{x^2 - 2x + 2}} + \sqrt{x^2 - 2x + 2}$$
$$= \frac{(x - 1)^2 + x^2 - 2x + 2}{\sqrt{x^2 - 2x + 2}} = \frac{2x^2 - 4x + 3}{\sqrt{x^2 - 2x + 2}} \ .$$

Return to frame **Q128** and select the one that is not correct.

C   YOUR ANSWER: If $xy + x - 2y - 1 = 0$, then $y' = (1 + y)/(2 - x)$.
There is nothing wrong with this. If $xy + x - 2y - 1 = 0$, differentiating term by term, we obtain

$$(xy' + y) + 1 - 2y' = 0$$
$$(x - 2)y' + (y + 1) = 0$$
$$y' = \frac{-(y + 1)}{x - 2}$$
$$y' = \frac{1 + y}{2 - x}.$$

Return to frame **Q128** and select the one that is not correct.

REVIEW TEST

1   For each of the following use the definition of derivative to find $f'(x)$.
   (a) $f(x) = 3x^2 - x + 2$ (b) $f(x) = 3/x$

Find the derivative of the functions in Exercises 2-12.

2 $f(x) = 4x^3 - 2x^2 + x - 5$

3 $g(x) = (x^3 + 5)(2x^2 - 3)$

4 $h(s) = \dfrac{4s - 1}{2s + 3}$

5 $f(t) = \dfrac{t^2 + 3t - 1}{t^3 + 1}$

6 $f(x) = (x^3 - x + 1)^4$

7 $h(x) = \dfrac{x^2}{(2x^2 - 1)^3}$

8 $F(y) = \left(\dfrac{y + 1}{y^2 - 3}\right)^4$

9 $f(x) = \sqrt{x^2 + 3}$

10 $h(x) = (x^2 - x + 3)^{-3/5}$

11 $G(x) = \left(\dfrac{2x}{x^3 - 1}\right)^{2/3}$

12 $f(x) = \sqrt{(x^3 + 1)(3x^2 - 1)^3}$

13   Find an equation of the tangent line to the graph of $y = 2/(1 - x)$ at the point $P(0, 2)$.

14   Find an equation of the tangent line to the graph of $y = 2x^2 - 3x + 1$ which is perpendicular to the line $3y - 2x + 1 = 0$.

15   If $y = 3x^2 - x + 5$, $x = 3$, and $\Delta x = 0.1$, find Δy and dy.

16   Use differentials to approximate $\sqrt{26}$.

17   A box in the form of a cube has an edge of length $x = 3$ cm with a possible error of .05 cm. What is the possible error in the volume of the box?

18   If there is a differentiable function f defined implicitly by $4x^3 + 3x^2y + 2y^2 = 6$, find y'.

19   Find an equation of the tangent line to $x + x^2y^2 - y = 1$ at $P(1, 1)$.

20   Find the first and second derivatives of the following functions.
   (a) $f(x) = 3x^3 - 4x^2 + x - 5$ (b) $h(y) = (\sqrt{2y + 1})^3$

21   If there is a differentible function f defined implicitly by $xy - x^2 - y = 0$, find y''.

22   If $f(x) = (ax + b)^{-1}$, find the nth derivative.

SAMPLE TEST

1 For each of the following use the definition of derivative to find $f'(x)$.
   (a) $f(x) = -x^2 + 5$ (b) $f(x) = \sqrt{2x - 1}$

Find the derivatives of the functions in Exercises 2-12.

2 $f(x) = 8x^2 - 2x + 3$

3 $h(x) = (y^2 - 2y + 3)(y + 1)$

4 $H(x) = \dfrac{2x + 1}{x - 3}$

5 $f(t) = (t^3 + 2t^2 - t + 1)^5$

6 $H(y) = \dfrac{(y + 1)^3}{y^2 + 2}$

7 $g(x) = \dfrac{\sqrt{2x - 1}}{x^2}$

8 $f(y) = \dfrac{(y - 1)^{2/3}}{(y + 1)^{1/3}}$

9 $f(t) = \sqrt{2t^2 - 1}$

10 $H(z) = (z^2 + 1)^{-2/3}$

11 $g(x) = \left(\dfrac{x}{2x^2 + 1}\right)^{1/3}$

12 $h(x) = \sqrt{1 + (1/x^2)}$

13 Find an equation of the tangent line to the graph of $y = 3x^2 - 2x + 1$ at the point $P(1, 2)$.

14 Find an equation of the tangent line to the graph of $y = 1/(x - 1)$ which is parallel to the line $x + y + 1 = 0$.

15 If $y = 1/x^2$, $x = 2$, and $\Delta x = 0.2$, find Δy and dy.

16 Use differentials to approximate $\sqrt[3]{996}$.

17 A circular disc has a diameter of 8 cm with a possible error of .01 cm. What is the possible error in the area of the disc?

18 If there is a differentiable function f defined implicitly by $x^3 - x = y^3 - y^2 + 24$, find y'.

19 Find an equation of the tangent line to $xy = 4$ at $P(-2, -2)$.

20 Find the first and second derivatives of the following functions.
   (a) $f(x) = x^4 - 3x^2 + 5$ (b) $g(t) = \sqrt{t^2 + 1}$

21 If there is a differentiable function f defined implicitly by $x + x\sqrt{y} = 1 - \sqrt{y}$, find y''.

22 If $f(t) = at^{-1}$, find the nth derivative.

CHAPTER 4

Applications
of the
Derivative

4.1 LOCAL EXTREMA OF FUNCTIONS

OBJECTIVES

You should know the definition of the maximum and minimum value of a function and the local maximum and minimum value of a function. You should know what is meant by critical numbers and how to find the critical numbers. You should also be able to find the absolute maximum and minimum of a function on a closed interval.

Q129 A function has a local maximum value at c if the values of f near c are smaller than $f(c)$.

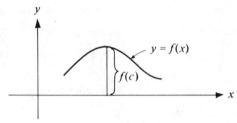

Notice that the values of f near c are less than $f(c)$. Similarly, a function has a local minimum value at c if the values of f near c are greater than $f(c)$.

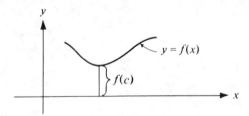

This is stated more precisely in the definition on page 138 of the text.
    Consider the following graph:

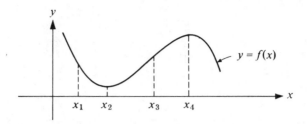

Which one of the following statements is correct?

> f is increasing at $x = x_1$ and has a local maximum at $x = x_4$.   Frame **A**
> f is increasing at $x = x_3$ and has a local minimum at $x = x_2$.   Frame **B**
> f has a local maximum at $x = x_2$ and a local minimum at $x = x_4$.   Frame **C**
> f is decreasing at $x = x_1$ and has a local minimum at $x = x_3$.   Frame **D**

A   **YOUR ANSWER:** f is increasing at $x = x_1$ and has a local maximum at $x = x_4$. Be careful. The values of f to the left of x_1 are greater than $f(x_1)$ and the values to the right of x_1 are smaller than $f(x_1)$. Therefore, f is decreasing at $x = x_1$.

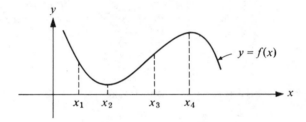

Now return to frame **Q129** and try again.

B   **YOUR ANSWER:** f is increasing at $x = x_3$ and has a local minimum at $x = x_2$. You are correct.

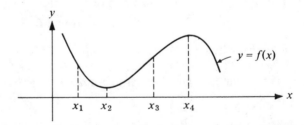

The function f is increasing at $x = x_3$ because the values of f to the left of x_3 are smaller than $f(x_3)$ and the values of f to the right of x_3 are larger than $f(x_3)$. We have a local minimum at $x = x_2$ because the values of f near $x = x_2$ are larger than $f(x_2)$.

C   **YOUR ANSWER:** f has a local maximum at $x = x_2$ and a local minimum at $x = x_4$. Don't you have maximum and minimum mixed up? Since the values of f near x_2 are greater than $f(x_2)$, we have a local minimum at $x = x_2$. Similarly, since the values of f near x_4 are smaller than $f(x_4)$, we have a local maximum at $x = x_4$.

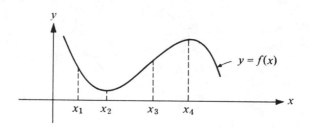

Now return to frame **Q129** and try again.

D **YOUR ANSWER:** f is decreasing at $x = x_1$ and has a local minimum at $x = x_3$.
Be careful. The function f is increasing at $x = x_3$ because the values of f to the left of x_3 are smaller than $f(x_3)$ and the values to the right of x_3 are greater than $f(x_3)$. In order to have a local minimum at $x = x_3$, the values of f near x_3 have to be greater than $f(x_3)$.

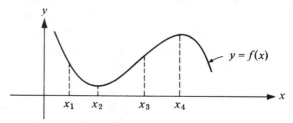

Now return to frame **Q129** and try again.

Q130 It can be shown that if a function f has a local extremum at a number c, then either $f'(c) = 0$ or $f'(c)$ does not exist. These numbers are called *critical numbers*. Every critical number is not necessarily a local extremum, but at least the critical numbers give us the candidates for local extrema. The function $f(x) = 5x^2 - 10x + 3$ may have a local extremum for which one of the following values of x?

$x = 2$ Frame **A** $x = 1$ Frame **B** $x = -1$ Frame **C**

A **YOUR ANSWER:** $x = 2$.
No. If $f(x) = 5x^2 - 10x + 3$, $f'(x) = 10x - 10$. Since $f'(2) = 10(2) - 10 = 10$, f is not a critical number. Now return to frame **Q130** and try again.

B **YOUR ANSWER:** $x = 1$.
Right. If $f(x) = 5x^2 - 10x + 3$, $f'(x) = 10x - 10$. Now when $f'(c) = 0$, we know that f may have a local extremum at $x = c$. Therefore, $x = 1$ may provide a local extremum because $f'(1) = 10(1) - 10 = 0$ and hence is a critical number.

C **YOUR ANSWER:** $x = -1$.
No. If $f(x) = 5x^2 - 10x + 3$, $f'(x) = 10x - 10$. Since $f'(-1) = 10(-1) - 10 = -20$, f is not a critical number. Now return to frame **Q130** and try again.

Q131 If $f(x) = x^3 + x^2 - x + 2$, what are the critical numbers?

$3x^2 + 2x - 1$

$3x - ?(x + 1)$

1/3 and −1	Frame **A**
0 and 1	Frame **B**
1 and −1	Frame **C**

A YOUR ANSWER: 1/3 and −1.
Right. If $f(x) = x^3 + x^2 - x + 2$, $f'(x) = 3x^2 + 2x - 1$.
$$3x^2 + 2x - 1 = 0$$
$$(3x - 1)(x + 1) = 0$$
$$x = 1/3 \text{ or } x = -1$$
Therefore, 1/3 and −1 are critical numbers, and hence f may have extrema at $x = 1/3$ or at $x = -1$.

B YOUR ANSWER: 0 and 1.
Where did you get these values? If $f(x) = x^3 + x^2 - x + 2$, then $f'(x) = 3x^2 + 2x - 1$. Now if $f'(x) = 0$, we have $3x^2 + 2x - 1 = (3x - 1)(x + 1) = 0$. The solutions of $f'(x) = 0$ are the critical numbers. Now return to frame **Q131** and try again.

C YOUR ANSWER: 1 and −1.
Where did you get these values? If $f(x) = x^3 + x^2 - x + 2$, then $f'(x) = 3x^2 + 2x - 1$. Now if $f'(x) = 0$, we have $3x^2 + 2x - 1 = (3x - 1)(x + 1) = 0$. The solutions of $f'(x) = 0$ are the critical numbers. Now return to frame **Q131** and try again.

Q132　We found that the critical numbers for $f(x) = x^3 + x^2 - x + 2$ are 1/3 and −1. Later we will develop an elegant method of checking the critical numbers in order to determine if they are in fact extrema. However, we could sketch the graph of f and thus determine if f has extrema at 1/3 or −1.
　　Can you sketch the graph and thus answer the question?

　　Yes　　Frame **A**　　No　　Frame **B**

A YOUR ANSWER: Yes.
Good. If $f(x) = x^3 + x^2 - x + 2$, we have $f(-2) = 0$, $f(-1) = 3$, $f(0) = 2$, $f(1/3) = 49/27$, and $f(1) = 3$. Plotting these points, we have

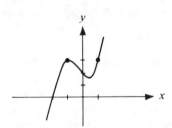

B YOUR ANSWER: No.
Let's see if we can help. We have $f(x) = x^3 + x^2 - x + 2$. Calculating a few functional values we obtain $f(-2) = 0$, $f(-1) = 3$, $f(0) = 2$, $f(1/3) = 49/27$, and $f(1) = 3$. Plot these points, sketch the graph, and determine the extrema. Now return to frame **Q132** and select the other alternative.

$(x^2-4)^{1/3}$
$\frac{1}{3}(x^2-4)^{-2/3}(2x)$

Q133　Let's try one more. Find the critical numbers of $f(x) = \sqrt[3]{x^2 - 4}$.

−2 and 2   Frame **A**   0   Frame **B**   0, −2, and 2   Frame **C**

A   **YOUR ANSWER:**   −2 and 2.
Almost, but you left out one number. If $f(x) = \sqrt[3]{x^2 - 4} = (x^2 - 4)^{1/3}$, then

$$f'(x) = \frac{1}{3}(x^2 - 4)^{-2/3}(2x) = \frac{2x}{3(x^2 - 4)^{2/3}} \ .$$

When is $f'(x) = 0$? Return to frame **Q133** and try again.

B   **YOUR ANSWER:**   0.
If $f'(x)$ does not exist for certain numbers, then these numbers are also critical numbers.

$$f(x) = \sqrt[3]{x^2 - 4} = (x^2 - 4)^{1/3}$$
$$f'(x) = \frac{1}{3}(x^2 - 4)^{-2/3}(2x) = \frac{2x}{3(x^2 - 4)^{2/3}}$$

The derivative $f'(x)$ does not exist for certain numbers. Return to frame **Q133**, think about this, and then try again.

C   **YOUR ANSWER:**   0, −2, and 2.
Correct.

$$f(x) = \sqrt[3]{x^2 - 4} = (x^2 - 4)^{1/3}$$
$$f'(x) = \frac{1}{3}(x^2 - 4)^{-2/3}(2x) = \frac{2x}{3(x^2 - 4)^{2/3}}$$

Therefore, 0, 2, and −2 are the critical numbers because $f'(0) = 0$ and $f'(2)$ and $f'(-2)$ do not exist.

Q134   In order to find the absolute maximum and mininum values of a function f on a closed interval $[a, b]$, calculate $f(c)$ for each critical number c in $[a, b]$ and calculate $f(a)$ and $f(b)$. Now the absolute maximum and minimum of f on $[a, b]$ will be the largest and smallest of these functional values.
   If $f(x) = 2x^2 - 3x + 5$ on $[0, 2]$, find the absolute maximum and minimum values.

Absolute maximum 5, absolute minimum 3/4   Frame **A**

Absolute maximum 7, absolute minimum $3\frac{7}{8}$ Frame **B**

Absolute maximum 7, absolute minimum 5   Frame **C**

A   **YOUR ANSWER:**   Absolute maximum 5, absolute minimum 3/4.
Be careful. Neither one is correct. If $f(x) = 2x^2 - 3x + 5$, then $f'(x) = 4x - 3$ and thus the only critical number is 3/4. We want $f((3/4))$, not 3/4. We also want $f(0)$ and $f(2)$, the values of the end-points. Now compare these values and then return to frame **Q134** and select the correct answer.

B   **YOUR ANSWER:**   Absolute maximum 7, absolute minimum $3\frac{7}{8}$.

Of course. If $f(x) = 2x^2 - 3x + 5$ on $[0, 2]$, then $f'(x) = 4x - 3$ and thus the only critical number is 3/4.

$$f\left(\frac{3}{4}\right) = 2\left(\frac{3}{4}\right)^2 - 3\left(\frac{3}{4}\right) + 5 = \frac{31}{8} = 3\frac{7}{8}$$
$$f(0) = 2(0)^2 - 3(0) + 5 = 5$$
$$f(2) = 2(2)^2 - 3(2) + 5 = 7$$

Therefore, the absolute maximum is 7 and the absolute minimum is $3\frac{7}{8}$. Notice that 7 is an end-point extremum.

C   **YOUR ANSWER:**   Absolute maximum 7, absolute minimum 5.
No. The absolute minimum is not 5. If $f(x) = 2x^2 - 3x + 5$, then $f'(x) = 4x - 3$ and thus the only critical number is 3/4. Find $f(3/4)$, compare with the values of the end-points, and then return to frame **Q134** and try again.

4.2   ROLLE'S THEOREM AND THE MEAN VALUE THEOREM

OBJECTIVES

You should know Rolle's Thoerem and the Mean Value Theorem and how to use these theorems.

Q135   Rolle's Thoerem states that if a function f is continuous on a closed interval $[a, b]$, and differentiable on the open interval (a, b), and if $f(a) = f(b)$, then $f'(c) = 0$ for at least one number c in (a, b). This is proved on page 144 of the text.
   If $f(x) = x^{2/3}$, then $f'(x) = 2/3x^{1/3}$. Notice that $f(-1) = f(1) = 1$, but $f'(x)$ is not 0 for any number in the interval $(-1, 1)$. Does this contradict Rolle's Theorem?

   Yes   Frame **A**   No   Frame **B**

A   **YOUR ANSWER:**   Yes.
The conclusion of a theorem does not have to follow unless the hypothesis is met. Return to frame **Q135,** determine if the hypothesis of the theorem is met for the function in the interval $(-1, 1)$, and then try again.

B   **YOUR ANSWER:**   No.
Right. The function $f(x) = x^{2/3}$ is continuous on $[-1, 1]$, but is not differentiable on $(-1, 1)$.

$$f(x) = x^{2/3}$$
$$f'(x) = \frac{2}{3x^{1/3}}$$

Since f' does not exist at $x = 0$, f is not differentiable at $x = 0$. Therefore, the conclusion of Rolle's Theorem does not have to follow.

Q136   The function $f(x) = x^2 - x - 2$ meets all of the conditions of Rolle's Theorem. The function f is continuous on $[-1, 2]$, f is differentiable on $(-1, 2)$, $f(-1) = f(2)$. What is the number c of Rolle's Theorem? That is, what is the number c such that $f'(c) = 0$?

   $-1/2$ Frame **A**   0   Frame **B**
   $1/2$ Frame **C**   1   Frame **D**

A **YOUR ANSWER:** $-1/2$.
Sorry, but you missed a sign. Return to frame **Q136** and try again.

B **YOUR ANSWER:**   0.
We want the number c such that $f'(c) = 0$ where $f(x) = x^2 - x - 2$. This is not necessarily 0. Return to frame **Q136** and try again.

C **YOUR ANSWER:** $1/2$.
Of course.

$$f(x) = x^2 - x - 2$$
$$f'(x) = 2x - 1$$

If $f'(c) = 0$, $2c - 1 = 0$, or $c = 1/2$.

D **YOUR ANSWER:**   1.
Where did you get 1?

$$f(x) = x^2 - x - 2$$
$$f'(x) = 2x - 1$$

Now we want c such that $f'(c) = 0$. Return to frame **Q136** and try again.

Q137 Now let's consider the *Mean Value Theorem* which is proved on page 145 of the text.

If a function f is continuous on a closed interval $[a, b]$ and is differentiable on the open interval (a, b), then there exists a number c in (a, b) such that

$$f(b) - f(a) = f'(c)(b - a).$$

What is the value of c satisfying the Mean Value Theorem if $f(x) = 3x^2 + 4x - 3$, $a = 1$, and $b = 3$?

| 13/2 | Frame **A** | 2 | Frame **B** |
| 8/3 | Frame **C** | I don't understand. | Frame **D** |

A **YOUR ANSWER:**   13/2.
Your calculations are off. The Mean Value Theorem states that there exists a c between a and b such that

$$f(b) - f(a) = (b - a)f'(c).$$

We have $a = 1$ and $b = 3$ with $f(x) = 3x^2 + 4x - 3$. Therefore, we are looking for c such that

$$f(3) - f(1) = (3 - 1)f'(c).$$

Now return to frame **Q137** and find c.

B **YOUR ANSWER:**   2.
You are correct. The Mean Value Theorem states that there exists a c between a and b such that

$$f(b) - f(a) = (b - a)f'(c).$$

Since $f(x) = 3x^2 + 4x - 3$, $a = 1$, and $b = 3$, we have

$$f(3) - f(1) = (3 - 1)f'(c)$$
$$36 - 4 = (3 - 1)(6c + 4)$$
$$32 = 2(6c + 4)$$
$$16 = 6c + 4$$
$$c = 2.$$

C   YOUR ANSWER: 8/3.

Your calculations are off. The Mean Value Theorem states that there exists a c between a and b such that

$$f(b) - f(a) = (b - a)f'(c).$$

We have $a = 1$ and $b = 3$ with $f(x) = 3x^2 + 4x - 3$. Therefore, we are looking for c such that

$$f(3) - f(1) = (3 - 1)f'(c).$$

Now return to frame **Q137** and find c.

D   YOUR ANSWER: I don't understand.

The Mean Value Theorem states that there exists a c between a and b such that

$$f(b) - f(a) = (b - a)f'(c).$$

We have $a = 1$ and $b = 3$ with $f(x) = 3x^2 + 4x - 3$. Substitute these values in the above and solve for c. Now return to frame **Q137** and try again.

4.3   THE FIRST DERIVATIVE TEST

OBJECTIVES

You should be able to determine when a function is increasing or decreasing by using the derivative. You should also know how to use the first derivative test to find the local extrema of a function.

Q138   If $f'(x) > 0$ for all x in (a, b), then f is increasing on $[a, b]$.
If $f'(x) < 0$ for all x in (a, b), then f is decreasing on $[a, b]$.

This means that by considering the derivative of a function, we can determine when it is increasing and when it is decreasing, except when the derivative is zero. If the derivative is zero, then we are in doubt as to whether the function is increasing or decreasing. Of course, when the derivative is zero it may be neither increasing nor decreasing, as we will see later.

Let's look at an example. If $f(x) = 2x^2 + 4x - 6$, then $f'(x) = 4x + 4$. Now if $4x + 4 > 0$, we have $4(x + 1) > 0$ or $x + 1 > 0$ which implies $x > -1$. Therefore, f is increasing when $x > -1$. Similarly, f is decreasing when $x < -1$. The graph is sketched below. Notice that f is neither increasing nor decreasing at $x = -1$.

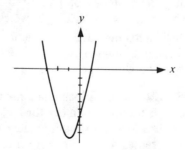

If $f(x) = 3x^2 - 5x + 8$, for what values of x is f decreasing?

$x > 5/6$ Frame **A** $x < 5/3$ Frame **B** $x < 5/6$ Frame **C**

A   **YOUR ANSWER:** $x > 5/6$.
Don't you have the values of x for which f is increasing instead of decreasing? If $f(x)$ = $3x^2 - 5x + 8$, then $f'(x) = 6x - 5$. Therefore, f is decreasing when $6x - 5 < 0$. Now return to frame **Q138** and select the correct answer.

B   **YOUR ANSWER:** $x < 5/3$.
Sorry, but you made a mistake in the derivative. If $f(x) = 3x^2 - 5x + 8$, then $f'(x)$ = $6x - 5$. Now if $6x - 5 < 0$, then f is decreasing. Return to frame **Q138** and select the correct answer.

C   **YOUR ANSWER:** $x < 5/6$.
Certainly. If $f(x) = 3x^2 - 5x + 8$, then $f'(x) = 6x - 5$. Therefore, f is decreasing if $6x - 5 < 0$ or $x < 5/6$.

Q139   Does the function $f(x) = -8x + 5$ increase for any value of x?

Yes   Frame **A**   No   Frame **B**

A   **YOUR ANSWER:** Yes.
Let's take a look. If $f(x) = -8x + 5$, then $f'(x) = -8$. Now $f'(x) < 0$ for every x. Can f ever increase? Think about this and then return to frame **Q139** and select the other alternative.

B   **YOUR ANSWER:** No.
Good. If $f(x) = -8x + 5$, $f'(x) = -8$. Therefore, f is a decreasing function for every x because $f'(x) < 0$ for every x.

Q140   If a function has a local extremum, then it must occur at a critical number. Therefore, in order to determine the local extrema, we check each critical number. One method of checking the critical numbers to determine if they are local extrema is referred to as the First Derivative Test. This is described on page 149 of the text. If $f'(x)$ changes sign as x increases through a critical number c, then f has a local extremum at c. If $f'(x)$ changes from positive to negative through c, we have a local maximum at c, and if $f'(x)$ changes from negative to positive through c, we have a local minimum at c. Of course, if there is no change, then there is no local extremum. Study the examples on pages 150-152.
If $f(x) = 2x^3 - 9x^2 + 12x + 3$, which one of the following is correct?

f has a local maximum at 2.   Frame **A**
f has a local minimum at 1.   Frame **B**
f has a local maximum at 1.   Frame **C**

A   **YOUR ANSWER:** f has a local maximum at 2.
It is true that 2 is a critical number for $f(x) = 2x^3 - 9x^2 + 12x + 3$. However, it does not provide a local maximum because the derivative changes from negative to positive as x increases through 2. Return to frame **Q140** and try again.

B   YOUR ANSWER: f has a local minimum at 1.
It is true that 1 is a critical number for $f(x) = 2x^3 - 9x^2 + 12x + 3$. However, it does not provide a local minimum because the derivative changes from positive to negative as x increases through 1. Return to frame **Q140** and try again.

C   YOUR ANSWER: f has a local maximum at 1.
Very good.

$$f(x) = 2x^3 - 9x^2 + 12x + 3$$
$$f'(x) = 6x - 18x + 12$$

Since $6x^2 - 18x + 12 = 6(x - 1)(x - 2)$, 1 and 2 are critical numbers.

Interval	$x - 1$	$x - 2$	$f'(x)$	f
$(-\infty, 1)$	$-$	$-$	$+$	increasing
$(1, 2)$	$+$	$-$	$-$	decreasing
$(2, \infty)$	$+$	$+$	$+$	increasing

Now $f'(x)$ changes from positive to negative as x increases through 1. Therefore, f has a local maximum at 1. Notice that f has a local minimum at 2 since $f'(x)$ changes from negative to positive as x increases through 2.

Q141   Find the local extrema of $f(x) = x^2(x - 2)^{1/3}$. Were you successful?

   Yes   Frame **A**   No   Frame **B**

A   YOUR ANSWER: Yes.
Wonderful.

$$f(x) = x^2(x - 2)^{1/3}$$
$$f'(x) = x^2\left(\frac{1}{3}\right)(x - 2)^{-2/3} + (x - 2)^{1/3}(2x)$$
$$= \frac{x^2}{3(x - 2)^{2/3}} + (x - 2)^{1/3}(2x)$$
$$= \frac{x^2 + 6x(x - 2)}{3(x - 2)^{2/3}} = \frac{x(7x - 12)}{3(x - 2)^{2/3}}$$

The critical numbers are 0, 12/7, and 2 because $f'(0) = 0$, $f'(12/7) = 0$, and $f'(2)$ does not exist.

Interval	x	$7x - 12$	$(x - 2)^{2/3}$	$f'(x)$	f
$(-\infty, 0)$	$-$	$-$	$+$	$+$	increasing
$(0, 12/7)$	$+$	$-$	$+$	$-$	decreasing
$(12/7, 2)$	$+$	$+$	$+$	$+$	increasing
$(2, \infty)$	$+$	$+$	$+$	$+$	increasing

The function f has a local maximum at 0 because f' changes from positive to negative as x increases through 0, and f has a local minimum at 12/7 because f' changes from negative to positive as x increases through 12/7. There is no local extremum at 2 because f' does not change as x increases through 2.

   The point on the graph where the local maximum occurs is $(0, 0)$, and the point where the local minimum occurs is $(12/7, (-144/49)\sqrt[3]{2/7})$ because $f(0) = 0$ and $f(12/7) = (-144/49)\sqrt[3]{2/7}$.

B   YOUR ANSWER: No.
Let's see if we can get you started.

$$f(x) = x^2(x - 2)^{1/3}$$
$$f'(x) = x^2 \left(\frac{1}{3}\right)(x - 2)^{-2/3} + (x - 2)^{1/3}(2x)$$
$$= \frac{x^2}{3(x - 2)^{2/3}} + (x - 2)^{1/3}(2x)$$
$$= \frac{x^2 + 6x(x - 2)}{3(x - 2)^{2/3}} = \frac{x(7x - 12)}{3(x - 2)^{2/3}}$$

The critical numbers are 0, 12/7, and 2 because $f'(0) = 0$, $f'(12/7) = 0$, and $f'(2)$ does not exist. Determine if $f'(x)$ changes sign as x increases through the critical numbers. Now return to frame **Q141** and select the other alternative.

4.4 CONCAVITY AND THE SECOND DERIVATIVE TEST

OBJECTIVES

You should know the definition of concavity and the test for concavity. You should know what is meant by a point of inflection. You should also know how to use the Second Derivative Test to find the local extrema of a function.

Q142 We have said that if $f'(c) = 0$, then c may provide an extremum. We are now going to explore another method of determining if f has an extremum at c when $f'(c) = 0$.

First we need the concept of concavity. In order to visualize this concept geometrically, consider the following: In the neighborhood of a point P where the graph is concave upward, the graph is above its tangent both to the right and to the left of P.

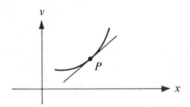

Similarly, if the graph is concave downward at P, the graph is below its tangent both to the right and to the left of P, and if P is a point of inflection, then the graph of P will be below its tangent on one side of P and above the tangent on the other side of P.

Which one of the following graphs is concave downward at the point A?

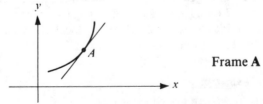

Frame A

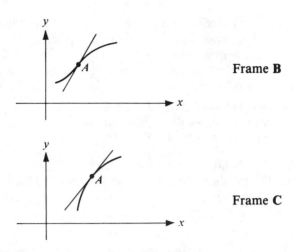

Frame **B**

Frame **C**

A   YOUR ANSWER:

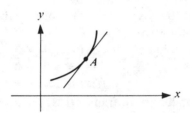

Watch out. The graph is above the tangent line both to the right and left of A and hence is concave upward at A. Return to frame **Q142** and try again.

B   YOUR ANSWER:

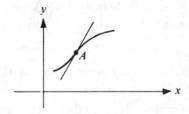

Watch out. The graph is above the tangent line to the left of A, but below the tangent line to the right of A. Therefore, A is an inflection point. Return to frame **Q142** and try again.

C   YOUR ANSWER:

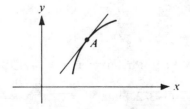

Correct. The graph is below the tangent line both to the left and right of A and hence is concave downward.

Q143   The graph of f is *concave upward* at c if f' is increasing at c and *concave downward* at c if f' is decreasing at c. Therefore, the graph of f is concave upward if $f''(c) > 0$ and is concave downward if $f''(c) < 0$.

Is the graph of the function $f(x) = 3x^3 + 4x^2 - 6x + 5$ concave upward or concave downward at $x = 1$?

Concave upward   Frame **A**
Concave downward   Frame **B**
I don't understand.   Frame **C**

A   **YOUR ANSWER:**   Concave upward.
Right. The graph of f is concave upward at c if $f''(c) > 0$.

$$f(x) = 3x^3 + 4x^2 - 6x + 5$$
$$f'(x) = 9x^2 + 8x - 6$$
$$f''(x) = 18x + 8$$

Therefore, $f''(1) > 0$ and hence the graph of f is concave upward.

B   **YOUR ANSWER:**   Concave downward.
Sorry, but you are wrong. The graph of f is concave downward at c if $f''(c) < 0$ and is concave upward at c if $f''(c) > 0$.

$$f(x) = 3x^3 + 4x^2 - 6x + 5$$
$$f'(x) = 9x^2 + 8x - 6$$
$$f''(x) = 18x + 8$$

What is $f''(1)$? Return to frame **Q143**, think about this, and then select the correct answer.

C   **YOUR ANSWER:**   I don't understand.
The graph of f is concave downward at c if $f''(c) < 0$ and concave upward at c if $f''(c) > 0$. Therefore, evaluate $f''(1)$ and thus determine whether the graph of f is concave upward or downward. Now return to frame **Q143** and try again.

Q144   You might wonder how concavity helps with the problem of extrema. This relationship is developed on pages 157-158 of the text and results in the following theorem:

If $f'(c) = 0$ and $f''(c) > 0$, then f has a local minimum at c.
If $f'(c) = 0$ and $f''(c) < 0$, then f has a local maximum at c.

If $f'(c) = 0$ and $f''(c) = 0$, then anything is still possible. This is the Second Derivative Test given on page 158 of the text.

Using the above theorem, what is the extremum of $y = x^2 + 3x - 5$?

Minimum at $x = -3/2$ Frame **A**
Maximum at $x = -3/2$ Frame **B**
Maximum at $x = 3/2$ Frame **C**

A   **YOUR ANSWER:**   Minimum at $x = -3/2$.
Right. If $y = x^2 + 3x - 5$, $y' = 2x + 3$. The extremum will have to occur where $2x + 3 = 0$ or $x = -3/2$. Since $y'' = 2$, $y'' > 0$ when $x = -3/2$. Therefore, we have a minimum at $x = -3/2$.

B   **YOUR ANSWER:**   Maximum at $x = -3/2$.
Sorry, but you are wrong. If $y = x^2 + 3x - 5$, $y' = 2x + 3$. The extremum will

have to occur where $2x + 3 = 0$, which is $x = -3/2$. What is y'' when $x = -3/2$? Return to frame **Q144** and try again.

C YOUR ANSWER: Maximum at $x = 3/2$.
Sorry, but you are wrong. If $y = x^2 + 3x - 5$, $y' = 2x + 3$. The extremum will have to occur where $2x + 3 = 0$ which is $x = -3/2$. Return to frame **Q144** and try again.

Q145 A point of inflection occurs where the concavity changes from upward to downward or from downward to upward. Study the examples given in the text on pages 159-162. Now let's find the points where f may have an extremum when $f(x) = x^3 + x^2 - x - 4$.

−1 and 1/3	Frame **A**	−1 and 3	Frame **B**
1 and 1/3	Frame **C**	I don't know.	Frame **D**

A YOUR ANSWER: −1 and 1/3.
You are correct. If $f(x) = x^3 + x^2 - x - 4$, $f'(x) = 3x^2 + 2x - 1$.
$$3x^2 + 2x - 1 = 0$$
$$(3x - 1)(x + 1) = 0$$
$$x = 1/3 \text{ or } x = -1.$$
Therefore, 1/3 and −1 may provide us with an extremum because $f'(x) = 0$ when $x = 1/3$ or −1.

B YOUR ANSWER: −1 and 3.
Be careful. If $f(x) = x^3 + x^2 - x - 4$, then $f'(x) = 3x^2 + 2x - 1$. Now we want the values of x for which $f'(x) = 0$. Return to frame **Q145** and try again.

C YOUR ANSWER: 1 and 1/3.
Be careful. If $f(x) = x^3 + x^2 - x - 4$, then $f'(x) = 3x^2 + 2x - 1$. Now we want the values of x for which $f'(x) = 0$. Return to frame **Q145** and try again.

D YOUR ANSWER: I don't know.
The values of x for which f may have an extremum are the values of x for which $f'(x) = 0$. If $f(x) = x^3 + x^2 - x - 4$, $f'(x) = 3x^2 + 2x - 1$. Now return to frame **Q145**, find where $f'(x) = 0$, and select the correct answer.

Q146 We have $f(x) = x^3 + x^2 - x - 4$ with critical numbers −1 and 1/3. For which value does f have a local maximum? (*Hint*: Check second derivatives.)

1/3	Frame **A**	−1	Frame **B**

A YOUR ANSWER: 1/3.
Watch out. If $f(x) = x^3 + x^2 - x - 4$, $f'(x) = 3x^2 + 2x - 1$, and $f''(x) = 6x + 2$. Since $f''(1/3) = 6(1/3) + 2 = 4$, f has a local minimum at $x = 1/3$ because $f''(1/3) > 0$. Return to frame **Q146**, calculate $f''(-1)$, and select the other alternative.

B YOUR ANSWER: −1.
Right. If $f(x) = x^3 + x^2 - x - 4$, $f'(x) = 3x^2 + 2x - 1$, and $f''(x) = 6x + 2$. Since $f''(-1) = 6(-1) + 2 = -4$, f has a local maximum at $x = 1$ because $f''(-1) < 0$.

Similarly, $f''(1/3) = 6(1/3) + 2 = 4$. Therefore, f has a minimum at $x = 1/3$ because $f''(1/3) > 0$.

Q147 We have $f(x) = x^3 + x^2 - x - 4$, $f'(x) = 3x^2 + 2x - 1$, and $f''(x) = 6x + 2$. Now the values of x for which f may have an inflection point are the values for which $f''(x) = 0$. We have $f''(x) = 6x + 2$. Therefore, f may have an inflection point at $x = -1/3$. Does f have an inflection point at $x = -1/3$?

Yes   Frame **A**   No   Frame **B**

A **YOUR ANSWER:** Yes.
Certainly. We have $f(x) = x^3 + x^2 - x - 4$, $f'(x) = 3x^2 + 2x - 1$, $f''(x) = 6x + 2$. If $x = -1/3$, then $f''(x) = 0$. The function f has an inflection point at $x = -1/3$ because the concavity changes from downward to concave upward. In summary, we have

Interval	$f''(x) = 6x + 2$	Concavity
$(-\infty, -1/3)$	< 0	downward
$(-1/3, \infty)$	> 0	upward

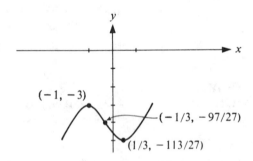

Notice that the inflection point is where the graph changes from concave downward to concave upward.

B **YOUR ANSWER:** No.
Why not? We have $f'(x) = 3x^2 + 2x - 1$ and $f''(x) = 6x + 2$. If $x = -1/3$, $f''(x) = 0$. What happens to the concavity on each side of $-1/3$? Think about this and then return to frame **Q147** and select the other alternative.

Q148 If $f(x) = (1/3)x^3 + (1/2)x^2 - 6x + 8$, find all the extrema and points of inflection. Were you successful?

Yes   Frame **A**   No   Frame **B**   I need help.   Frame **C**

A **YOUR ANSWER:** Yes.
Very good. We have

$$f(x) = \frac{1}{3}x^3 + \frac{1}{2}x^2 - 6x + 8;$$
$$f'(x) = x^2 + x - 6;$$
$$f''(x) = 2x + 1.$$

If $f'(x) = 0$, then

$$x^2 + x - 6 = 0$$
$$(x - 2)(x + 3) = 0$$
$$x = 2 \text{ or } x = -3.$$

Since $f''(2) = 2(2) + 1 = 5$, f has a minimum at $x = 2$. Since $f''(-3) = 2(-3) + 1 = -5$, f has a maximum at $x = -3$. If $f''(x) = 0$, then $2x + 1 = 0$ or $x = (-1/2)$. Since $f''(x) < 0$ if $x < -1/2$ and $f''(x) > 0$ if $x > -1/2$, f has an inflection point at $x = -1/2$.

B   YOUR ANSWER: No.
We need the first two derivatives.

$$f(x) = \frac{1}{3}x^3 + \frac{1}{2}x^2 - 6x + 8;$$
$$f'(x) = x^2 + x - 6;$$
$$f''(x) = 2x + 1.$$

Now if f has any extrema, they must occur where $f'(x) = 0$, and if f has any inflection points, they must occur where $f''(x) = 0$. Find these values, check them as in the examples in the text on pages 159-162, and then return to frame **Q148** and try again.

C   YOUR ANSWER: I need help.
If f has any extrema, they must occur where $f'(x) = 0$, and if f has any inflection points, they must occur where $f''(x) = 0$. Find these values, check them as in the examples in the text on pages 159-162, and then return to frame **Q148** and try again.

Q149   Does $f(x) = 2x^3 + 3x - 1$ have any extrema?

　　　　　Yes　　　Frame **A**　　　　No　　　Frame **B**

A   YOUR ANSWER: Yes.
Be careful. We have

$$f(x) = 2x^3 + 3x - 1;$$
$$f'(x) = 6x^2 + 3.$$

Now since $f'(x) = 6x^2 + 3 \neq 0$ for any x, f cannot have any extrema. Think about this and then return to frame **Q149** and select the other alternative.

B   YOUR ANSWER: No.
Correct. We have

$$f(x) = 2x^3 + 3x - 1;$$
$$f'(x) = 6x^2 + 3.$$

Since $f'(x) = 6x^2 + 3 \neq 0$ for any x, f cannot have any extrema.

Q150   Does f have an inflection point where $f(x) = 2x^3 + 3x - 1$?

　　　　　Yes　　　Frame **A**　　　　No　　　Frame **B**

A   YOUR ANSWER: Yes.
Right. We have

$$f(x) = 2x^3 + 3x - 1;$$
$$f'(x) = 6x^2 + 3;$$
$$f''(x) = 12x.$$

Since $f''(x) = 12x$ is zero if $x = 0$, and when $x < 0$, $f''(x) < 0$, and when $x > 0$, $f''(x) > 0$, f has an inflection point at $x = 0$.

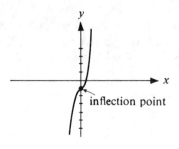

inflection point

B   YOUR ANSWER: No.
Why not? We have

$$f(x) = 2x^3 + 3x - 1;$$
$$f'(x) = 6x^2 + 3.$$
$$f''(x) = 12x.$$

Now $f''(x) = 12x$ is zero if $x = 0$. Return to frame **Q150**, see if f doesn't have an inflection point at $x = 0$, and select the other alternative.

Q151   Let's try one more. Find all extrema and points of inflection if $f(x) = (1/3)x^3 - x$. How did it go?

Great   Frame **A**   Bad   Frame **B**   Miserable   Frame **C**

A   YOUR ANSWER: Great.
Very good. If $f(x) = (1/3)x^3 - x$, then

$$f'(x) = x^2 - 1;$$
$$f''(x) = 2x.$$

If $f'(x) = x^2 - 1 = 0$, then $x = 1$ or $x = -1$. These are the values of x for which f may have an extremum. Since $f''(1) = 2(1) = 2 > 0$, f has a local minimum at $x = 1$. Since $f''(-1) = 2(-1) = -2 < 0$, f has a local maximum at $x = -1$. If $f''(x) = 2x = 0$, then $x = 0$. This is the only value for which f may have a point of inflection. Since $f''(x) < 0$ when $x < 0$ and $f''(x) > 0$ when $x > 0$, f does have a point of inflection at $x = 0$.

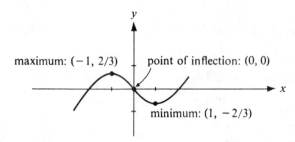

maximum: $(-1, 2/3)$ point of inflection: $(0, 0)$

minimum: $(1, -2/3)$

B   YOUR ANSWER: Bad.
It's not too bad. If $f(x) = (1/3)x^3 - x$, then

$$f'(x) = x^2 - 1;$$
$$f''(x) = 2x.$$

First find all values of x for which $f'(x) = 0$. Check these values for extrema by using the second derivative. Next find all values of x for which $f''(x) = 0$ and check these values for points of inflection by using concavity. Now return to frame **Q151** and try again.

C   YOUR ANSWER: Miserable.

Is it really that bad? If $f(x) = (1/3)x^3 - x$, then

$$f'(x) = x^2 - 1;$$
$$f''(x) = 2x.$$

First find all values of x for which $f'(x) = 0$. Check these values for extrema by using the second derivative. Next find all values of x for which $f''(x) = 0$ and check these values for points of inflection by using concavity. Now return to frame **Q151** and try again.

4.5   HORIZONTAL AND VERTICAL ASYMPTOTES

OBJECTIVES

You should know how to find limits involving infinity. You should also be able to use limits to determine vertical and horizontal asymptotes.

Q152   If $f(x)$ approaches a real number L as we let x increase without bound, we say that the limit of $f(x)$ is L as x becomes infinite and write

$$\lim_{x \to \infty} f(x) = L.$$

This is defined and discussed on pages 164 and 165 of the text. We may also have

$$\lim_{x \to -\infty} f(x) = L.$$

An important tool for calculating limits as x becomes infinite is given in Theorem (4.21) which says that if k is a positive rational number, c is any nonzero real number, and x^k is defined, then

$$\lim_{x \to \infty} \left(\frac{c}{x^k}\right) = 0 \quad \text{and} \quad \lim_{x \to -\infty} \left(\frac{c}{x^k}\right) = 0.$$

Using this theorem and our other limit theorems, what is

$$\lim_{x \to \infty} \left(3 + \frac{2}{x^2}\right)?$$

2   Frame **A**   3   Frame **B**   0   Frame **C**

A   YOUR ANSWER: 2.

No. Using our limit theorems,

$$\lim_{x \to \infty} \left(3 + \frac{2}{x^2}\right) = \lim_{x \to \infty} 3 + \lim_{x \to \infty} \left(\frac{2}{x^2}\right).$$

Now compute the value of each of these limits and return to frame **Q152** and select the correct answer.

B   YOUR ANSWER: 3.
Good.

$$\lim_{x\to\infty}\left(3+\frac{2}{x^2}\right)=\lim_{x\to\infty}3+\lim_{x\to\infty}\left(\frac{2}{x^2}\right)=3+0=3.$$

$\text{Lim}_{x\to\infty}\,3=3$ because the limit of a constant is the constant. $\text{Lim}_{x\to\infty}\,(2/x^2)=0$ by Theorem (4.21) on page 166 of the text.

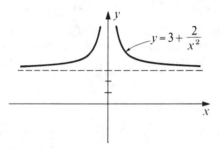

Notice in the graph of $f(x)=3+2/x^2$ that $f(x)$ approaches the line $y=3$. The line $y=3$ is called a horizontal asymptote. The limit of $f(x)$ as $x\to\infty$ provides us with a horizontal asymptote. In our problem, since

$$\lim_{x\to\infty}\,f(x)=3,$$

$y=3$ is a horizontal asymptote.

C   YOUR ANSWER: 0.
Be careful. We do have $\lim_{x\to\infty}(2/x^2)=0$, but what about $\lim_{x\to\infty}(3+2/x^2)$? Return to frame **Q152**, think about this, and then try again.

Q153   Study Example 1 on page 166 of the text. Now what is

$$\lim_{x\to\infty}\left(\frac{2x^3-4x+6}{5x^3+2x^2-1}\right)?$$

| 0 | Frame **A** | 2/5 | Frame **B** |
| 2 | Frame **C** | I don't know. | Frame **D** |

A   YOUR ANSWER: 0.
We do need to use

$$\lim_{x\to\infty}\left(\frac{c}{x^k}\right)=0,$$

but the limit of the entire function as $x\to\infty$ may not be zero. Return to frame **Q153** and try again.

B   YOUR ANSWER: 2/5.
Very good. Dividing numerator and denominator by x^3, we obtain

$$\lim_{x \to \infty} \left(\frac{2x^3 - 4x + 6}{5x^3 + 2x^2 - 1} \right) = \lim_{x \to \infty} \left(\frac{2 - 4/x^2 + 6/x^3}{5 + 2/x - 1/x^3} \right)$$

$$= \frac{2 - 0 + 0}{5 + 0 - 0} = \frac{2}{5} \; .$$

It follows that $y = 2/5$ is a horizontal asymptote for the graph of

$$f(x) = \frac{2x^3 - 4x + 6}{5x^3 + 2x - 1} \; .$$

C   YOUR ANSWER: 2.
Didn't you overlook the denominator? Dividing numerator and denominator by x^3, we obtain

$$\lim_{x \to \infty} \left(\frac{2x^3 - 4x + 6}{5x^3 + 2x^2 - 1} \right) = \lim_{x \to \infty} \left(\frac{2 - 4/x^2 + 6/x^3}{5 + 2/x - 1/x^3} \right)$$

Now return to frame **Q153**, complete the problem, and then try again.

D   YOUR ANSWER: I don't know.
In order to find a limit like

$$\lim_{x \to \infty} \left(\frac{2x^3 - 4x + 6}{5x^3 + 2x^2 - 1} \right)$$

we divide numerator and denominator by x^k where k is the largest exponent in the expression. In our problem, this is x^3. Now return to frame **Q153** and try again.

Q154   Let's put it all together. Can you find the horizontal asymptotes and sketch the graph of $y = x^3/(2 + x^2)$?

　　　Sure　　　Frame **A**　　　I'm not so certain.　　　Frame **B**

A   YOUR ANSWER: Sure.
Excellent. We have $y = x^2/(2 + x^2)$.

$$\lim_{x \to \infty} \left(\frac{x^2}{2 + x^2} \right) = \lim_{x \to \infty} \left(\frac{1}{2/x^2 + 1} \right) = \frac{1}{0 + 1} = 1$$

Also, the limit as $x \to -\infty$ is 1. Therefore, $y = 1$ is a horizontal asymptote.

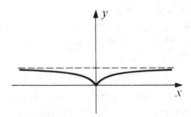

B   YOUR ANSWER: I'm not so certain.
Let's see if we can get you started. Find the horizontal asymptotes by evaluating

$$\lim_{x \to \infty} \left(\frac{x^2}{2 + x^2} \right) \quad \text{and} \quad \lim_{x \to -\infty} \left(\frac{x^2}{2 + x^2} \right) .$$

Now return to frame **Q154**, complete the problem, and then select the other answer.

Q155   If $f(x)$ increases without bound as x approaches a real number a, we say limit of $f(x)$ is ∞ as $x \to a$ and write

$$\lim_{x \to a} f(x) = \infty.$$

Of course, $f(x)$ could approach $-\infty$ and x could approach a from the right or left. This gives us the following additional possibilities:

$$\lim_{x \to a} f(x) = -\infty, \lim_{x \to a^+} f(x) = \infty, \lim_{x \to a^+} f(x) = -\infty,$$

$$\lim_{x \to a^-} f(x) = \infty, \lim_{x \to a^-} f(x) = -\infty.$$

Graphs of all six possibilities are presented on pages 169 and 170 of the text. The line $x = a$ gives us a vertical asymptote for the graph.

Theorem (4.25) on page 170 of the text is very useful in finding the value of limits which become infinite. Rather than memorizing the theorem, one can usually determine the answer intuitively. For example,

$$\lim_{x \to 3^+} \left(\frac{2}{x - 3} \right) = \infty.$$

When x approaches 3 from the right, $x - 3$ approaches 0, but through positive numbers. Therefore, $2/(x - 3)$ get numerically larger in a positive direction. The main point is that if we have a constant in the numerator and an expression in the denominator that approaches 0, then the fraction gets numerically large (either positive or negative, depending on how the expression approaches zero).

Let's try one. What is $\lim_{x \to 1^-} \left(\frac{5}{(x - 1)^3} \right)$?

∞ Frame **A** $-\infty$ Frame **B**

A   YOUR ANSWER: ∞.
Wrong. We want

$$\lim_{x \to 1^-} \left(\frac{5}{(x - 1)^3} \right).$$

The expression $(x - 1)$ approaches 0 through negative values as x approaches 1 from the left. What does this do to the limit? Think about this and then return to frame **Q155** and select the other alternative.

B   YOUR ANSWER: $-\infty$.
Right. Since $x - 1$ approaches 0 through negative values as x approaches 1 from the left and the cube of a negative number is still negative, we have

$$\lim_{x \to 1^-} \left(\frac{5}{(x - 1)^3} \right) = -\infty.$$

Notice, the numerator is the constant 5 and the denominator approaches 0 through negative numbers. Hence, the fraction gets numerically larger in a negative direction.

Q156   What is $\lim_{x \to 2^+} \left(\frac{-1}{(x - 2)^5} \right)$?

∞ Frame **A** $-\infty$ Frame **B**

A   YOUR ANSWER: ∞.
Be careful. It is true that as $x \to 2^+$, $(x - 2)^5$ approaches 0 through positive numbers, but the constant in the numerator is negative. Study the problem again, return to

frame **Q156,** and select the other alternative.

B YOUR ANSWER: $-\infty$.
Correct.

$$\lim_{x \to 2^+} \left(\frac{-1}{(x - 2)^5} \right) = -\infty$$

The expression $(x - 2)^5$ approaches 0 through positive numbers as x approaches 2 from the right. However, since the constant in the numerator is negative, the fraction gets numerically larger in a negative direction.

Q157 What is $\lim_{x \to 1} \left(\frac{3}{(x - 1)^4} \right)$?

∞ Frame **A** $-\infty$ Frame **B**

A YOUR ANSWER: ∞.
Of course.

$$\lim_{x \to 1} \left(\frac{3}{(x - 1)^4} \right) = \infty$$

The expression $(x - 1)^4$ approaches 0 through positive numbers regardless of whether x approaches 1 from the right or left because of the even exponent on $x - 1$.

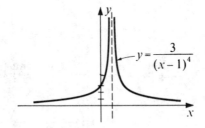

$$y = \frac{3}{(x - 1)^4}$$

B YOUR ANSWER: $-\infty$.
Watch out. The expression $(x - 1)^4$ approaches 0 through positive numbers as x approaches 1 from the right or left. Return to frame **Q157** and select the other alternative.

Q158 Theorem (4.27) on page 172 of the text gives us some properties of sums, products, and quotients of functions which become infinite.

Can you find $\lim_{x \to 2^+} \left(\frac{3x^2}{(x - 2)(x + 1)} \right)$?

Yes   Frame **A**   No   Frame **B**

A YOUR ANSWER: Yes.
Excellent.

$$\lim_{x \to 2^+} \left(\frac{3x^2}{(x - 2)(x + 1)} \right) = \lim_{x \to 2^+} \left(\frac{1}{(x - 2)} \cdot \frac{3x^2}{(x + 1)} \right)$$

$$\lim_{x \to 2^+} \left(\frac{1}{x - 2} \right) = \infty \quad \text{and} \quad \lim_{x \to 2^+} \left(\frac{3x^2}{x + 1} \right) = 4$$

Therefore,

$$\lim_{x \to 2^+} \left(\frac{3x^2}{(x - 2)(x + 1)} \right) = \infty.$$

If one limit of a product is ∞ and the other limit is a positive real number, then the limit of the product is ∞.

B   **YOUR ANSWER:** No.
Let's see if we can get you started. We need to factor the expression in such a manner that we get the factor $x - 2$ isolated because we are approaching 2. This can be done as follows:

$$\frac{3x^2}{(x - 2)(x + 1)} = \frac{1}{x - 2} \cdot \frac{3x^2}{x + 1} \, .$$

Now return to frame **Q158,** find the limit using the fact that the limit of the product is the product of the limits, and then select the other alternative.

Q159   Let's find $\lim_{x \to 3} \left(\frac{1}{x^2(x - 3)^2} \right)$. Were you successful?

Yes   Frame **A**   No   Frame **B**

A   **YOUR ANSWER:** Yes.
Good.

$$\lim_{x \to 3} \left(\frac{1}{x^2(x - 3)^2} \right) = \lim_{x \to 3} \left(\frac{1}{x^2} \cdot \frac{1}{(x - 3)^2} \right)$$

$$\lim_{x \to 3} \left(\frac{1}{x^2} \right) = \frac{1}{9} \quad \text{and} \quad \lim_{x \to 3} \left(\frac{1}{(x - 3)^2} \right) = \infty$$

Therefore,

$$\lim_{x \to 3} \left(\frac{1}{x^2(x - 3)^2} \right) = \infty.$$

B   **YOUR ANSWER:** No.
This is very much like the last problem. We need to factor the expression.

$$\lim_{x \to 3} \left(\frac{1}{x^2(x - 3)^2} \right) = \lim_{x \to 3} \left(\frac{1}{x^2} \cdot \frac{1}{(x - 3)^2} \right)$$

Now return to frame **Q159** and try again.

Q160   We have found $\lim_{x \to 3} \left(\frac{1}{x^2(x - 3)^2} \right) = \infty$. Therefore, $x = 3$ is a vertical asymptote. Find the horizontal asymptotes and any other vertical asymptotes and sketch the graph. How did it go?

Great   Frame **A**   Terrible   Frame **B**

A   **YOUR ANSWER:** Great.
Very good.

$$\lim_{x \to 0} \left(\frac{1}{x^2(x - 3)^2} \right) = \lim_{x \to 0} \left(\frac{1}{x^2} \cdot \frac{1}{(x - 3)^2} \right) = \infty$$

because

$$\lim_{x \to 0} \left(\frac{1}{x^2}\right) = \infty \quad \text{and} \quad \lim_{x \to 0} \left(\frac{1}{(x-3)^2}\right) = \frac{1}{9} \, .$$

Therefore, $x = 0$ is also a vertical asymptote as well as $x = 3$.

$$\lim_{x \to \infty} \left(\frac{1}{x^2(x-3)^2}\right) = 0 \quad \text{and} \quad \lim_{x \to -\infty} \left(\frac{1}{x^2(x-3)^2}\right) = 0$$

Therefore, $y = 0$ is a horizontal asymptote. A sketch of the graph looks something like the following:

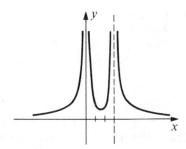

B   YOUR ANSWER: Terrible.
It can't be all bad. We want to sketch the graph of

$$y = \frac{1}{x^2(x-3)^2} \, .$$

We discovered that

$$\lim_{x \to 3} \left(\frac{1}{x^2(x-3)^2}\right) = \infty$$

and thus $x = 3$ is a vertical asymptote. Are there other values that x could approach and give us ∞? If so, we have other vertical asymptotes. In order to find horizontal asymptotes, we want the limit as $x \to \infty$ or $-\infty$. Now return to frame **Q160,** find the asymptotes, sketch the graph, and then select the other alternative.

4.6   APPLICATIONS OF EXTREMA

OBJECTIVES

You should be able to solve certain applied problems involving extrema.

Q161   It is frequently possible to solve a problem which asks for the largest volume, or least area, or something similar by recognizing that the solution of the problem is a maximum or minimum value of some function. There are some examples given on pages 177-184 of the text.

   Let's try a problem. A rectangular field is to be adjacent to a river and is to have fencing on the three sides not adjacent to the river. If 200 yards of fencing are available, find the dimensions of the field with the largest area. In order to solve this

problem, we need a relationship for the area of the field in terms of the lengths of the sides. Let the two sides of the field which are perpendicular to the river each have length x yards. What is the length in yards of the third side?

   $200 - 2x$ Frame **A** $200 - x$ Frame **B** $100 - x$ Frame **C**

A   YOUR ANSWER: $200 - 2x$.
Right. The two sides of the field which are perpendicular to the river each have length x yards. We have a total of 200 yards of fencing available. Therefore, the third side has length $200 - 2x$ yards.

B   YOUR ANSWER: $200 - x$.
Watch out. The two sides of the field which are perpendicular to the river each have length x yards. We have a total of 200 yards of fencing available. Now what is the length of the third side? Return to frame **Q161** and try again.

C   YOUR ANSWER: $100 - x$.
Watch out. We don't want to fence the side by the river. The two sides of the field perpendicular to the river each have length x yards. We have a total of 200 yards of fencing available. Now what is the length of the third side? Return to frame **Q161** and try again.

Q162   We have the following:

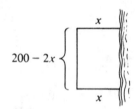

Now what is the area of the field?

   $(200 - 2x)x$ Frame **A**
   200 Frame **B**
   $(200 - 2x)x^2$ Frame **C**

A   YOUR ANSWER: $(200 - 2x)x$.
Of course.

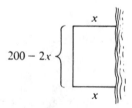

The area of the field is the length times the width. Therefore, $A = (200 - 2x)x$.

B   YOUR ANSWER: 200.
Don't you have the length of the fence instead of the area of the field? Return to

frame **Q162** and find the area.

C **YOUR ANSWER:** $(200 - 2x)x^2$.
Almost, but don't you have an extra factor of x? The area of the field is the length times the width. Return to frame **Q162** and select the correct answer.

Q163 We have $A = (200 - 2x)x$. Now we simply want the value of x for which A is maximum. What is this value?

25	Frame **A**	50	Frame **B**
100	Frame **C**	I don't know.	Frame **D**

A **YOUR ANSWER:** 25.
You are off base. We have $A = (200 - 2x)x = 200x - 2x^2$. Therefore, $A' = 200 - 4x$. Now what value of x will make $A' = 0$? Return to frame **Q163** and try again.

B **YOUR ANSWER:** 50.
You are correct. If $A = (200 - 2x)x = 200x - 2x^2$, $A' = 200 - 4x$. If $A' = 200 - 4x = 0$, then $x = 50$. Since $A'' = -4$, we know A has a maximum at $x = 50$. Remember, x was the length of each side perpendicular to the river. Therefore, the dimensions of the field are 50 yards by $200 - 2(50) = 100$ yards.

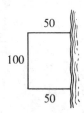

The maximum area is $(100)(50) = 5000$ square yards.

C **YOUR ANSWER:** 100.
You are off base. We have $A = (200 - 2x)x = 200x - 2x^2$. Therefore, $A' = 200 - 4x$. Now what value of x will make $A' = 0$? Return to frame **Q163** and try again.

D **YOUR ANSWER:** I don't know.
We have $A = (200 - 2x)x = 200x - 2x^2$. If A has a maximum, it must occur where $A' = 0$. Now return to frame **Q163** and try again.

Q164 If the total cost of producing x radio sets per day is $(1/4)x^2 + 35x + 25$ dollars and the total selling price of x radio sets per day is $50x - (1/2)x^2$ dollars, how many should be produced daily to obtain a maximum profit?

70	Frame **A**	10	Frame **B**
15	Frame **C**	I need some help.	Frame **D**

A **YOUR ANSWER:** 70.
Your calculations are off. Let P denote profit. Then

$$P = \left(50x - \frac{1}{2}x^2\right) - \left(\frac{1}{4}x^2 + 35x + 25\right)$$

$$= 15x - \frac{3}{4}x^2 - 25.$$

Now return to frame **Q164**, find P', and solve the problem.

B   YOUR ANSWER: 10.

Correct. Since the total selling price of x radio sets is $50x - (1/2)x^2$ and the total cost of producing x radio sets is $(1/4)x^2 + 35x + 25$, the profit is

$$P = \left(50x - \frac{1}{2}x^2\right) - \left(\frac{1}{4}x^2 + 35x + 25\right)$$

$$= 15x - \frac{3}{4}x^2 - 25;$$

$$P' = 15 - \frac{3}{2}x;$$

$$P'' = -\frac{3}{2}.$$

If $P' = 15 - (3/2)x = 0$, then $x = 10$. Since $P''(10) < 0$, P has a maximum when $x = 10$.

C   YOUR ANSWER: 15.

Your calculations are off. Let P denote profit.

$$P = \left(50x - \frac{1}{2}x^2\right) - \left(\frac{1}{4}x^2 + 35x + 25\right)$$

$$= 15x - \frac{3}{4}x^2 - 25.$$

Now return to frame **Q164**, find P', and solve the problem.

D   YOUR ANSWER: I need some help.

Since the total selling price of x radio sets is $50x - (1/2)x^2$ and the total cost of producing x radio sets is $(1/4)x^2 + 35x + 25$, the profit is

$$P = \left(50x - \frac{1}{2}x^2\right) - \left(\frac{1}{4}x^2 + 35x + 25\right).$$

Now the problem is to find the value of x for which P is a maximum. Return to frame **Q164** and try again.

Q165   Let's try one more. A cylindrical can with open top is to hold 64 cubic inches. Find the dimensions so as to use the least amount of material. Were you successful?

　　　　Yes   Frame **A**   No   Frame **B**

A   YOUR ANSWER: Yes.

Excellent. Letting r and h, respectively, be the radius of the base and height in inches of the container, and since $V = 64$, we have

$$\pi r^2 h = 64 \quad \text{and} \quad A = 2\pi r h + \pi r^2.$$

In order to express A as a function of one variable, we solve for h in the first relation and substitute in the second to obtain

$$A = 2\pi r\left(\frac{64}{\pi r^2}\right) + \pi r^2 = \frac{128}{r} + \pi r^2;$$

$$A' = \frac{-128}{r^2} + 2\pi r = \frac{2(\pi r^3 - 64)}{r^2}.$$

If $A' = 0$, then $\pi r^3 - 64 = 0$ or $r = 4/\sqrt[3]{\pi}$. Then

$$h = \frac{64}{\pi r^2} = \frac{64}{\pi(4/\sqrt[3]{\pi})^2} = \frac{4}{\sqrt[3]{\pi}}.$$

Thus, $r = h = 4/\sqrt[3]{\pi}$ yields the required volume with the least amount of material.

B   YOUR ANSWER: No.

Let's see if we can get you started. Let r and h, respectively, be the radius of the base and height in inches of the container, A the amount of material, and V the volume of the container. This gives us

$$V = \pi r^2 h \quad \text{and} \quad A = 2\pi rh + \pi r^2.$$

These are the formulas for volume and surface area. Since $V = 64$, we have

$$\pi r^2 h = 64 \quad \text{and} \quad A = 2\pi rh + \pi r^2.$$

Notice that A is expressed in terms of r and h. We may eliminate r by using $\pi r^2 h = 64$ or $h = 64/\pi r^2$. Hence,

$$A = 2\pi r\left(\frac{64}{\pi r^2}\right) + \pi r^2 = \frac{128}{r} + \pi r^2.$$

Now the problem is to find r for which A is a minimum. Return to frame **Q165** and try again.

4.7   THE DERIVATIVE AS A RATE OF CHANGE

OBJECTIVES

You should know how to interpret the derivative as a rate of change and how to solve problems using this concept.

Q166   If the position s at time t of an object moving on a straight line is determined by a relation $s = f(t)$, then the *average velocity* of the object in the time interval from t to $t + h$ is

$$\frac{f(t + h) - f(t)}{h},$$

whereas the *velocity* at time t is

$$f'(t) = \lim_{h \to 0} \frac{f(t + h) - f(t)}{h}.$$

If $s = -t^2 + 8t + 4$, where s is in feet and t is in seconds, what is the average velocity in the time interval from $t = 0$ to $t = 6$?

1 foot/second	Frame **A**
2 feet/second	Frame **B**
8 feet/second	Frame **C**

A **YOUR ANSWER:** 1 foot/second.
Sorry, but your calculations are off. The average velocity from $t = 0$ to $t = 6$ where $f(t) = -t^2 + 8t + 4$ is

$$\frac{f(6) - f(0)}{6} .$$

Return to frame **Q166**, carry out the calculations, and then select the correct answer.

B **YOUR ANSWER:** 2 feet/second.
Right. If $s = f(t) = -t^2 + 8t + 4$, then the average velocity from $t = 0$ to $t = 6$ is

$$\frac{f(6) - f(0)}{6} = \frac{-(6)^2 + 8(6) + 4 - 4}{6} = \frac{12}{6} = 2.$$

C **YOUR ANSWER:** 8 feet/second.
Don't you have the velocity at $t = 0$ which is $f'(t)$ at $t = 0$? The average velocity from $t = 0$ to $t = 6$ where $f(t) = -t^2 + 8t + 4$ is

$$\frac{f(6) - f(0)}{6} .$$

Return to frame **Q166**, carry out the calculations, and then select the correct answer.

Q167 If $s = -t^2 + 8t + 4$, where s is in feet and t is in seconds, we found that the average velocity in the time interval from $t = 0$ to $t = 6$ is 2 feet/second. What is the velocity at $t = 0$?

8 feet/second	Frame **A**
2 feet/second	Frame **B**
I don't know.	Frame **C**

A **YOUR ANSWER:** 8 feet/second.
Correct. If $s = f(t) = -t^2 + 8t + 4$, then $f'(t) = -2t + 8$. The velocity at $t = 0$ is $f'(0) = 8$.

B **YOUR ANSWER:** 2 feet/second.
The velocity at $t = 0$ is not necessarily the same as the average velocity. The velocity at $t = 0$ is $f'(t)$ evaluated at $t = 0$. Now return to frame **Q167** and select the correct answer.

C **YOUR ANSWER:** I don't know.
The velocity at $t = 0$ is $f'(t)$ evaluated at $t = 0$. Now return to frame **Q167**, find $f'(0)$, and select the correct answer.

Q168 If $s = f(t)$, we have seen that the velocity v at time t is $f'(t)$. Now in a similar manner, the *average acceleration* in the time interval from t to $t + h$ is

$$\frac{f'(t + h) - f'(t)}{h}$$

and the *acceleration* at time t is

$$f''(t) = \lim_{h \to 0} \frac{f'(t + h) - f'(t)}{h} .$$

If $s = f(t) = t^3 - 3t$, where s is in feet and t is in seconds, what is the acceleration at $t = 2$?

$3t^2 - 3$

$6t$

9 feet/sec²	Frame **A**
12 feet/sec²	Frame **B**
6 feet/sec²	Frame **C**

A **YOUR ANSWER:** 9 feet/sec².
Sorry, but you found the velocity instead of acceleration. If $s = f(t)$, then $v = f'(t)$, and $a = f''(t)$. Return to frame **Q168**, calculate $f''(t)$ at $t = 2$, and select the correct answer.

B **YOUR ANSWER:** 12 feet/sec².
Right. If $s = f(t) = t^3 - 3t$, then $v = f'(t) = 3t^2 - 3$, and $a = f''(t) = 6t$. Therefore, if $t = 2$, $a = 6(2) = 12$.

C **YOUR ANSWER:** 6 feet/sec².
Sorry, but your calculations are off. If $s = f(t)$, then $v = f'(t)$, and $a = f''(t)$. Return to frame **Q168**, calculate $f''(t)$ at $t = 2$, and select the correct answer.

4.8 RELATED RATES

OBJECTIVES

You should know what is meant by related rates and how to solve problems using related rates.

Q169 If two quantities x and y are both functions of t, and if x and y are connected by some relation, then the rates of change dx/dt and dy/dt are called *related rates*. There are several kinds of problems involving related rates. Some examples are given on pages 195-198 of the text.

Let's try a problem involving related rates. Suppose the length of the side of a square is increasing at the rate of 0.3 inch per second. Find the rate at which the area is increasing at the instant when the side is 15 inches long. Let x denote the length of the side of the square. Which one of the following indicates the length is increasing at the rate of 0.3 inch per second?

$x = 0.3$	Frame **A**
$\dfrac{dx}{dt} = 0.3$	Frame **B**
$\dfrac{dx}{dt} = 15$	Frame **C**

A **YOUR ANSWER:** $x = 0.3$.
No. Read the problem again. The length of the side of a square is increasing at the rate of 0.3 inch per second. Find the rate at which the area is increasing at the instant when the side is 15 inches long.

If x denotes the length of the side of the square, what represents the rate of change of x? Now return to frame **Q169,** think about this, and then try again.

B YOUR ANSWER: $dx/dt = 0.3$.

Certainly. The problem states: The length of the side of a square is increasing at the rate of 0.3 inch per second. Find the rate at which the area is increasing at the instant when the side is 15 inches long. Therefore, we are given that $dx/dt = 0.3$.

C YOUR ANSWER: $dx/dt = 15$.

No. Read the problem again. The length of the side of a square is increasing at the rate of 0.3 inch per second. Find the rate at which the area is increasing at the instant when the side is 15 inches long.

   The expression dx/dt does represent the rate of change of x, but what is given as this rate of change? Now return to frame **Q169**, think about this, and then try again.

Q170 Now we want to find dA/dt when $x = 15$. Since $A = x^2$, which one of the following is dA/dt?

$$\frac{dA}{dt} = 2x\frac{dx}{dt} \qquad \text{Frame **A**}$$

$$\frac{dA}{dt} = 2x \qquad \text{Frame **B**}$$

$$\frac{dA}{dt} = 0.3 \qquad \text{Frame **C**}$$

A YOUR ANSWER: $\dfrac{dA}{dt} = 2x\dfrac{dx}{dt}$.

Correct.

B YOUR ANSWER: $dA/dt = 2x$.

Not exactly. We have $A = x^2$, but we want the derivative of both sides with respect to t. You have the derivative of A with respect to x. Think about this and then return to frame **Q170** and try again.

C YOUR ANSWER: $dA/dt = 0.3$.

No. We have $dx/dt = 0.3$ and $A = x^2$. Differentiate both sides of $A = x^2$ with respect to t. Now return to frame **Q170** and try again.

Q171 The problem is as follows: The length of the side of a square is increasing at the rate of 0.3 inch per second. Find the rate at which the area is increasing at the instant when the side is 15 inches long.

   We have $dx/dt = 0.3$ and $dA/dt = 2x(dx/dt)$. Now you are in a position to determine dA/dt when $x = 15$, aren't you? What do you get?

30 inches per second	Frame **A**
9 inches per second	Frame **B**
4.5 inches per second	Frame **C**

A YOUR ANSWER: 30 inches per second.

Sorry, but your calculations are off. We have $dx/dt = 0.3$ and $x = 15$. Therefore,

$$\frac{dA}{dt} = 2x\frac{dx}{dt} = 2(15)(0.3).$$

Return to frame **Q171**, calculate the result, and select the correct answer.

B **YOUR ANSWER:** 9 inches per second.
Of course. We have $dx/dt = 0.3$ and $x = 15$. Therefore,

$$\frac{dA}{dt} = 2x\frac{dx}{dt} = 2(15)(0.3) = 9.$$

C **YOUR ANSWER:** 4.5 inches per second.
Sorry, but your calculations are off. We have $dx/dt = 0.3$ and $x = 15$. Therefore,

$$\frac{dA}{dt} = 2x\frac{dx}{dt} = 2(15)(0.3).$$

Return to frame **Q171**, calculate the result, and select the correct answer.

Q172 If a point moves on the parabola with equation $y = 2x^2$ in such a way that x increases uniformly at the rate of 3 units per second, what is the rate of change of y at the instant when $x = 2$?

6 units per second	Frame **A**
12 units per second	Frame **B**
24 units per second	Frame **C**

A **YOUR ANSWER:** 6 units per second.
No. If $y = 2x^2$, then $dy/dt = 4x(dx/dt)$. We want to find dy/dt when x and dx/dt are given, don't we? Return to frame **Q172** and try again.

B **YOUR ANSWER:** 12 units per second.
No. If $y = 2x^2$, then $dy/dt = 4x(dx/dt)$. We want to find dy/dt when x and dx/dt are given, don't we? Return to frame **Q172** and try again.

C **YOUR ANSWER:** 24 units per second.
Good. We were given $dx/dt = 3$ and we want to determine dy/dt when $x = 2$ where $y = 2x^2$. Therefore,

$$\frac{dy}{dt} = 4x\frac{dx}{dt} = 4(2)(3) = 24.$$

Q173 Let's try one more. Gas is escaping from a spherical balloon at the rate of 2 cubic feet per minute. How fast is the surface area shrinking when the radius is 12 feet? Can you solve this problem?

Yes	Frame **A**
No	Frame **B**
I need some help to get started.	Frame **C**

A **YOUR ANSWER:** Yes.
Excellent. The problem is as follows: Gas is escaping from a spherical balloon at the rate of 2 cubic feet per minute. How fast is the surface area shrinking when the radius is 12 feet? The volume and surface area of a sphere are

$$V = \frac{4}{3}\pi r^3 \quad \text{and} \quad S = 4\pi r^2.$$

Differentiating with respect to t, we obtain

$$\frac{dV}{dt} = 4\pi r^2 \frac{dr}{dt} \quad \text{and} \quad \frac{dS}{dt} = 8\pi r \frac{dr}{dt}.$$

Since gas is escaping at the rate of 2 cubic feet per minute, we have

$$4\pi r^2 \frac{dr}{dt} = -2 \quad \text{or} \quad \frac{dr}{dt} = \frac{-1}{2\pi r^2}.$$

Now

$$\frac{dS}{dt} = 8\pi r \frac{dr}{dt} = 8\pi r \left(\frac{-1}{2\pi r^2}\right) = -\frac{4}{r}.$$

But when $r = 12$, we have $-4/12 = -1/3$ square feet per minute.

B   YOUR ANSWER: No.

Sure you can. The problem is as follows: Gas is escaping from a spherical balloon at the rate of 2 cubic feet per minute. How fast is the surface area shrinking when the radius is 12 feet?

Both volume and surface area of a sphere are involved in the problem. These formulas are

$$V = \frac{4}{3}\pi r^3 \quad \text{and} \quad S = 4\pi r^2.$$

Since gas is escaping at the rate of 2 cubic feet per minute, $dV/dt = -2$. Now find dS/dt. Return to frame **Q173** and try again.

C   YOUR ANSWER: I need some help to get started.

The problem is as follows: Gas is escaping from a spherical balloon at the rate of 2 cubic feet per minute. How fast is the surface area shrinking when the radius is 12 feet? Both volume and surface area of a sphere are involved in the problem. These formulas are

$$V = \frac{4}{3}\pi r^3 \quad \text{and} \quad S = 4\pi r^2.$$

Calculate dV/dt and dS/dt and find dS/dt in terms of what is given. Now return to frame **Q173** and try again.

4.9 ANTIDERIVATIVES

OBJECTIVES

You should know the definition of an antiderivative. You should know some of the rules for finding an antiderivative and how to express the general antiderivative of a function.

Q174 If $f'(x)$ exists for every number x in a given domain, then f is called an *antiderivative* of f'. That is, a function H is an antiderivative of a function h if $H' = h$. For example, $H(x) = x^2 + 3$ is an antiderivative of $h(x) = 2x$ because $H'(x) = 2x = h(x)$.

Which one of the following is an antiderivative of $f(x) = 3$?

$F(x) = 3x + 5$	Frame **A**
$F(x) = 3x^2$	Frame **B**
$F(x) = 3$	Frame **C**

A **YOUR ANSWER:** $F(x) = 3x + 5$.
Correct. If $F(x) = 3x + 5$, then $F'(x) = 3$ which is equal to $f(x)$. Therefore, F is called an antiderivative of f. We speak of *an* antiderivative rather than *the* antiderivative because it is not unique. For example, $G(x) = 3x + 6$ is also an antiderivative of f because $G'(x) = 3$.

B **YOUR ANSWER:** $F(x) = 3x^2$.
No. The function F is an antiderivative of f if $F' = f$. If $F(x) = 3x^2$, then $F'(x) = 6x$. Therefore, F is not an antiderivative of f because $F' \neq f$. Return to frame **Q174** and try again.

C **YOUR ANSWER:** $F(x) = 3$.
No. The function F is an antiderivative of f if $F' = f$. If $F(x) = 3$, then $F'(x) = 0$. Therefore, F is not an antiderivative of f because $F' \neq f$. Return to frame **Q174** and try again.

Q175 Which one of the following is an antiderivative of $f(x) = 2x + 5$?

$F(x) = 2x^2 + 5$	Frame **A**
$F(x) = x^2 + 5$	Frame **B**
$F(x) = x^2 + 5x + 3$	Frame **C**

A **YOUR ANSWER:** $F(x) = 2x^2 + 5$.
Watch out. The function F is an antiderivative of f if $F' = f$. If $F(x) = 2x^2 + 5$, then $F'(x) = 4x$, which is not f. Therefore, F is not an antiderivative of f. Return to frame **Q175** and try again.

B **YOUR ANSWER:** $F(x) = x^2 + 5$.
Watch out. The function F is an antiderivative of f if $F' = f$. If $F(x) = x^2 + 5$, then $F'(x) = 2x$, which is not f. Therefore, F is not an antiderivative of f. Return to frame **Q175** and try again.

C **YOUR ANSWER:** $F(x) = x^2 + 5x + 3$.
Good. If $F(x) = x^2 + 5x + 3$, then $F'(x) = 2x + 5$. Therefore, $F(x) = x^2 + 5x + 3$ is an antiderivative of $f(x) = 2x + 5$.

Q176 THEOREM: If f has a derivative everywhere in the closed interval $[a, b]$, and if $f'(x) = 0$ for every x in $[a, b]$, then f is a constant. That is, f assigns to every x in $[a, b]$ the same number c.

THEOREM: If F and G are both antiderivatives of the same function f, then $G(x) = F(x) + C$.

Both of the above theorems are proved in the text on pages 201 and 202. We have already observed that an antiderivative of a function f is not unique. Because of the latter theorem above, we may speak of $F(x) + C$ as the *general antiderivative* of $f(x)$ if $F(x)$ is an antiderivative of $f(x)$. For example, we know that x^2 is an antiderivative of $2x$. But we also know that $x^2 + 3$ is an antiderivative of $2x$ and $x^2 + 5$ is an antiderivative of $2x$. Now we simply say that $x^2 + C$ (C an arbitrary constant) is the general antiderivative of $2x$.

Which one of the following is the general antiderivative of $2x + 3$?

$x^2 + 3x + C$ Frame **A**
$x^2 + C$ Frame **B**
$x^2 + 3 + C$ Frame **C**

A **YOUR ANSWER:** $x^2 + 3x + C$.
Right. The derivative of $x^2 + 3x + C$ is $2x + 3 + 0 = 2x + 3$. Notice that the derivative of $x^2 + 3x$ is also $2x + 3$, and we simply add on the arbitrary constant C to obtain the general antiderivative.

B **YOUR ANSWER:** $x^2 + C$.
Be careful. The derivative of $x^2 + C$ is $2x$, whereas, we want the derivative to be $2x + 3$. Remember, C is simply an arbitrary constant. Return to frame **Q176** and try again.

C **YOUR ANSWER:** $x^2 + 3 + C$.
What you have is essentially the same as $x^2 + k$ where k is an arbitrary constant, because we could let $k = 3 + C$, since 3 and C are both constants. The derivative of $x^2 + k$ is $2x$, whereas, we want the derivative to be $2x + 3$. Return to frame **Q176** and try again.

Q177 What is the general antiderivative of 5?

$5x$ Frame **A** $5x^2 + C$ Frame **B** $5x + C$ Frame **C**

A **YOUR ANSWER:** $5x$.
It is true that the derivative of $5x$ is 5, but we want the general antiderivative. What do we do to obtain the general antiderivative? Think about this and then return to frame **Q177** and try again.

B **YOUR ANSWER:** $5x^2 + C$.
No. The derivative of $5x^2 + C$ is not 5, is it? Return to frame **Q177** and try again.

C **YOUR ANSWER:** $5x + C$.
Of course. The derivative of $5x + C$ is 5. This is the general antiderivative because of the arbitrary constant.

Q178 Let a be any real number, r any rational number different from -1, and C an arbitrary constant.

$$\text{If } f(x) = ax^r, \text{ then } F(x) = \left(\frac{a}{r + 1}\right)x^{r+1} + C$$

is the most general antiderivative of $f(x)$. This is referred to as the Power Rule for Antidifferentiation and is given on page 202 of the text.

What is the most general antiderivative of $f(x) = 2x^{-3}$?

$$F(x) = (1/2)x^4 + C \qquad \text{Frame A}$$
$$F(x) = (-1/2)x^{-4} + C \qquad \text{Frame B}$$
$$F(x) = -x^{-2} + C \qquad \text{Frame C}$$

A **YOUR ANSWER:** $F(x) = (1/2)x^4 + C$.

No. If $f(x) = ax^r$, then $F(x) = \left(\dfrac{a}{r+1}\right)x^{r+1} + C$. Since $f(x) = 2x^{-3}$, we have $a = 2$

and $r = -3$. Now return to frame **Q178**, make the appropriate substitutions, and then select the correct answer.

B **YOUR ANSWER:** $F(x) = (-1/2)x^{-4} + C$.

Be careful. If $f(x) = ax^r$, then $F(x) = \left(\dfrac{a}{r+1}\right)x^{r+1} + C$. Since $f(x) = 2x^{-3}$, we have

$a = 2$ and $r = -3$. Now return to frame **Q178**, make the appropriate substitutions, and then select the correct answer.

C **YOUR ANSWER:** $F(x) = -x^{-2} + C$.

Of course. Since $f(x) = 2x^{-3}$, we have

$$F(x) = \left(\frac{2}{-3+1}\right)x^{-3+1} + C$$

$$= \left(\frac{2}{-2}\right)x^{-2} + C = -x^{-2} + C.$$

Q179 Find the most general antiderivative, $F(x)$, of $f(x) = 3x^3 - x^2 + 5x - 1$.

$$F(x) = x^4 - x^3 + x^2 - x + C \qquad \text{Frame A}$$
$$F(x) = (3/4)x^4 - (1/3)x^3 + (5/2)x^2 - x + C \qquad \text{Frame B}$$
$$F(x) = 3x^4 - x^3 + 5x^2 - x + C \qquad \text{Frame C}$$

A **YOUR ANSWER:** $F(x) = x^4 - x^3 + x^2 - x + C$.

Sorry, but you don't have the correct coefficients. Return to frame **Q179**, study the Power Rule for Antidifferentiation, and then try again.

B **YOUR ANSWER:** $F(x) = (3/4)x^4 - (1/3)x^3 + (5/2)x^2 - x + C$.

Right. We have $f(x) = 3x^3 - x^2 + 5x - 1$. Applying the Power Rule for Antidifferentiation to each term gives us

$$F(x) = \frac{3}{4}x^4 - \frac{1}{3}x^3 + \frac{5}{2}x^2 - x + C.$$

It is not necessary to use an aribitrary constant for each term since they could be added together to give us the one arbitrary constant C.

C **YOUR ANSWER:** $F(x) = 3x^4 - x^3 + 5x^2 - x + C$.

Didn't you forget to divide by the exponent when using the Power Rule for Antidifferentiation? Return to frame **Q179**, study the rule, and then try again.

Q180 Since $v = ds/dt$, s is an antiderivative of v. Therefore, if we know v as a function of t, we can find s provided we have an additional piece of information in order to determine the constant. Study the examples given on pages 204-205 of the text.

If $v = 4t + 1$, find s at time t provided $s = 1$ when $t = 2$.

$s = 2t^2 + t - 9$	Frame **A**
$s = 4t^2 + t - 17$	Frame **B**
$s = 2t^2 + t$	Frame **C**

A   **YOUR ANSWER:** $s = 2t^2 + t - 9$.
Good. If $v = 4t + 1$, then $s = 2t^2 + t + C$. We know that $s = 1$ when $t = 2$.
Hence, $1 = 2(2)^2 + 2 + C$ or $C = -9$. Therefore, $s = 2t^2 + t - 9$.

B   **YOUR ANSWER:** $s = 4t^2 + t - 17$.
Your calculations are off. If $v = 4t + 1$, then

$$s = 2t^2 + t + C.$$

If $s = 1$ when $t = 2$, we can determine C. Now return to frame **Q180** and try again.

C   **YOUR ANSWER:** $s = 2t^2 + t$.
Your calculations are off. If $v = 4t + 1$, then

$$s = 2t^2 + t + C.$$

If $s = 1$ when $t = 2$, then $C \neq 0$. Return to frame **Q180** and try again.

Q181   Since $a = dv/dt$, v is an antiderivative of a. If $a = 12t^2 + 6t$, find s at time t provided $v = -3$ and $s = 0$ when $t = 0$. (*Hint*: Find v and then s.) Were you successful?

  Yes   Frame **A**   No   Frame **B**

A   **YOUR ANSWER:**   Yes.
Very good. If $a = 12t^2 + 6t$, then $v = 4t^3 + 3t^2 + C$. Since $v = -3$ when $t = 0$, $C = -3$. Therefore, $v = 4t^3 + 3t^2 - 3$. Now $s = t^4 + t^3 - 3t + C$. Since $s = 0$ when $t = 0$, $C = 0$ and $s = t^4 + t^3 - 3t$.

B   **YOUR ANSWER:**   No.
Let's see if we can get you started. If $a = 12t^2 + 6t$, then

$$v = 4t^3 + 3t^2 + C.$$

We know that $v = -3$ when $t = 0$. Hence, $C = -3$. Therefore, $v = 4t^3 + 3t^2 - 3$. Now we can find s as before because we also know that $s = 0$ when $t = 0$. Return to frame **Q181**, complete the solution, and select the other alternative.

4.10   APPLICATIONS TO ECONOMICS

OBJECTIVES

You should know some of the applications of derivatives to economics, such as the cost function and demand function.

Q182   The cost function and related functions are discussed on pages 207 and 208 of the text. If

$$C(x) = 50 + \frac{8}{x} + \frac{x^2}{30} \, ,$$

what is the marginal cost function?

$$x\left(50 + \frac{8}{x} + \frac{x^2}{30}\right) \qquad \text{Frame A}$$

$$\frac{-8}{x^2} + \frac{x}{15} \qquad \text{Frame B}$$

$$\frac{50}{x} + \frac{8}{x^2} + \frac{x}{30} \qquad \text{Frame C}$$

A **YOUR ANSWER:** $x\left(50 + \frac{8}{x} + \frac{x^2}{30}\right)$.

Aren't you confusing some notions of cost and price? Return to frame **Q182**, study the definition of marginal cost function, and try again.

B **YOUR ANSWER:** $\frac{-8}{x^2} + \frac{x}{15}$.

Correct. If $C(x) = 50 + 8/x + x^2/30$, then $C'(x) = -8/x^2 + x/15$ is the marginal cost function. When the marginal cost function is zero, we have the minimum cost.

C **YOUR ANSWER:** $\frac{50}{x} + \frac{8}{x^2} + \frac{x}{30}$.

No. You have the average cost function. The marginal cost function is the derivative of the cost function. Now return to frame **Q182** and try again.

Q183 The notions of demand function, marginal demand function, total revenue function, and the marginal revenue function are discussed on pages 210 and 211 of the text.

If $x^2 - 6x + 2p - 15 = 0$ gives the relationship between the demand x and the price p of a commodity, what is $R(x)$, the total revenue function?

$$\frac{-x^2 + 6x + 15}{2} \qquad \text{Frame A}$$

$$-x + 3 \qquad \text{Frame B}$$

$$\frac{-x^3 + 6x^2 + 15x}{2} \qquad \text{Frame C}$$

A **YOUR ANSWER:** $\frac{-x^2 + 6x + 15}{2}$.

No. If $x^2 - 6x + 2p - 15 = 0$ gives the relationship between the demand x and the price p of a commodity, then

$$p = g(x) = \frac{-x^2 + 6x + 15}{2}$$

is the demand function. Study pages 210 and 211 of the text, and then return to frame **Q183** and find the total revenue function.

B **YOUR ANSWER:** $-x + 3$.

No. If $x^2 - 6x + 2p - 15 = 0$ gives the relationship between the demand x and the price p of a commodity, then

$$p = g(x) = \frac{-x^2 + 6x + 15}{2}$$

is the demand function and

$$p' = g'(x) = -x + 3$$

is the marginal demand function. Study pages 210 and 211 of the text and then return to frame **Q183** and find the total revenue function.

C   YOUR ANSWER: $\dfrac{-x^3 + 6x^2 + 15x}{2}$.

Yes. If

$$p = g(x) = \frac{-x^2 + 6x + 15}{2}$$

is the demand function, then, by definition, $R(x) = xg(x)$ is the total revenue function. Therefore,

$$R(x) = \frac{-x^3 + 6x^2 + 15x}{2} \, .$$

Since $g(x)$ is the price per unit when there is a demand for x units, $R(x) = xg(x)$ is the revenue obtained by selling x units.

Q184   We have total revenue,

$$R(x) = \frac{-x^3 + 6x^2 + 15x}{2} \, .$$

Can you determine how many units must be produced to yield the maximum revenue?

　　　　Yes　　　Frame **A**　　　No　　　Frame **B**

A   YOUR ANSWER: Yes.
Good.

$$R(x) = \frac{-x^3 + 6x^2 + 15x}{2}$$

$$R'(x) = \frac{-3x^2 + 12x + 15}{2}$$

If $R'(x) = 0$, then $-3x^2 + 12x + 15 = -3(x + 1)(x - 5) = 0$. The critical numbers are -1 and 5. Since R' changes from positive to negative as x increases through 5, we have a maximum at 5. Therefore, the revenue is a maximum when 5 units are produced.

B   YOUR ANSWER: No.
Sure you can. The problem is one of finding the maximum if

$$R(x) = \frac{-x^3 + 6x^2 + 15x}{2} \, .$$

Therefore, find the critical numbers and determine which one produces a maximum. Now return to frame **Q184**, find the number of units that will produce the maximum revenue, and select the other alternative.

REVIEW TEST

1   Find the absolute maximum and minimum of $f(x) = x^3 + 6x^2 + 12x$ on $[-4, 4]$.

2   Find the critical numbers of the following functions.
  (a) $f(x) = 2x^3 - 9x^2 + 12x + 7$ (b) $f(x) = x^2 - 5x + 3$ (c) $f(x) = 1/(1 - x^2)$

3   Prove that $f(x) = ax^4$ $(a \neq 0)$ has exactly one local extremum and that it is a local maximum if $a < 0$ and a local minimum if $a > 0$.

4   If $f(x) = 3x^{2/3} + 1$, show that $f(-1) = f(1)$ and $f'(c) \neq 0$ for every c in $(-1, 1)$. Why does this not contradict Rolle's Theorem?

5   Show that $f(x) = 3x^2 - 2x + 6$ satisfies the conditions of the Mean Value Theorem on $[0, 3]$, and find the value or values of C in $[0, 3]$ satisfying the Mean Value Theorem.

6   Using the First Derivative Test, find the local extrema of each of the following.
  (a) $f(x) = 2x^3 + 3x^2 - 12x + 5$ (b) $f(x) = (2/3)x^3 + 2/x$

7   Find the absolute maximum and minimum values for $f(x) = 2x^3 + 3x^2 - 12x + 5$ on the interval $[0, 3]$.

8   Where is the graph of $y = 3x^3 + 4x^2 - 6x + 5$ concave upward?

9   If $y = x/(x - 1)$, determine where the graph is increasing, decreasing, concave upward, and concave downward, and sketch the graph.

10 For each of the following, find the local extrema and points of inflection.
  (a) $f(x) = 2x^3 - x^2 - 4x - 5$ (b) $f(x) = 1/(x^2 + 3)$

11 Prove that $f(x) = ax^2 + bx + c$ can have no inflection points.

12 Find the following limits.
  (a) $\lim\limits_{x \to \infty} \dfrac{2x^3 + x^2 - 5}{5x^3 - 2x + 1}$ (b) $\lim\limits_{x \to \infty} \dfrac{\sqrt{x^2 - 1}}{x + 2}$
  (c) $\lim\limits_{x \to 2^+} \dfrac{3}{x - 2}$ (d) $\lim\limits_{x \to -1^-} \dfrac{2x}{(x + 1)^3}$

13 For each of the following, find the vertical and horizontal asymptotes and sketch the graph.
  (a) $f(x) = x^2/(x^2 + x - 6)$ (b) $f(x) = -2x/(x - 3)^2$

14 A peach orchard now has 20 trees per acre, and the average yield is 320 peaches per tree. For each additional tree planted per acre, the average yield per tree is reduced by approximately 8 peaches. How many trees per acre will give the largest crop of peaches?

15 The temperature T (degrees Celsius) of a solution at time t (minutes) is given by $T(t) = 1 + t^2 - 1/(1 + t)$, where $1 \leq t \leq 20$. What is the rate of change of $T(t)$ with respect to t at $t = 8$ minutes?

16 The position function s of a point P on a coordinate line is given by $s(t) = 20 - 5t + t^3$ where t is measured in seconds and $s(t)$ in cm. What is the velocity and acceleration at 5 seconds?

17 Gas is leaking from a spherical balloon at a constant rate, changing from 10 in. to 6 in. in 30 minutes. How fast was the volume changing when the radius was 8 in.?

18 A point moves on the graph of the equation $y = 2x^2 - x + 1$, the x-coordinate changing at a rate of 3 units per second. How fast is the ordinate changing at the point $(1, 2)$?

19　Find the most general antiderivative of the following functions.
　　(a)　$f(x) = 3x - 5$　　　　　　　　　　(b)　$f(x) = x^2 - 2x + 3$
　　(c)　$f(x) = \sqrt{x} + x^{2/3} - 1$　　　　(d)　$f(x) = (2x - 3)(x + 5)$

20　Solve the differential equation

$$f'(x) = 2x^3 - x + 5, f(1) = 2.$$

21　A point moves rectilinearly such that the acceleration $a(t) = 2t^2 - t + 3$. If the initial conditions are $v(0) = 2$ and $s(0) = 4$, find $s(t)$.

22　A toy company estimates that the cost (in dollars) of producing x toys is given by $C(x) = 100 + 0.03x + 0.001x^2$.
　　(a)　Find the cost of producing 300 toys.
　　(b)　Find the average cost of producing 300 toys.
　　(c)　Find the marginal cost of producing 300 toys.

SAMPLE TEST

1　Find the absolute maximum and minimum of $f(x) = x^4 + 8x^2 + 5$ on $[-1, 1]$.

2　Find the critical numbers of the following functions.
　　(a)　$f(x) = 1/x$　　(b)　$f(x) = 3x^2 - 5x + 1$　　(c)　$f(x) = x/(1 + x)$

3　If $f(x) = x^{1/5}$, prove that f has no local extrema.

4　Show that $f(x) = 2x - x^2$ satisfies the hypothesis of Rolle's Theorem on $[0, 2]$, and find the value of c in $(0, 2)$ such that $f'(c) = 0$.

5　Does $f(x) = |x|$ on the interval $[-1, 2]$ satisfy the Mean Value Theorem?

6　Using the First Derivative Test, find the local extrema of each of the following.
　　(a)　$f(x) = x^3 + 6x^2 + 9x - 2$　　　(b)　$f(x) = x\sqrt{3x - 4}$

7　Find the absolute maximum and minimum values for $f(x) = x^3 + 6x^2 + 9x - 2$ on the interval $[-4, -1]$.

8　Where is the graph of $y = 2x^3 + x^2 - 3x + 1$ concave downward?

9　If $y = 1/(x + 1)$, determine where the graph is increasing, decreasing, concave upward, and concave downward, and sketch the graph.

10　For each of the following, find the local extrema and points of inflection.
　　(a)　$f(x) = x^3 - 2x^2 + x - 1$　　(b)　$f(x) = x^2/4 + 4/x$

11　Prove that $f(x) = x^3$ has no local extrema, but does have an inflection point.

12　Find the following limits.
　　(a)　$\displaystyle\lim_{x \to -\infty} \frac{x^3 - 2x^2 + 3}{2x^3 + x - 1}$　　(b)　$\displaystyle\lim_{x \to \infty} (\sqrt{x^2 - 2} - x)$

　　(c)　$\displaystyle\lim_{x \to 1^-} \frac{2}{(x - 1)^5}$　　(d)　$\displaystyle\lim_{x \to 3^+} \frac{-3x}{(x - 3)^2}$

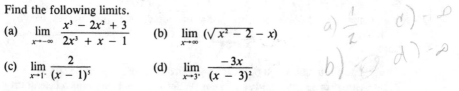

13　For each of the following, find the vertical and horizontal asymptotes and sketch the graph.
　　(a)　$f(x) = (x + 3)/(x^2 - 9)$　　(b)　$f(x) = -5/(x - 2)^2$

14　A farmer has 600 yd of wire fencing which he is going to use to enclose a rectangular field and then subdivide the field into two plots with a fence parallel to a side. What are the dimensions of the largest field which can be fenced with the given fencing?

15 Suppose that t seconds after a runner starts to run, his pulse rate (beats/min) is given by $P(t)$ $= 3t^2 - 2t + 42$. What is the rate of change of $P(t)$ with respect to t when $t = 3$ minutes?

16 The position function s of a point P on a coordinate line is given by $s(t) = \sqrt{t} - t^2 + 1$ where t is measured in seconds and $s(t)$ in cm. What is the velocity and acceleration at 9 seconds?

17 A kite is rising vertically at a rate of 2 ft/sec. An observer is situated 30 ft from a point on the ground directly below the balloon. At what rate is the distance between the balloon and the observer changing when the altitude of the balloon is 40 ft?

18 A point moves on the graph of the equation $y^2 = x^2 - 1$, the abscissa changing at the rate of 2 units per second. How fast is the ordinate changing at the point $(2, \sqrt{3})$?

19 Find the most general antiderivative of the following functions.
  (a) $f(x) = x^2 - 2$ (b) $f(x) = x^3 + 2x^2 - x + 1$
  (c) $f(x) = x^{1/3} - x^{3/5} + \sqrt{x}$ (d) $f(x) = (x - 1)^3$

20 Solve the differential equation $f'(x) = 3x^2 - 2x + 3$, $f(-1) = 1$.

21 A ball is thrown directly upward from a point 20 ft above the ground with an initial velocity of 40 ft/sec. Assuming no air resistance, how high will the ball rise?

22 A company determines that the cost $C(x)$ of manufacturing x units of a commodity may be approximated by $C(x) = 200 + 5/x + x^2/400$. How many units should be produced in order to minimize the cost?

CHAPTER 5

The
Definite
Integral

5.1 AREA

OBJECTIVES

You should be familiar with and be able to use summation notation. You should also be able to find the area under the graph of a "nice" function over an interval using either inscribed or circumscribed rectangles.

Q185 In order to find the area of the region under the graph of a function f, we need to use the notion of summation. The summation notation $\sum_{i=1}^{m} a_i$ is defined as

$$\sum_{i=1}^{m} a_i = a_1 + a_2 + \ldots + a_m.$$

The letter i is called the index of summation and is arbitrary. That is, $\sum_{i=1}^{m} a_i = \sum_{k=1}^{m} a_k$.
Which one of the following is equal to $\sum_{n=1}^{3} n$?

3   Frame **A**   6   Frame **B**

A   **YOUR ANSWER:**   3.
Be careful. $\sum_{n=1}^{3} n = 1 + 2 + 3$. Now return to frame **Q185**, compute $\sum_{n=1}^{3} n$, and then try again.

B   **YOUR ANSWER:**   6.
Of course. $\sum_{n=1}^{3} n = 1 + 2 + 3 = 6$.

Q186 Which one of the following is equal to $\sum_{i=1}^{3} (i^2 + 1)$?

17   Frame **A**   3   Frame **B**   14   Frame **C**

A   **YOUR ANSWER:**   17.
You are exactly right. $\sum_{i=1}^{3} (i^2 + 1) = (1^2 + 1) + (2^2 + 1) + (3^2 + 1) = 2 + 5 + 10 = 17$.

B   **YOUR ANSWER:**   3.
Be careful. $\sum_{i=1}^{3} (i^2 + 1) = (1^2 + 1) + (2^2 + 1) + (3^2 + 1)$. Return to frame **Q186**, carry out the computations, and then select the correct answer.

C   YOUR ANSWER: 14.
Be careful. $\Sigma_{i=1}^{3} (i^2 + 1) = (1^2 + 1) + (2^2 + 1) + (3^2 + 1)$. Return to frame **Q186,** carry out the computations, and then select the correct answer.

Q187   From Theorems (5.1) and (5.2) on page 220 of the text, we have the following properties of summation:

$$\Sigma_{i=1}^{n} c = nc,$$
$$\Sigma_{i=1}^{n} (a_i + b_i) = \Sigma_{i=1}^{n} a_i + \Sigma_{i=1}^{n} b_i,$$
$$\text{and } \Sigma_{i=1}^{n} ca_i = c \Sigma_{i=1}^{n} a_i.$$

Using the above properties, which one of the following is equal to $\Sigma_{i=1}^{n} (i^2 + i + 2)$?

$\Sigma_{i=1}^{n} i^2 + \Sigma_{i=1}^{n} i + 2n$ Frame **A**

$3 \Sigma_{i=1}^{n} i$ Frame **B**

$\Sigma_{i=1}^{n} i^2 + 2 \Sigma_{i=1}^{n} i$ Frame **C**

A   YOUR ANSWER: $\Sigma_{i=1}^{n} i^2 + \Sigma_{i=1}^{n} i + 2n$.
Right. $\Sigma_{i=1}^{n} (i^2 + i + 2) = \Sigma_{i=1}^{n} i^2 + \Sigma_{i=1}^{n} i + \Sigma_{i=1}^{n} 2$
$= \Sigma_{i=1}^{n} i^2 + \Sigma_{i=1}^{n} i + 2n.$

B   YOUR ANSWER: $3 \Sigma_{i=1}^{n} i$.
You are off base. Return to frame **Q187,** study the properties of summation, and then try again.

C   YOUR ANSWER: $\Sigma_{i=1}^{n} i^2 + 2 \Sigma_{i=1}^{n} i$.
You are off base. Return to frame **Q187,** study the properties of summation, and then try again.

Q188   Examples 3 and 4 on pages 224-227 of the text illustrate how to use the definition of area and the properties of summation to find the area of a "nice" region in a coordinate plane. After studying the examples, let's try one. If f is defined by $f(x) = 2 + x^2$, find the area of the region under the graph of f from 1 to 4.

Let's get started. If we divide the interval from 1 to 4 into n equal subintervals, what is the length, Δx, of each subinterval?

$4/n$ Frame **A** $3/n$ Frame **B** n Frame **C**

A   YOUR ANSWER: $4/n$.
Be careful. The length of the interval from 1 to 4 is $4 - 1 = 3$. Now what is the length of each subinterval if we divide the given interval into n equal subintervals? Return to frame **Q188** and select the correct answer.

B   YOUR ANSWER: $3/n$.
Of course. The length of the interval [1, 4] is $4 - 1 = 3$. Therefore, if we divide the interval into n equal subintervals, the length of each subinterval is $\Delta x = 3/n$.

C   YOUR ANSWER: n.
No. We want n equal subintervals. If we divide the interval [1, 4] into n equal subintervals, what is the length of each subinterval? Now return to frame **Q188** and try again.

Q189

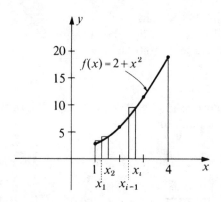

If we divide the interval [1, 4] into n equal subintervals, the length of each subinterval is $\Delta x = 3/n$. Therefore,

$$x_1 = 1 + \frac{3}{n}$$

$$x_2 = 1 + 2\left(\frac{3}{n}\right)$$

$$x_i = 1 + i\left(\frac{3}{n}\right)$$

Since f is increasing, the right endpoint of each subinterval produces the number in each subinterval at which f takes on its maximum value. The area of the ith rectangle is

$$f(x_i)\,\Delta x = f\left(1 + \frac{3i}{n}\right)\left(\frac{3}{n}\right) = \left[2 + \left(1 + \frac{3i}{n}\right)^2\right]\left(\frac{3}{n}\right).$$

Now can you find the area of the region under the graph of $f(x) = 2 + x^2$ from 1 to 4 using circumscribed rectangles?

   Yes   Frame **A**   No   Frame **B**

A   YOUR ANSWER: Yes.
Excellent. The area of the ith rectangle is

$$f(x_i)\,\Delta x = f\left(1 + \frac{3i}{n}\right)\left(\frac{3}{n}\right)$$

$$= \left[2 + \left(1 + \frac{3i}{n}\right)^2\right]\left(\frac{3}{n}\right) = \left(2 + 1 + \frac{6i}{n} + \frac{9i^2}{n^2}\right)\left(\frac{3}{n}\right)$$

$$= \left(3 + \frac{6i}{n} + \frac{9i^2}{n^2}\right)\left(\frac{3}{n}\right) = \frac{9}{n} + \frac{18i}{n^2} + \frac{27i^2}{n^3}.$$

Now the area is

$$A = \lim_{n\to\infty} \Sigma_{i=1}^{n}\left(\frac{9}{n} + \frac{18i}{n^2} + \frac{27i^2}{n^3}\right)$$

$$= \lim_{n\to\infty}\left(9 + \frac{18}{n^2}\,\Sigma_{i=1}^{n}\,i + \frac{27}{n^3}\,\Sigma_{i=1}^{n}\,i^2\right)$$

$$= \lim_{n\to\infty}\left[9 + \frac{18}{n^2}\left(\frac{n(n+1)}{2}\right) + \frac{27}{n^3}\left(\frac{n(n+1)(2n+1)}{6}\right)\right]$$

$$= \lim_{n\to\infty}\left(9 + 9 + \frac{9}{n} + 9 + \frac{27}{2n} + \frac{9}{2n^2}\right)$$

$$= \lim_{n\to\infty}\left(27 + \frac{9}{n} + \frac{27}{2n} + \frac{9}{2n^2}\right) = 27.$$

B   YOUR ANSWER: No.

We have

$$f(x_i) \, \Delta x = \left[2 + \left(1 + \frac{3i}{n}\right)^2\right]\left(\frac{3}{n}\right).$$

The area is given by

$$A = \lim_{n \to \infty} \Sigma_{i=1}^{n} f(x_i) \, \Delta x.$$

Simplify the expression

$$\left[2 + \left(1 + \frac{3i}{n}\right)^2\right]\left(\frac{3}{n}\right)$$

and find the limit as $n \to \infty$, because as $\Delta x \to 0$, $n \to \infty$. Now complete the work and return to frame **Q189** and select the other alternative.

5.2   DEFINITION OF DEFINITE INTEGRAL

OBJECTIVES

You should know the definition of a Riemann sum and the definition of the definite integral in terms of the limit of a sum. You should know the notation and terminology of the definite integral. You should also know Definitions (5.17) and (5.18) and Theorem (5.19) and how to use them.

Q190   Study the definition of Riemann sums given on page 229 of the text. If $f(x) = 2 + x^2$, find the Riemann sum where P is the partition of $[1, 4]$ into four subintervals determined by $x_0 = 1$, $x_1 = 2$, $x_2 = 2.5$, $x_3 = 3$, $x_4 = 4$, and $w_1 = 1.5$, $w_2 = 2.1$, $w_3 = 2.6$, $w_4 = 3.5$.

        26.085   Frame **A**   33.67   Frame **B**   25.67   Frame **C**

A   YOUR ANSWER: 26.085.

Very good. We have $f(x) = 2 + x^2$ where P is the partition of $[1, 4]$ into four subintervals determined by $x_0 = 1$, $x_1 = 2$, $x_2 = 2.5$, $x_3 = 3$, $x_4 = 4$, and $w_1 = 1.5$, $w_2 = 2.1$, $w_3 = 2.6$, $w_4 = 3.5$.

$$\begin{aligned}
R = \Sigma_{i=1}^{n} f(w_i) \, \Delta x_i &= (1)f(1.5) + (.5)f(2.1) + (.5)f(2.6) + (1)f(3.5) \\
&= (1)(4.25) + (.5)(6.41) + (.5)(8.76) + (1)(14.25) \\
&= 26.085.
\end{aligned}$$

B   YOUR ANSWER: 33.67.

No. $R = \Sigma_{i=1}^{n} f(w_i) \, \Delta x_i$. You apparently didn't multiply each term by Δx_i. Return to frame **Q190** and try again.

C YOUR ANSWER: 25.67.
Your calculations are off. Return to frame **Q190**, find $R = \sum_{i=1}^{n} f(w_i)\,\Delta x_i$, and try again.

Q191 The definite integral

$$\int_a^b f(x)\,dx$$

is defined on pages 232-233 of the text.

    In **Q189**, we found that for $f(x) = 2 + x^2$, if we partition [1, 4] into n equal subintervals and find the limit as $n \to \infty$, we obtain 27. Therefore,

$$\int_1^4 (2 + x^2)\,dx = 27.$$

Notice how closely this agrees with the Reimann sum that we found in the previous frame.

    Fortunately, for some functions, there is a better way to find the value of a definite integral. Before we proceed, though, let's consider the following. If the definite integral of f from a to b exists, then f is said to be integrable on $[a, b]$. It turns out that if f is continuous on $[a, b]$, then f is integrable on $[a, b]$. Which one of the following is guaranteed to exist?

$$\int_0^2 \frac{1}{x-1}\,dx \qquad \text{Frame } \mathbf{A}$$

$$\int_0^2 \frac{x^2}{x-3}\,dx \qquad \text{Frame } \mathbf{B}$$

$$\int_0^2 \frac{x}{x^2-4}\,dx \qquad \text{Frame } \mathbf{C}$$

A YOUR ANSWER: $\int_0^2 \frac{1}{x-1}\,dx.$
No. There is no guarantee that this integral exists because $1/(x-1)$ is not continuous on [0, 2]. Return to frame **Q191** and try again.

B YOUR ANSWER: $\int_0^2 \frac{x^2}{x-3}\,dx.$
Yes. Since $x^2/(x-3)$ is continuous on [0, 2], the integral exists.

C YOUR ANSWER: $\int_0^2 \frac{x^2}{x^2-4}\,dx.$
No. There is no guarantee that this integral exists because $x/(x^2-4)$ is not continuous on [0, 2]. Return to frame **Q191** and try again.

5.3 PROPERTIES OF THE DEFINITE INTEGRAL

OBJECTIVES

You should know the properties concerning the definite integral and how to use them.

Q192   Our first formula of integration is

$$\int_a^b k \, dx = k(b - a)$$

and is proved on page 237 of the text. What is $\int_1^4 2 \, dx$?

   3   Frame **A**   2   Frame **B**   6   Frame **C**

A   **YOUR ANSWER:** 3.
Watch out.

$$\int_a^b k \, dx = k(b - a).$$

Don't you simply have $b - a$? Now return to frame **Q192** and try again.

B   **YOUR ANSWER:** 2.
You are off base. Return to frame **Q192,** study the theorem again, and then select the correct answer.

C   **YOUR ANSWER:** 6.
Of course.

$$\int_1^4 2 \, dx = 2(4 - 1) = 2(3) = 6.$$

Q193   Study the properties of the definite integral on pages 236-240 of the text. Which one of the following is *not* correct?

$$\int_1^5 \frac{5x}{x + 1} \, dx = \int_1^2 \frac{5x}{x + 1} \, dx + \int_2^5 \frac{5x}{x + 1} \, dx \qquad \text{Frame } \mathbf{A}$$

$$\int_1^5 \frac{5x}{x + 1} \, dx \geq 0 \qquad \text{Frame } \mathbf{B}$$

$$\int_1^5 \frac{5x}{x + 1} \, dx = 5x \int_1^5 \frac{dx}{x + 1} \qquad \text{Frame } \mathbf{C}$$

A   **YOUR ANSWER:** $\int_1^5 \dfrac{5x}{x + 1} \, dx = \int_1^2 \dfrac{5x}{x + 1} \, dx + \int_2^5 \dfrac{5x}{x + 1} \, dx.$
There is nothing wrong with this (see Theorem (5.26) on page 239 of the text). Return to frame **Q193** and determine which one is not correct.

B   **YOUR ANSWER:** $\int_1^5 \dfrac{5x}{x + 1} \, dx \geq 0.$
No. Since $5x/(x + 1) \geq 0$ for every x in [1, 5], the integral is positive. Now return to frame **Q193** and determine which one is not correct.

C   **YOUR ANSWER:** $\int_1^5 \dfrac{5x}{x + 1} \, dx = 5x \int_1^5 \dfrac{dx}{x + 1}.$
Right. This is the one that is not correct. Theorem (5.22) states

$$\int_a^b kf(x) \, dx = k \int_a^b f(x) \, dx.$$

This says that the constant can be factored from the integral. The correct statement would be

$$\int_1^5 \frac{5x}{x + 1} \, dx = 5 \int_1^5 \frac{x}{x + 1} \, dx.$$

5.4   THE MEAN VALUE THEOREM FOR DEFINITE INTEGRALS

OBJECTIVES

You should know the Mean Value Theorem for Definite Integrals and how to use it.

Q194   The Mean Value Theorem is given on page 242 of the text. Suppose

$$\int_1^3 2x^2 \, dx = \frac{52}{3} \; .$$

Find the number which satisfies the conclusion of the Mean Value Theorem.

$\sqrt{13/3}$ Frame **A** $\sqrt{26}$ Frame **B** $\sqrt{26/3}$ Frame **C**

A   **YOUR ANSWER:** $\sqrt{13/3}$.
Right. We have $\int_1^3 2x^2 \, dx = 52/3$. By the Mean Value Theorem, there exists a number z in [1, 3] such that

$$2z^2(3 - 1) = \frac{52}{3}$$

$$z^2 = \frac{52}{12} = \frac{13}{3} \; .$$

Therefore, $z = \sqrt{13/3}$ is the number which satisfies the Mean Value Theorem. Notice that $-\sqrt{13/3}$ is not in [1, 3].

B   **YOUR ANSWER:** $\sqrt{26}$.
You made a mistake in your calculations. We have $\int_1^3 2x^2 \, dx = 52/3$. By the Mean Value Theorem, there exists a number z in [1, 3] such that

$$2z^2(3 - 1) = \frac{52}{3} \; .$$

Now find the required value of z and return to frame **Q194** and try again.

C   **YOUR ANSWER:** $\sqrt{26/3}$.
Sorry, but you forgot to divide by $(b - a)$ in the Mean Value Theorem. Study the Mean Value Theorem, return to frame **Q194,** and then select the correct answer.

Q195   If $\int_{-3}^{-1} 2x^{-2} \, dx = 4/3$, can you find the number which satisfies the Mean Value Theorem?

Yes   Frame **A**   No   Frame **B**

A   **YOUR ANSWER:** Yes.
Very good. We have $\int_{-3}^{-1} 2x^{-2} \, dx = 4/3$. By the Mean Value Theorem,

$$(2z^{-2})(-1 - (-3)) = \frac{4}{3}$$

$$4z^{-2} = \frac{4}{3}$$

$$\frac{1}{z^2} = \frac{1}{3}$$

$$z^2 = 3.$$

Therefore, $z = -\sqrt{3}$ is the required number because $-\sqrt{3}$ is in the interval $[-3, -1]$ and $\sqrt{3}$ is not in the interval $[-3, -1]$.

B   YOUR ANSWER: No.
Sure you can. We have $\int_{-3}^{-1} 2x^{-2} \, dx = 4/3$. By the Mean Value Theorem,

$$(2z^{-2})(-1 - (-3)) = \frac{4}{3} \quad \text{or} \quad 4z^{-2} = \frac{4}{3} \,.$$

Now return to frame **Q195**, find the required z, and select the other alternative.

5.5   THE FUNDAMENTAL THEOREM OF CALCULUS

OBJECTIVES

You should know the Fundamental Theorem of Calculus and how to use it.

Q196   The task of evaluating a definite integral by means of the definition is difficult even in the simplest cases. Needless to say, the concept of that limit is quite a difficult one. All is not lost, though, because it turns out that if F is an antiderivative of f, then

$$\int_a^b f(x) \, dx = F(b) - F(a).$$

This is called the *Fundamental Theorem of Calculus*. The Fundamental Theorem of Calculus is stated and proved on pages 245 and 246 of the text.
　　The theorem gives us a way to evaluate a definite integral. If f meets the conditions of the Fundamental Theorem and F is any antiderivative, then $\int_a^b f(x) \, dx$ can be determined by $F(b) - F(a)$. Notice that $\int_a^b f(x) \, dx$ is simply a real number.
　　We learned how to find some antiderivatives in Section 9 of Chapter 4. Study the examples on pages 248 and 249 of the text which illustrate the use of the Fundamental Theorem.
　　What is $\int_1^2 4x \, dx$?

　　6　　Frame **A**　　　4　　Frame **B**　　　1　　Frame **C**

A   YOUR ANSWER: 6.
Great. Since $F(x) = 2x^2$ is an antiderivative of $f(x) = 4x$, we have

$$\int_1^2 4x \, dx = F(2) - F(1) = 2(2)^2 - 2(1)^2 = 8 - 2 = 6.$$

B   YOUR ANSWER: 4.
Be careful. We want to evaluate $\int_1^2 4x \, dx$. Since $F(x) = 2x^2$ is an antiderivative of $f(x) = 4x$, we have $\int_1^2 4x \, dx = F(2) - F(1)$. Return to frame **Q196**, compute $F(2) - F(1)$, and select the correct answer.

C   YOUR ANSWER: 1.
Be careful. We want to evaluate $\int_1^2 4x \, dx$. Since $F(x) = 2x^2$ is an antiderivative of $f(x) = 4x$, we have $\int_1^2 4x \, dx = F(2) - F(1)$. Return to frame **Q196**, compute $F(2) - F(1)$, and select the correct answer.

Q197 What is $\int_1^3 (3x + 2)\, dx$?

16   Frame **A**   6   Frame **B**   28   Frame **C**

A **YOUR ANSWER:** 16.
You are correct. Since $F(x) = 3x^2/2 + 2x$ is an antiderivative of $f(x) = 3x + 2$, we have

$$\int_1^3 (3x + 2)\, dx = F(3) - F(1)$$
$$= \left(\frac{3(3)^2}{2} + 2(3)\right) - \left(\frac{3}{2} + 2\right)$$
$$= \left(\frac{27}{2} + 6\right) - \left(\frac{3}{2} + 2\right) = 16.$$

B **YOUR ANSWER:** 6.
Sorry, but your calculations are off. Are you having trouble finding an antiderivative of $3x + 2$? An antiderivative of $3x + 2$ is $3x^2/2 + 2x$. Now return to frame **Q197** and try again.

C **YOUR ANSWER:** 28.
Sorry, but your calculations are off. Are you having trouble finding an antiderivative of $3x + 2$? An antiderivative of $3x + 2$ is $3x^2/2 + 2x$. Now return to frame **Q197** and try again.

Q198 Now find $\int_{-1}^1 (4t^2 - t + 2)\, dt$.

17/3   Frame **A**   20/3   Frame **B** -1 Frame **C**

A **YOUR ANSWER:** 17/3.
Sorry, but you made a mistake with your signs.

$$\int_{-1}^1 (4t^2 - t + 2)\, dt = \left[\frac{4t^3}{3} - \frac{t^2}{2} + 2t\right]_{-1}^1$$

Now evaluate very carefully, return to frame **Q198,** and try again.

B **YOUR ANSWER:** 20/3.
Correct.

$$\int_{-1}^1 (4t^2 - t + 2)\, dt = \left[\frac{4t^3}{3} - \frac{t^2}{2} + 2t\right]_{-1}^1$$
$$= \left(\frac{4}{3} - \frac{1}{2} + 2\right) - \left(-\frac{4}{3} - \frac{1}{2} - 2\right) = \frac{20}{3}.$$

C **YOUR ANSWER:** -1.
Your calculations are off. We have $\int_{-1}^1 (4t^2 - t + 2)\, dt$. Now $4t^3/3 - t^2/2 + 2t$ is an antiderivative of $4t^2 - t + 2$. Return to frame **Q198,** use the Fundamental Theorem, and select the correct answer.

Q199 Let's try another one. Evaluate $\int_0^4 (\sqrt{x} + 2)^2\, dx$. How did it go?

Great   Frame **A**   Terrible   Frame **B**

A **YOUR ANSWER:** Great.
Very good.

$$\int_0^4 (\sqrt{x} + 2)^2 \, dx = \int_0^4 (x + 4x^{1/2} + 4) \, dx = \left[\frac{x^2}{2} + \frac{8x^{3/2}}{3} + 4x \right]_0^4$$

$$= \left(\frac{16}{2} + \frac{64}{3} + 16 \right) - (0) = \frac{136}{3} .$$

B **YOUR ANSWER:** Terrible.

It isn't as bad as you think. We have $\int_0^4 (\sqrt{x} + 2)^2 \, dx$. We begin by changing the form of the integral by squaring so that we can find an antiderivative. Therefore,

$$\int_0^4 (\sqrt{x} + 2)^2 \, dx = \int_0^4 (x + 4x^{1/2} + 4) \, dx.$$

Now complete the problem, return to frame **Q199**, and select the other response.

Q200 As a review find the following definite integrals:

1. $\displaystyle\int_1^3 (x^2 + 5) \, dx$ 2. $\displaystyle\int_1^9 \frac{\sqrt{t} - t^2}{t} \, dt$

3. $\displaystyle\int_0^1 t(\sqrt[3]{t} + 2\sqrt{t}) \, dt$ 4. $\displaystyle\int_1^2 \frac{x^2 - 4}{x + 2} \, dx$

After completing the problems, go to frame **A** and check your work.

A Let's see how well you did.

1. $\displaystyle\int_1^3 (x^2 + 5) \, dx = \left[x^3/3 + 5x \right]_1^3 = (9 + 15) - (1/3 + 5) = 56/3.$

2. $\displaystyle\int_1^9 \frac{\sqrt{t} - t^2}{t} \, dt = \int_1^9 \frac{t^{1/2} - t^2}{t} \, dt = \int_1^9 (t^{-1/2} - t) \, dt$

$$= \left[2t^{1/2} - t^2/2 \right]_1^9 = (6 - 81/2) - (2 - 1/2) = -36.$$

3. $\displaystyle\int_0^1 t(\sqrt[3]{t} + 2\sqrt{t}) \, dt = \int_0^1 t(t^{1/3} + 2t^{1/2}) = \int_0^1 (t^{4/3} + 2t^{3/2}) \, dt$

$$= \left[\frac{3t^{7/3}}{7} + \frac{4t^{5/2}}{5} \right]_0^1 = (3/7 + 4/5) - (0) = 43/35.$$

4. $\displaystyle\int_1^2 \frac{x^2 - 4}{x + 2} \, dx = \int_1^2 (x - 2) \, dx$

$$= \left[x^2/2 - 2x \right]_1^2 = (2 - 4) - (1/2 - 2) = -1/2.$$

5.6 INDEFINITE INTEGRALS AND CHANGE OF VARIABLES

OBJECTIVES

You should know what is meant by an indefinite integral and how to change variables. You should also be able to evaluate indefinite integrals.

Q201 The Fundamental Theorem of Calculus has provided us with a connection between antiderivatives and definite integrals. Because of this connection, we use integral signs to denote antiderivatives. If F is an antiderivative of f, we write

$$\int f(x) \, dx = F(x) + C$$

where C is an arbitrary constant. This is discussed on page 252 of the text.

Consider $\int (x^3 + 2)^{1/2}3x^2 \, dx$. At first glance, it may seem hopeless to find the indefinite integral, but the method of substitution will come to our aid. This is discussed in the text on page 254. If we let

$$u = x^3 + 2, \quad \text{then} \quad du = 3x^2 \, dx.$$

Therefore,

$$\int (x^3 + 2)^{1/2}3x^2 \, dx = \int u^{1/2} \, du$$

$$= \frac{u^{3/2}}{3/2} + C = \frac{2}{3}(x^3 + 2)^{3/2} + C.$$

The trick in substitution is to choose u in such a manner that du is part of the integrand and the resulting integral fits one of our formulas.

In order to find $\int (x^2 + 1)^3 2x \, dx$, what substitution would you make?

$u = x^2 + 1$ Frame **A** $u = 2x$ Frame **B** $u = (x^2 + 1)^3$ Frame **C**

A   **YOUR ANSWER:** $u = x^2 + 1$.
Very good. If $u = x^2 + 1$, then $du = 2x \, dx$. Therefore,

$$\int (x^2 + 1)^3 2x \, dx = \int u^3 \, du.$$

B   **YOUR ANSWER:** $u = 2x$.
No. If you use $u = 2x$, then the resulting integral does not fit any of our integration formulas. Remember, the task is to choose u in such a manner that du is part of the integrand and the resulting integral fits one of our formulas. Now return to frame **Q201** and try again.

C   **YOUR ANSWER:** $u = (x^2 + 1)^3$.
No. If you use $u = (x^2 + 1)^3$, then the resulting integral does not fit any of our integration formulas. In fact, the situation will be worse. Remember, the task is to choose u in such a manner that du is part of the integrand and the resulting integral fits one of our formulas. Now return to frame **Q201** and try again.

Q202   Now find $\int (x^2 + 1)^3 2x \, dx$.

$(1/4)(x^2 + 1)^4 + C$	Frame **A**
$(1/2)(x^2 + 1)^4 x + C$	Frame **B**
$(1/4)(x^2 + 1)^4 x^2 + C$	Frame **C**

A   **YOUR ANSWER:** $(1/4)(x^2 + 1)^4 + C$.
You are correct. If $u = x^2 + 1$, then $du = 2x \, dx$. Therefore,

$$\int (x^2 + 1)^3 2x \, dx = \int u^3 \, du = \frac{u^4}{4} + C = \frac{1}{4}(x^2 + 1)^4 + C.$$

B   **YOUR ANSWER:** $(1/2)(x^2 + 1)^4 x + C$.
You are not on the right track. We want $\int (x^2 + 1)^3 2x \, dx$.

$$\text{If } u = x^2 + 2, \quad \text{then} \quad du = 2x \, dx.$$

Therefore,

$$\int (x^2 + 1)^3 2x \, dx = \int u^3 \, du.$$

Now return to frame **Q202**, find $\int u^3 \, du$, and try again.

C   YOUR ANSWER: $(1/4)(x^2 + 1)^4 x^2 + C$.
You are not on the right track. We want $\int (x^2 + 1)^3 2x \, dx$.

$$\text{If } u = x^2 + 1, \quad \text{then} \quad du = 2x \, dx.$$

Therefore,

$$\int (x^2 + 1)^3 2x \, dx = \int u^3 \, du.$$

Now return to frame **Q202**, find $\int u^3 \, du$, and try again.

Q203   Find $\int \dfrac{3x^2 \, dx}{(x^3 + 2)^3}$.

$-\dfrac{1}{2(x^3 + 2)^2} + C$ Frame **A**

$-\dfrac{1}{4(x^3 + 2)^4} + C$ Frame **B**

I need some help.   Frame **C**

A   YOUR ANSWER: $-\dfrac{1}{2(x^3 + 2)^2} + C$.
Right. If $u = x^3 + 2$, then $du = 3x^2 \, dx$. Therefore,

$$\int \frac{3x^2 \, dx}{(x^3 + 2)^3} = \int u^{-3} \, du = \frac{u^{-2}}{-2} + C = -\frac{1}{2(x^3 + 2)^2} + C.$$

B   YOUR ANSWER: $-\dfrac{1}{4(x^3 + 2)^4} + C$.
Did you forget the integration formulas?

$$\text{If } u = x^3 + 2, \quad \text{then} \quad du = 3x^2 \, dx.$$

Therefore,

$$\int \frac{3x^2 \, dx}{(x^3 + 2)^3} = \int u^{-3} \, du.$$

Now return to frame **Q203**, find $\int u^{-3} \, du$, and then select the correct answer.

C   YOUR ANSWER: I need some help.
If $u = x^3 + 2$, then $du = 3x^2 \, dx$. Therefore,

$$\int \frac{3x^2 \, dx}{(x^3 + 2)^2} = \int u^{-3} \, du.$$

Notice that the choice of u enables us to reduce the given integral to one we know how to handle. Now return to frame **Q203** and try again.

Q204   What is $\int \sqrt{1 + x^2} \, x \, dx$?

$(1/3)(1 + x^2)^{3/2} + C$ Frame **A**
$(2/3)(1 + x^2)^{3/2} + C$ Frame **B**
Something is missing.   Frame **C**

A   YOUR ANSWER: $(1/3)(1 + x^2)^{3/2} + C$.
Very good.

$$\int \sqrt{1 + x^2}\, x\, dx = \frac{1}{2} \int \sqrt{1 + x^2}\, 2x\, dx.$$

Now if $u = 1 + x^2$, then $du = 2x\, dx$. Therefore,

$$\frac{1}{2} \int \sqrt{1 + x^2}\, 2x\, dx = \frac{1}{2} \int \sqrt{u}\, du$$

$$= \frac{1}{2} \int u^{1/2}\, du = \frac{1}{2} \frac{u^{3/2}}{3/2} + C$$

$$= \frac{1}{3} u^{3/2} + C = \frac{1}{3}(1 + x^2)^{3/2} + C.$$

B   YOUR ANSWER: $(2/3)(1 + x^2)^{3/2} + C.$
You overlooked a constant. Our integral is $\int \sqrt{1 + x^2}\, x\, dx.$

$$\text{If } u = 1 + x^2, \quad \text{then} \quad du = 2x\, dx.$$

Now we don't have the constant 2 in the integrand. However, it may be inserted in the following manner:

$$\int \sqrt{1 + x^2}\, x\, dx = \frac{1}{2} \int \sqrt{1 + x^2}\, 2x\, dx.$$

Now return to frame **Q204** and try again.

C   YOUR ANSWER: Something is missing.
Something is missing, but we can compensate for it. Our integral is $\int \sqrt{1 + x^2}\, x\, dx.$

$$\text{If } u = 1 + x^2, \quad \text{then} \quad du = 2x\, dx.$$

Now we don't have the constant 2 in the integrand. However, it may be inserted in the following manner:

$$\int \sqrt{1 + x^2}\, x\, dx = \frac{1}{2} \int \sqrt{1 + x^2}\, 2x\, dx.$$

Now return to frame **Q204** and try again.

Q205   Find $\int (1 - x^2)^{1/3} x\, dx.$ Were you successful?
    Yes   Frame **A**   No   Frame **B**

A   YOUR ANSWER: Yes.
Wonderful. Our integral is $\int (1 - x^2) x\, dx.$ If $u = 1 - x^2$, then $du = -2x\, dx.$ Therefore, we need a factor of -2 in the integrand.

$$\int (1 - x^2)^{1/3} x\, dx = -\frac{1}{2} \int (1 - x^2)^{1/3} (-2x\, dx) = -\frac{1}{2} \int u^{1/3}\, du$$

$$= -\frac{3}{8} u^{4/3} + C = -\frac{3}{8}(1 - x^2)^{4/3} + C.$$

B   YOUR ANSWER: No.
Don't despair. We want $\int (1 - x^2)^{1/3} x\, dx.$ If $u = 1 - x^2$, then $du = -2x\, dx.$ Therefore, we need a factor of -2. Inserting a factor of -2, we have

$$\int (1 - x^2)^{1/3} x\, dx = -\frac{1}{2} \int (1 - x^2)^{1/3} (-2x\, dx).$$

Now return to frame **Q205**, solve the problem, and select the other alternative.

Q206 Now let's consider the definite integral. When making a substitution of variables, if we change the limits of integration to their corresponding values in terms of the new variable, we can evaluate a definite integral without the need of expressing the indefinite integral in terms of the original variable. For example, consider

$$\int_0^2 (2 + x^2)^2\, 2x\, dx.$$

If $u = 2 + x^2$, then $du = 2x\, dx$. When $x = 0$, then $u = 2 + 0 = 2$, and when $x = 2$, then $u = 2 + 2^2 = 6$. Therefore,

$$\int_0^2 (2 + x^2)^2 2x\, dx = \int_2^6 u^2\, du = \frac{u^3}{3}\Big]_2^6 = 72 - \frac{8}{3} = \frac{208}{3}.$$

Study the example on page 257 of the text. Which one of the following integrals is equivalent to

$$\int_1^3 \sqrt{3 + 2x}\, dx$$

if we let $u = 3 + 2x$?

$$\int_5^9 u^{1/2}\, du \quad \text{Frame A} \qquad \frac{1}{2}\int_1^3 u^{1/2}\, du \quad \text{Frame B} \qquad \frac{1}{2}\int_5^9 u^{1/2}\, du \quad \text{Frame C}$$

A **YOUR ANSWER:** $\int_5^9 u^{1/2}\, du$.

Sorry, but you forgot the constant. Our integral is

$$\int_1^3 \sqrt{3 + 2x}\, dx.$$

If $u = 3 + 2x$, then $du = 2\, dx$. Therefore, we need a constant factor of 2. Inserting the constant 2, we obtain

$$\int_1^3 \sqrt{3 + 2x}\, dx = \frac{1}{2}\int_1^3 \sqrt{3 + 2x}\, 2dx.$$

Now return to frame **Q206**, make the required substitution, and select the correct answer.

B **YOUR ANSWER:** $\frac{1}{2}\int_1^3 u^{1/2}\, du$.

Watch out. Didn't you forget to change the limits of integration? Our integral is

$$\int_1^3 \sqrt{3 + 2x}\, dx = \frac{1}{2}\int_1^3 \sqrt{3 + 2x}\, 2\, dx.$$

If $u = 3 + 2x$, then $du = 2\, dx$. Now when $x = 1$, then $u = 3 + 2(1) = 5$, and when $x = 3$, then $u = 3 + 2(3) = 9$. Now return to frame **Q206**, make the required substitution, and select the correct answer.

C **YOUR ANSWER:** $\frac{1}{2}\int_5^9 u^{1/2}\, du$.

You are correct. Our integral is $\int_1^3 \sqrt{3 + 2x}\, dx$. If $u = 3 + 2x$, then $du = 2\, dx$. Therefore, we need a constant factor of 2. Inserting the constant 2, we have

$$\int_1^3 \sqrt{3 + 2x}\, dx = \frac{1}{2}\int_1^3 \sqrt{3 + 2x}\, 2dx.$$

Now when $x = 1$, $u = 5$, and when $x = 3$, $u = 9$. Therefore,

$$\frac{1}{2} \int_1^3 \sqrt{3 + 2x}\, 2dx = \frac{1}{2} \int_5^9 u^{1/2}\, du$$

$$= \frac{1}{2} \frac{u^{3/2}}{3/2} \bigg]_5^9 = \frac{1}{3} u^{3/2} \bigg]_5^9 = \frac{1}{3}(27 - 5\sqrt{5}).$$

5.7 NUMERICAL INTEGRATION

OBJECTIVES

You should know how to use the Trapezoidal Rule and Simpson's Rule to approximate a definite integral.

Q207   In order to evaluate a definite integral by means of the Fundamental Theorem, it is necessary to find an antiderivative of the integrand. If an antiderivative cannot be found, then numerical methods may be used to approximate the integral. Two techniques, the Trapezoidal Rule and Simpson's Rule, are discussed in the text.

    After studying Example 1 on page 261 of the text, use the Trapezoidal Rule to approximate

$$\int_0^5 \frac{x}{1 + x^2}\, dx$$

where $n = 10$. (*Hint*: Arrange your work in a table as in the text and use a calculator if possible.) After completing the work, go to Frame **A** and check your work.

A   The integral is

$$\int_0^5 \frac{x}{1 + x^2}\, dx.$$

i	x_i	$f(x_i)$	m	$mf(x_i)$
0	0.0	.0000	1	.0000
1	0.5	.4000	2	.8000
2	1.0	.5000	2	1.0000
3	1.5	.4615	2	.9230
4	2.0	.4000	2	.8000
5	2.5	.3448	2	.6896
6	3.0	.3000	2	.6000
7	3.5	.2642	2	.5284
8	4.0	.2353	2	.4706
9	4.5	.2118	2	.4236
10	5.0	.1923	1	.1923
				6.4275

Since $(b - a)/2n = (5 - 0)/20 = 1/4$, we have by the Trapezoidal Rule,

$$\int_0^5 \frac{x}{1 + x^2}\, dx \approx \left(\frac{1}{4}\right)(6.4275) = 1.6069.$$

Q208 Now study Example 2 on page 264 of the text and use Simpson's Rule to approximate

$$\int_0^5 \frac{x}{1 + x^2} \, dx$$

where $n = 10$. Arrange your work in a table and use a calculator if possible. After completing the work, go to frame **A** and check your work.

A The integral is

$$\int_0^5 \frac{x}{1 + x^2} \, dx.$$

i	x_i	$f(x_i)$	m	$mf(x_i)$
0	0.0	.0000	1	.0000
1	0.5	.4000	4	1.6000
2	1.0	.5000	2	1.0000
3	1.5	.4615	4	1.8460
4	2.0	.4000	2	.8000
5	2.5	.3448	4	1.3792
6	3.0	.3000	2	.6000
7	3.5	.2642	4	1.0568
8	4.0	.2353	2	.4706
9	4.5	.2118	4	.8472
10	5.0	.1923	1	.1923

9.7921

Since $(b - a)/3n = (5 - 0)/30 = 1/6$, we have by Simpson's Rule,

$$\int_0^5 \frac{x}{1 + x^2} \, dx \approx \left(\frac{1}{6}\right)(9.7921) = 1.6320.$$

REVIEW TEST

1 Find the following numbers.

(a) $\sum_{i=1}^4 (i - 1)$ 　　(b) $\sum_{i=1}^5 (i^2 + 1)$ 　　(c) $\sum_{i=1}^3 i(i^2 + 1)$

2 Find $\sum_{i=1}^n (2i^2 + i + 3)$.

3 Find the area of $f(x) = x^2 - 1$ from $a = 1$ to $b = 5$ using either inscribed or circumscribed rectangles.

4 If $f(x) = x^2 - 1$, find

(a) the Reimann sum R_p of f where P is the partition of $[1, 5]$ into four subintervals determined by $x_0 = 1, x_1 = 1.5, x_2 = 2.5, x_3 = 4, x_4 = 5$ and $w_1 = 1.1, w_2 = 2, w_3 = 3, w_4 = 4.5$.

(b) the Reimann sum R_p of f where P is the partition of $[1, 5]$ into six subintervals determined by $x_0 = 1, x_1 = 1.5, x_2 = 2, x_3 = 2.5, x_4 = 3.5, x_5 = 4.5, x_6 = 5$ and $w_1 = 1.1, w_2 = 1.7, w_3 = 2.1, w_4 = 3, w_5 = 4, w_6 = 4.7$.

5 If $\int_1^3 (2x^3 - 1) \, dx = 78$, find $\int_3^1 (2x^3 - 1) \, dx$.

6   Which one of the following definite integrals is guaranteed to exist?

$$\int_0^1 \frac{1}{x - 1} \, dx, \qquad \int_0^3 \frac{x^2}{x - 4} \, dx, \qquad \int_0^3 \frac{1}{x^2 - 4} \, dx$$

7   Without evaluating the integrals, verify the inequality

$$\int_1^4 x(x^2 + 1) \, dx < \int_1^4 (2x^3 + 5) \, dx.$$

8   If f is integrable on a closed interval containing a, b, c, and d, prove

$$\int_a^b f(x) \, dx + \int_b^c f(x) \, dx + \int_c^d f(x) \, dx = \int_a^d f(x) \, dx.$$

9   If $\int_1^3 (2x^2 + 1) \, dx = 58/3$, find a number z which satisfies the conclusion of the Mean Value Theorem for Definite Integrals.

Evaluate the definite integrals in Exercises 10-15.

10 $\int_{-1}^3 (x^2 - 2x + 3) \, dx$

11 $\int_1^2 \frac{t - 6}{t^3} \, dt$

12 $\int_{-1}^1 (1 + x^2)^2 \, dx$

13 $\int_0^4 |x - 2| \, dx$

14 $\int_2^3 \sqrt{x - 1} \, dx$

15 $\int_0^{\sqrt{3}} \frac{y}{\sqrt{y^2 + 1}} \, dy$

Evaluate the indefinite integrals in Exercises 16-20.

16 $\int (2x - 1)^5 \, dx$

17 $\int \sqrt{8 - y^2} \, dy$

18 $\int \frac{v^2}{(v^3 + 1)^2} \, dv$

19 $\int \frac{3}{\sqrt{1 - 4t}} \, dt$

20 $\int \frac{(\sqrt{x} + 1)^2}{\sqrt{x}} \, dx$

21 If $f(x) = 2x^2 - 1$, find the area of the region under the graph of f from 1 to 3.

22 Approximate the definite integral

$$\int_0^4 \frac{1}{1 + x^2} \, dx$$

for $n = 10$ using the (a) Trapezoidal Rule (b) Simpson's Rule. (Use calculator if possible with approximations to four decimal places.)

SAMPLE TEST

1   Find the following numbers.
   (a) $\Sigma_{i=1}^5 2$ (b) $\Sigma_{i=1}^3 (i^2 - 1)$ (c) $\Sigma_{i=1}^4 i^2(i + 1)$

2   Find $\Sigma_{i=1}^n (i^2 - i + 1)$.

3   Find the area of $f(x) = 2x^2 + 1$ from $a = 0$ to $b = 4$ using either inscribed or circumscribed rectangles.

4   If $f(x) = x^2 + x$, find the Riemann sum R^P of f where P is the partition of $[0, 4]$ into 5 subintervals determined by $x_0 = 0$, $x_1 = .5$, $x_2 = 1.5$, $x_3 = 2$, $x_4 = 3$, $x_5 = 4$ and $w_1 = .1$, $w_2 = 1$, $w_3 = 1.6$, $w_4 = 2.5$, $w_5 = 3.5$.

5   Find $\int_3^3 (x^2 - 2x + 1) \, dx$.

6 If $\int_0^3 (2x^2 - x + 1) \, dx = 33/2$, find $\int_0^3 (2y^2 - y + 1) \, dy$.

7 Without evaluating the integrals, verify the inequality

$$\int_2^5 (x^3 - 2x) \, dx \geqslant \int_2^5 (x - 1)^2 \, dx.$$

8 If f and g are integrable functions on $[a, b]$, prove

$$\int_a^b [f(x)]^2 \, dx + \int_a^b f(x) \cdot g(x) \, dx + \int_a^b [g(x)]^2 \, dx \geqslant 0.$$

9 If $\int_1^3 (3x^2 + 5) \, dx = 36$, find a number z which satisfies the conclusion of the Mean Value Theorem for Definite Integrals.

Evaluate the definite integrals in Exercises 10-15.

10 $\displaystyle\int_0^3 (2x^3 - x^2 + 1) \, dx$

11 $\displaystyle\int_0^2 (\sqrt{y} + y^{1/3} + 1) \, dy$

12 $\displaystyle\int_3^3 (1 - x)^5 (2x + 3) \, dx$

13 $\displaystyle\int_0^2 |x - 1| \, dx$

14 $\displaystyle\int_0^1 (t^2 + 1)^3 t \, dt$

15 $\displaystyle\int_2^3 \frac{x}{(x^2 - 1)^2} \, dx$

Evaluate the indefinite integrals in Exercises 16-20.

16 $\displaystyle\int (3t + 1)^6 \, dt$

17 $\displaystyle\int \frac{y}{\sqrt{1 - y^2}} \, dy$

18 $\displaystyle\int (t^3 - 1)^4 t^2 \, dt$

19 $\displaystyle\int \frac{x - 1}{(x^2 - 2x + 1)^2} \, dx$

20 $\displaystyle\int (2 + 1/x)^2 (1/x^2) \, dx$

21 If $f(x) = x^3 - 1$, find the area of the region under the graph of f from 0 to 3.

22 Approximate the definite integral

$$\int_1^3 \frac{1}{1 + x} \, dx$$

for $n = 8$ using the (a) Trapezoidal Rule (b) Simpson's Rule. (Use calculator if possible with approximations to four decimal places.)

CHAPTER 6

Applications of the
Definite
Integral

6.1 AREA

OBJECTIVES

*You should be able to sketch the region bounded by the graphs of given equations.
You should be able to illustrate a typical vertical or horizontal rectangle in a region
and, by using the definite integral, find the area of the region.*

Q209 If a region is bounded by the vertical lines $x = a$ and $x = b$ $(a < b)$, and by the continuous curves $y = g(x)$ and $y = f(x)$, where $g(x) \leqslant f(x)$ for $a \leqslant x \leqslant b$, then the area of the region is

$$A = \int_a^b [f(x) - g(x)]\ dx.$$

This definition is discussed on pages 269-270 of the text.

Look at Figure 6.1 on page 269 of the text. Intuitively, if we think of dividing the region into vertical rectangles with width dx and height $f(x) - g(x)$, then the area of one rectangle is $[f(x) - g(x)]\ dx$ and the total area is

$$\int_a^b [f(x) - g(x)]\ dx.$$

Let's find the area of the region bounded by the parabola $y = (1/2)x^2$ and $y = x$. Which one of the following integrals will give us the required area?

$\int_0^2 \left(x - \frac{1}{2}x^2\right) dx$ Frame **A**

$\int_0^2 \frac{1}{2}x^2\ dx$ Frame **B**

$\int_0^4 \left(\frac{1}{2}x^2 - x\right) dx$ Frame **C**

A **YOUR ANSWER:** $\int_0^2 \left(x - \frac{1}{2}x^2\right) dx.$

Excellent.

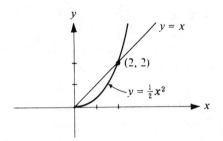

If we consider vertical rectangles, the width is dx and the height is the value of y of the upper boundary for $0 \leqslant x \leqslant 2$ minus the value of y of the lower boundary for $0 \leqslant x \leqslant 2$, which is $x - (1/2)x^2$. Therefore, the area is

$$\int_0^2 \left(x - \frac{1}{2}x^2 \right) dx.$$

B YOUR ANSWER: $\int_0^2 \frac{1}{2} x^2 \, dx.$

No. Let's take a look at the region.

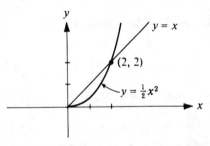

If we consider vertical rectangles, the width is dx and the height is the value of y of the upper boundary for $0 \leqslant x \leqslant 2$ minus the value of y of the lower boundary for $0 \leqslant x \leqslant 2$. What is the upper and lower boundary of the required region? Now return to frame **Q209** and try again.

C YOUR ANSWER: $\int_0^4 \left(\frac{1}{2}x^2 - x \right) dx.$

You are off base. Let's take a look at the region.

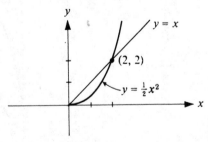

If we consider vertical rectangles, the width is dx and the height is the value of y of the upper boundary for $0 \leqslant x \leqslant 2$ minus the value of y of the lower boundary for $0 \leqslant x \leqslant 2$. What is the upper and lower boundary of the required region? Now return to frame **Q209** and try again.

Q210   The area of the region bounded by the parabola $y = (1/2)x^2$ and $y = x$ is

$$\int_0^2 \left(x - \frac{1}{2}x^2 \right) dx.$$

What is this area?

2/3 square units	Frame **A**
4/3 square units	Frame **B**
2 square units	Frame **C**

A **YOUR ANSWER:** 2/3 square units.
Right.

$$\int_0^2 \left(x - \frac{1}{2}x^2 \right) dx = \left[\frac{x^2}{2} - \frac{x^3}{6} \right]_0^2 = \frac{4}{2} - \frac{8}{6} = \frac{2}{3} \text{ square units.}$$

B **YOUR ANSWER:** 4/3 square units.
No.

$$\int_0^2 \left(x - \frac{1}{2}x^2 \right) dx = \left[\frac{x^2}{2} - \frac{x^3}{6} \right]_0^2.$$

Now return to frame **Q210** and try again.

C **YOUR ANSWER:** 2 square units.
No.

$$\int_0^2 \left(x - \frac{1}{2}x^2 \right) dx = \left[\frac{x^2}{2} - \frac{x^3}{6} \right]_0^2.$$

Now return to frame **Q210** and try again.

Q211   Find the area bounded by the parabolas $y = 6x - x^2$ and $y = x^2 - 2x$. How did it go?

Wonderful	Frame **A**	Terrible	Frame **B**

A **YOUR ANSWER:** Wonderful.
Very good.

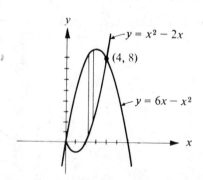

Considering vertical rectangles, the upper boundary of this region has equation

$$y = 6x - x^2 \quad \text{for} \quad 0 \leqslant x \leqslant 4$$

and the lower boundary has equation

$$y = x^2 - 2x \quad \text{for} \quad 0 \leqslant x \leqslant 4.$$

$$\int_0^4 [(6x - x^2) - (x^2 - 2x)] \, dx = \int_0^4 (8x - 2x^2) \, dx$$

$$= \left[4x^2 - \frac{2}{3}x^3 \right]_0^4 = \frac{64}{3} \quad \text{square units.}$$

B   YOUR ANSWER: Terrible.

Let's take a look at the graph.

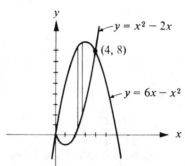

If we consider vertical rectangles, the upper boundary of the required region has equation $y = 6x - x^2$ for $0 \leqslant x \leqslant 4$ and the lower boundary has equation $y = x^2 - 2x$ for $0 \leqslant x \leqslant 4$. Therefore, the height of a vertical rectangle is $(6x - x^2) - (x^2 - 2x)$. Now return to frame **Q211**, calculate the area, and select the other alternative.

Q212   Sometimes it is more convenient to split the region into horizontal rectangles. In this case, we think of the height as the value of x of the right boundary minus the value of x of the left boundary, and for convenience think of the width as dy. Let's find the area bounded by the parabola $y^2 = 4x$ and the line $y = 2x - 4$.

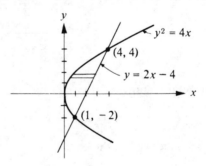

Splitting the region into horizontal rectangles, what is the area?

$$\int_{-2}^4 (y^2 - y) \, dy \qquad \text{Frame A}$$

$$\int_{-2}^4 \left[\frac{1}{4}y^2 - \frac{1}{2}(y + 4) \right] dy \qquad \text{Frame B}$$

$$\int_{-2}^4 \left(2 + \frac{1}{2}y - \frac{1}{4}y^2 \right) dy \qquad \text{Frame C}$$

A   YOUR ANSWER: $\int_{-2}^4 (y^2 - y) \, dy.$

Be careful.

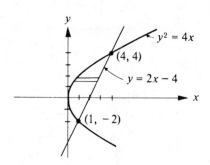

The area of a horizontal rectangle is dy times the value of x of the right boundary minus the value of x of the left boundary. Return to frame **Q212,** solve both equations for x, and try again.

B   YOUR ANSWER: $\int_{-2}^{4} \left[\frac{1}{4}y^2 - \frac{1}{2}(y + 4) \right] dy.$

Almost, but you subtracted the right boundary from the left which will give you the negative of the area. Return to frame **Q212** and select the correct answer.

C   YOUR ANSWER: $\int_{-2}^{4} \left(2 + \frac{1}{2}y - \frac{1}{4}y^2 \right) dy.$

You are right.

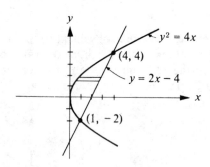

Using horizontal rectangles, the right boundary has the equation

$$x = 2 + \frac{1}{2}y \quad \text{for} \quad -2 \leqslant y \leqslant 4$$

and the left boundary has the equation

$$x = \frac{1}{4}y^2 \quad \text{for} \quad -2 \leqslant y \leqslant 4.$$

Therefore, the area is

$$\int_{-2}^{4} \left(2 + \frac{1}{2}y - \frac{1}{4}y^2 \right) dy = \left[2y + \frac{1}{4}y^2 - \frac{y^3}{12} \right]_{-2}^{4} = 9 \text{ square units.}$$

Q213   Can you find the area of the region bounded by the parabola $y^2 = 4x$ and the line $y = 2x - 4$ in **Q212** by using vertical rectangles?

   Yes   Frame **A**   No   Frame **B**

A YOUR ANSWER: Yes.
Very good.

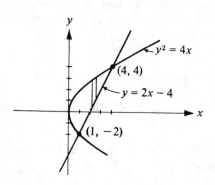

If we divide the region into vertical rectangles, then the upper boundary of the
region has the equation

$$y = 2\sqrt{x} \quad \text{for} \quad 0 \leqslant x \leqslant 4$$

but the lower boundary of the region has the equation

$$y = -2\sqrt{x} \quad \text{for} \quad 0 \leqslant x \leqslant 1;$$
$$y = 2x - 4 \quad \text{for} \quad 1 \leqslant x \leqslant 4.$$

Therefore, two integrals will be required to express the area.

$$\int_0^1 [2\sqrt{x} - (-2\sqrt{x})] \, dx + \int_1^4 [2\sqrt{x} - (2x - 4)] \, dx =$$
$$\int_0^1 4\sqrt{x} \, dx + \int_1^4 (2\sqrt{x} - 2x + 4) \, dx = \left[\frac{8x^{3/2}}{3} \right]_0^1 + \left(\frac{4}{3}x^{3/2} - x^2 + 4x \right)\Big]_1^4$$
$$= \frac{8}{3} + \frac{19}{3} = 9 \text{ square units.}$$

Notice that this is the same result as that obtained using horizontal rectangles.

B YOUR ANSWER: No.
We want the area bounded by the parabola $y^2 = 4x$ and the line $y = 2x - 4$.

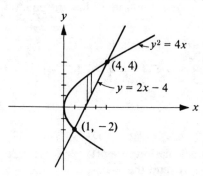

If we divide the region into vertical rectangles, then the upper boundary of the
region has the equation

$$y = 2\sqrt{x} \quad \text{for} \quad 0 \leqslant x \leqslant 4$$

but the lower boundary of the region has the equation

$$y = -2\sqrt{x} \quad \text{for} \quad 0 \leqslant x \leqslant 1;$$
$$y = 2x - 4 \quad \text{for} \quad 1 \leqslant x \leqslant 4.$$

Therefore, two integrals will be required to express the area. Return to frame **Q213**, study Example 3 on page 275 of the text, find the area, and then select the other alternative.

Q214 Let's try one more. Find the area of the region bounded by the parabola $x = 4 - y^2$ and the y-axis.

32/3 square units	Frame **A**	64/3 square units	Frame **B**
16 square units	Frame **C**	I am having trouble.	Frame **D**

A **YOUR ANSWER:** 32/3 square units.
You are right.

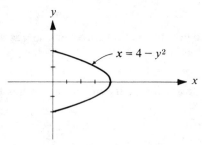

Using horizontal rectangles, the right boundary has the equation
$$x = 4 - y^2 \quad \text{for} \quad -2 \leqslant y \leqslant 2$$
and the left boundary has the equation
$$x = 0 \quad \text{for} \quad -2 \leqslant y \leqslant 2.$$
Therefore, the area is
$$\int_{-2}^{2} (4 - y^2)\, dy = \left[4y - \frac{y^3}{3} \right]_{-2}^{2} = \frac{16}{3} - \left(-\frac{16}{3} \right) = \frac{32}{3} \text{ square units.}$$
Using vertical rectangles, the upper boundary has equation
$$y = \sqrt{4 - x} \quad \text{for} \quad 0 \leqslant x \leqslant 4$$
and the lower boundary has the equation
$$y = -\sqrt{4 - x} \quad \text{for} \quad 0 \leqslant x \leqslant 4.$$
Therefore, the area is
$$\int_{0}^{4} [\sqrt{4 - x} - (-\sqrt{4 - x})]\, dx = 2 \int_{0}^{4} \sqrt{4 - x}\, dx = \left[-\frac{4}{3}(4 - x)^{3/2} \right]_{0}^{4}$$
$$= 0 - \left(-\frac{32}{3} \right) = \frac{32}{3} \text{ square units.}$$

B **YOUR ANSWER:** 64/3 square units.
Your calculations are off. We want the area of the region bounded by the parabola $x = 4 - y^2$ and the y-axis.

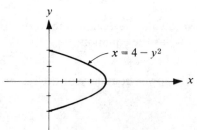

Notice that the region lends itself to vertical or horizontal rectangles without too much trouble. Return to frame **Q214,** study the examples in the text, and then try again.

C   YOUR ANSWER: 16 square units.
Your calculations are off. We want the area of the region bounded by the parabola $x = 4 - y^2$ and the y-axis.

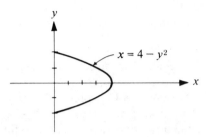

Notice that the region lends itself to vertical or horizontal rectangles without too much trouble. Return to frame **Q214,** study the examples in the text, and then try again.

D   YOUR ANSWER: I am having trouble.
Don't panic. Let's take a look at the problem. We want the area of the region bounded by the parabola $x = 4 - y^2$ and the y-axis.

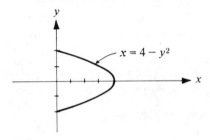

Using horizontal rectangles, the right boundary has the equation

$$x = 4 - y^2 \quad \text{for} \quad -2 \leqslant y \leqslant 2$$

and the left boundary has the equation

$$x = 0 \quad \text{for} \quad -2 \leqslant y \leqslant 2.$$

Now return to frame **Q214,** set up the proper integral, and try again.

6.2   SOLIDS OF REVOLUTION

OBJECTIVES

You should know the definition of a solid of revolution. You should be able to find the volume of a solid of revolution when a cross section of the solid is a disk or a washer.

Q215   Consider the shaded region below:

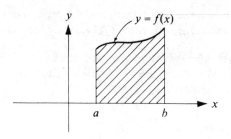

If this region is revolved about the *x*-axis, then a solid is generated which is referred to as a *solid of revolution*.

We can find the volume of this solid in a manner similar to finding area in the last section. If we revolve a vertical rectangle about the *x*-axis, then a disk is generated of thickness *dx* and radius $f(x)$. (Again, this is simply a convenient memory device.) Therefore, the volume of this disk is $\pi[f(x)]^2 \, dx$ and the volume of the solid is

$$V = \pi \int_a^b [f(x)]^2 \, dx.$$

This notion is discussed in more detail on pages 279–281 of the text.

Find the volume generated by revolving the region bounded by $y^2 = 8x$, the *x*-axis, and $x = 2$ about the *x*-axis.

32π/3 cubic units	Frame **A**	16π cubic units	Frame **B**
16π/3 cubic units	Frame **C**	I need help.	Frame **D**

A   **YOUR ANSWER:**   32π/3 cubic units.
Sorry, but you used the method of finding area instead of volume. Return to frame **Q215**, study the technique of finding volume, and then try again.

B   **YOUR ANSWER:**   16π cubic units.
Right.

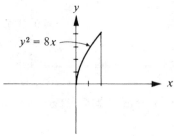

The volume generated by revolving the region about the *x*-axis is

$$V = \pi \int_a^b [f(x)]^2 \, dx = \pi \int_0^2 8x \, dx$$
$$= \left[\pi(4x^2) \right]_0^2 = 16\pi \text{ cubic units.}$$

C   **YOUR ANSWER:**   16π/3 cubic units.
You made a mistake somewhere. We want the volume generated by revolving the region bounded by $y^2 = 8x$, the *x*-axis, and $x = 2$ about the *x*-axis.

$$V = \pi \int_a^b [f(x)]^2 \, dx.$$

In our problem, $a = 0$, $b = 2$, and $[f(x)]^2 = 8x$. Now return to frame **Q215** and try again.

D **YOUR ANSWER:** I need help.

All right. We want the volume generated by revolving the region bounded by $y^2 = 8x$, the x-axis, and $x = 2$ about the x-axis.

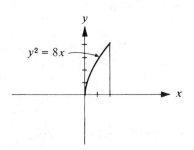

The formula for volume is

$$V = \pi \int_a^b [f(x)]^2 \, dx.$$

In our problem, isn't $a = 0$, $b = 2$, and $[f(x)]^2 = 8x$? Now return to frame **Q215** and try again.

Q216 Can you find the volume generated by revolving the region bounded by $y = 1/x$, the x-axis, $x = 1$, and $x = 3$ about the x-axis?

　　　Yes　　Frame **A**　　　No　　Frame **B**

A **YOUR ANSWER:** Yes.

Excellent.

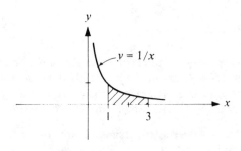

We want to revolve the above region about the x-axis. Since the radius of a generated disk is $1/x$, the volume of one disk is $\pi \cdot (1/x^2) \, dx$. Therefore,

$$V = \pi \int_1^3 \frac{1}{x^2} \, dx = \left[-\pi \, \frac{1}{x} \right]_1^3 = -\pi \left(\frac{1}{3} - 1 \right) = \frac{2\pi}{3} \text{ cubic units.}$$

B **YOUR ANSWER:** No.

Sure you can.

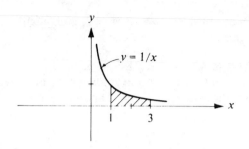

We want to revolve the above region about the x-axis. Since the radius of a generated disk is $1/x$, the volume of one disk is $\pi \cdot (1/x^2)\ dx$. Therefore,

$$V = \pi \int_1^3 \frac{1}{x^2}\ dx.$$

Now return to frame **Q216**, compute V, and select the other alternative.

Q217 A similar technique is employed if we rotate about the y-axis. Find the volume generated by rotating the region bounded by $y = 4x^2$, the y-axis, and $y = 16$ about the y-axis.

> $256\pi/3$ cubic units   Frame **A**
> 32π cubic units   Frame **B**
> I am having trouble.   Frame **C**

A **YOUR ANSWER:** $256\pi/3$ cubic units.
No. We want the volume generated by rotating the region bounded by $y = 4x^2$, the y-axis, and $y = 16$ about the y-axis.

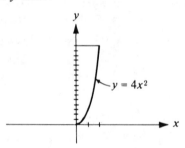

Our problem is to revolve the above region about the y-axis. If we rotate a horizontal rectangle about the y-axis, then we can think of the width as dy and the radius as the value of x. Therefore, the volume of the generated disk is $\pi((1/4)y)\ dy$ since $x^2 = (1/4)y$. Now return to frame **Q217**, compute the proper integral, and try again.

B **YOUR ANSWER:** 32π cubic units.
Good.

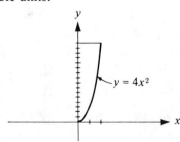

Since we are revolving about the y-axis, we can think of the width of a horizontal rectangle as dy and the radius as the value of x. Therefore, the volume of the generated disk is $\pi((1/4)y) \, dy$ since $x^2 = (1/4)y$. Now

$$V = \pi \int_0^{16} \frac{1}{4} y \, dy = \left[\frac{\pi y^2}{8} \right]_0^{16} = 32\pi \text{ cubic units.}$$

C   YOUR ANSWER: I am having trouble.

Let's see if we can help. We want the volume generated by rotating the region bounded by $y = 4x^2$, the y-axis, and $y = 16$ about the y-axis.

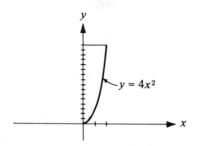

Our problem is to revolve the above region about the y-axis. If we rotate a horizontal rectangle about the y-axis, then we can think of the width as dy and the radius as the value of x. Therefore, the volume of the generated disk is $\pi((1/4)y) \, dy$ since $x^2 = (1/4)y$. Now return to frame **Q217** and try again.

Q218   Let's try finding the volume of a solid of revolution when we revolve about a line other than one of the coordinate axes. Find the volume generated by revolving the region bounded by the parabola $y^2 = 8x$ and the line $x = 2$ about the line $x = 2$. How did it go?

   Great   Frame **A**   Terrible   Frame **B**

A   YOUR ANSWER: Great.

Very good.

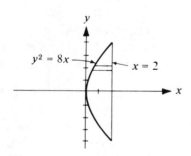

When a horizontal rectangle is revolved about the line $x = 2$, we can think of a generated disk whose radius is $2 - x$, whose height is dy, and thus whose volume is $\pi(2 - x)^2 \, dy$. Therefore,

$$V = \pi \int_{-4}^{4} (2 - x)^2 \, dy = \pi \int_{-4}^{4} \left(2 - \frac{y^2}{8}\right)^2 dy$$

$$= \pi \int_{-4}^{4} \left(4 - \frac{1}{2}y^2 + \frac{y^4}{64}\right) dy$$

$$= \pi \left[4y - \frac{y^3}{6} + \frac{y^5}{320}\right]_{-4}^{4}$$

$$= \frac{256\pi}{15} \text{ cubic units.}$$

B   YOUR ANSWER: Terrible.
Is it really that bad?

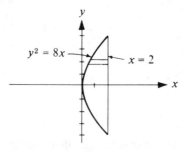

When a horizontal rectangle is revolved about the line $x = 2$, we can think of a generated disk whose radius is $2 - x$, whose height is dy, and whose volume is $\pi(2 - x)^2 \, dy$. Now return to frame **Q218**, evaluate the proper integral, and then select the other alternative.

6.3   VOLUMES USING CYLINDRICAL SHELLS

OBJECTIVES

You should be able to find the volume of a solid of revolution by the method of cylindrical shells.

Q219   This method uses cylindrical shells of the type illustrated in Figure 6.21 on page 289 of the text. It turns out that the volume of the cylindrical shell is

$2\pi \cdot$ (average radius of the inside and outside cylinders) $\cdot$
(altitude of the cylinder) $\cdot$ (thickness of the shell).

Now suppose we want the volume of a solid of the type below.

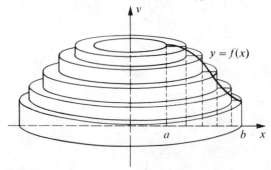

Intuitively, this volume is obtained by stacking cylindrical shells around each other from a to b. If we consider x as the average radius of the inside and outside cylinders of a typical shell, $f(x)$ as the altitude, and dx as the thickness, then the volume of a typical cylindrical shell is $2\pi x f(x)\, dx$ and the volume of the solid is indicated by

$$2\pi \int_a^b x f(x)\, dx.$$

This is discussed in detail on pages 289 and 290 of the text.

Which one of the following integrals indicates the volume of the solid generated by revolving the region bounded by $y = x^2$, the x-axis, $x = 1$, and $x = 2$ about the y-axis?

$$2\pi \int_1^2 x^4\, dx \qquad \text{Frame A}$$

$$2\pi \int_1^2 x^3\, dx \qquad \text{Frame B}$$

$$\pi \int_1^2 x^4\, dx \qquad \text{Frame C}$$

A **YOUR ANSWER:** $2\pi \int_1^2 x^4\, dx.$

Didn't you simply square $f(x)$? The volume is

$$2\pi \int_1^2 x f(x)\, dx.$$

In our problem, $f(x) = x^2$. Now return to frame **Q219** and select the correct answer.

B **YOUR ANSWER:** $2\pi \int_1^2 x^3\, dx.$

You are correct.

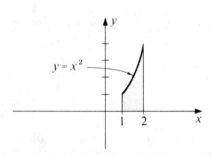

A typical vertical rectangle in the shaded region rotated about the y-axis generates a cylindrical shell. Therefore, the volume using the method of cylindrical shells is

$$2\pi \int_1^2 x f(x)\, dx = 2\pi \int_1^2 x(x^2)\, dx = 2\pi \int_1^2 x^3\, dx.$$

C **YOUR ANSWER:** $\pi \int_1^2 x^4\, dx.$

No. You have the volume obtained by rotating the required region about the x-axis instead of the y-axis, using the method of the previous section. Now return to frame **Q219** and try again.

Q220 Let's try another one. Find the volume generated by rotating the region bounded by

$y = 4x^2$, the y-axis, and $y = 16$ about the y-axis. How did it go?

    Terrific   Frame **A**   I need help.   Frame **B**

A   **YOUR ANSWER:**   Terrific.

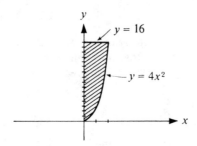

We want the volume generated by rotating the shaded region about the y-axis using cylindrical shells. The altitude of a typical shell is $16 - 4x^2$. Therefore, the volume is

$$2\pi \int_0^2 x(16 - 4x^2)\, dx = 2\pi \int_0^2 (16x - 4x^3)\, dx$$

$$= 2\pi \left[8x^2 - x^4 \right]_0^2 = 2\pi(32 - 16) = 32\pi.$$

Notice that this is the same result as in **Q217,** when we found this same volume using another method.

B   **YOUR ANSWER:**   I need help.

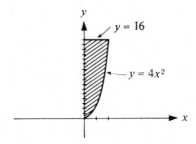

We want to rotate the shaded region about the y-axis. When a vertical rectangle is rotated about the y-axis, a cylindrical shell is generated where the altitude of a typical shell is $16 - 4x^2$. Now return to frame **Q220** and try again.

6.4   VOLUMES BY SLICING

OBJECTIVES

You should be able to find the volume of a solid which has the property that for every x in a closed interval [a, b] on a coordinate line ℓ, the plane perpendicular to ℓ at the point with coordinate x intersects the solid in a cross section whose area can be expressed as a function of x.

Q221 If a plane intersects a solid, then the region common to the plane and the solid is called a cross section of the solid. The technique for finding the volume of a solid by using the areas of a cross section is discussed in detail in the text on pages 294 and 295. Let's try one.

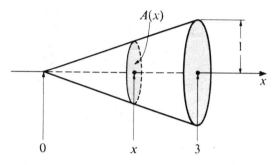

The volume of the solid above is

$$\int_0^3 A(x)\,dx$$

where the cross section is made by a plane perpendicular to the x-axis and, in this problem, $A(x)$ is the area of a circle depending on x. In order to use the slicing technique, the solid must have this property, namely, that any slice has an area that is a function of x.

Now in order to find the volume of the solid above, we need $A(x)$. What is $A(x)$?

$\pi x^2/3$	Frame **A**	9π	Frame **B**
$\pi x^2/9$	Frame **C**	I don't understand.	Frame **D**

A YOUR ANSWER: $\pi x^2/3$.
No. The area of a circle is πr^2 where r is the radius of the circle. We need to find the radius r for any x. Now return to frame **Q221** and try again.

B YOUR ANSWER: 9π.
You are off base. In order to find $A(x)$, which is the area of a circle, we need to find the radius r for any x. Now return to frame **Q221** and try again.

C YOUR ANSWER: $\pi x^2/9$.
Excellent. In order to find the radius r for any x, consider a side view of the solid.

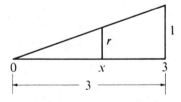

By similar triangles, $r/1 = x/3$. Therefore, $r = x/3$ and the area $A(x)$ of a typical cross section is

$$\pi r^2 = \pi\left(\frac{x}{3}\right)^2 = \pi\frac{x^2}{9}\ .$$

D   YOUR ANSWER: I don't understand.
In order to find $A(x)$, which is the area of a circle, we need to find the radius r for any x. Consider a side view of the solid.

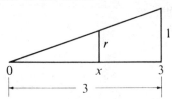

Find r in terms of x and then $A(x)$ which is πr^2. Now return to frame **Q221** and try again.

Q222   We want the volume of the following solid.

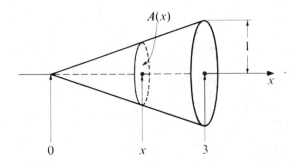

We found that $A(x) = \pi x^2 / 9$. Now find the volume of the solid. Were you successful?

   Yes   Frame **A**   No   Frame **B**

A   YOUR ANSWER: Yes.
Good. Since the cross sections are made by a plane perpendicular to the x-axis and $A(x) = \pi x^2/9$ for any x, the volume is

$$\int_0^3 A(x)\ dx = \frac{\pi}{9} \int_0^3 x^2\ dx$$

$$= \frac{\pi}{9} \left[\frac{x^3}{3} \right]_0^3 = \frac{\pi}{9}(9) = \pi \text{ cubic units.}$$

B   YOUR ANSWER: No.
Let's get you started. Since the cross sections are made by a plane perpendicular to the x-axis and $A(x) = \pi x^2/9$ for any x, the volume is

$$\int_0^3 A(x)\ dx.$$

Now return to frame **Q222**, compute the value of the integral, and then select the other alternative.

Q223   Let's try one more problem using the method of slicing. Find the volume of the solid generated by rotating about the x-axis the region bounded by the line $x = 6$ and the curve $y^2 = x$. How did it go?

Great   Frame **A**   Not so good   Frame **B**

A   YOUR ANSWER: Great.
Very good. This solid of revolution is shaped somewhat like a headlight of a car.

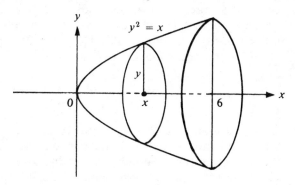

For each x in [0, 6], $A(x)$ is the area of a circle with radius y and thus

$$A(x) = \pi y^2 = \pi x$$

since we have $y^2 = x$. Therefore,

$$V = \int_0^6 \pi x \, dx = \left[\pi \frac{x^2}{2} \right]_0^6 = 18\pi.$$

B   YOUR ANSWER: Not so good.
If we rotate $y^2 = x$ about the x-axis, each cross section made by a plane perpendicular to the x-axis is a circle of radius y.

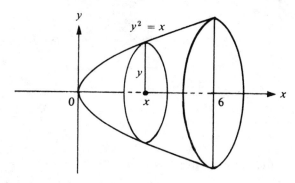

Therefore, for each x in [0, 6], $A(x)$ is the area of a circle with radius y. Now return to frame **Q223**, complete the solution, and select the other alternative.

6.5   WORK

OBJECTIVES

You should be able to solve problems involving work done using the definite integral.

Q224   If a constant force F is applied to an object moving at a distance d in the direction of the force, then the work W done on the object is given by

$$W = fd.$$

Now if a variable force is applied to an object moving it a certain distance in the direction of the force, then the methods of calculus are needed to find the work done. It turns out that if the force at the point with coordinate x on a coordinate line l is $f(x)$, where f is continuous on $[a, b]$, and if the force acts in the direction of l, then the work W done in moving an object from the point with coordinate a to the point with coordinate b is given by

$$\int_a^b f(x)\ dx.$$

This is discussed on pages 298-301 of the text.

Study the examples in the text and then try this problem. A boat is anchored so that the anchor rests on the bottom 50 feet directly below where the anchor chain is wound. In the water the anchor weighs 2000 lb and the chain weighs 15 lb per foot. How much work is done in bringing up the anchor? Were you successful?

Yes   Frame **A**   I need a hint.   Frame **B**

A   YOUR ANSWER: Yes.
Excellent. When the anchor has been raised to a height of x feet above the bottom, then the force required to hold the anchor is the sum of the weight of the anchor and the weight of the remaining length of chain. The weight of the anchor is 2000 lb and the weight of the chain is 15 lb per foot.

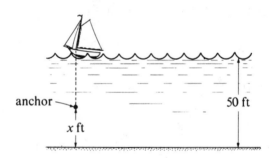

Therefore, force is given by

$$F(x) = 2000 + (50 - x)15 \text{ lb.}$$

Now the work done in bringing up the anchor is

$$\int_0^{50} [2000 + (50 - x)15]\ dx = \int_0^{50} (2750 - 15x)\ dx$$
$$= \left[2750x - 15\frac{x^2}{2} \right]_0^{50}$$
$$= 137,500 - 18,750 = 118,750 \text{ ft-lb.}$$

B   YOUR ANSWER: I need a hint.
All right. First, you need to find the force. When the anchor has been raised x feet, the force required to hold the anchor is the sum of the weight of the anchor and the weight of the remaining length of chain.

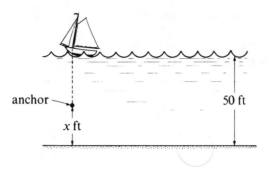

Therefore, force is given by

$$F(x) = 2000 + (50 - x)15 \text{ lb.}$$

Since the anchor has to be wound from 0 to 50, the work done is the integral of $F(x)$ from 0 to 50. Now return to frame **Q224,** complete the problem, and select the other alternative.

6.6   FORCE EXERTED BY A LIQUID

OBJECTIVES

You should be able to solve the problem of force exerted by a liquid using the definite integral.

Q225   The force F exerted by a liquid of constant density ρ on a region of the type below,

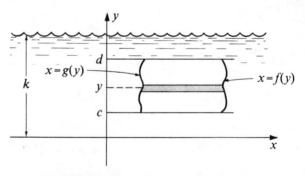

where the functions f and g are continuous on $[c, d]$, is

$$\int_c^d \underbrace{\rho(k - y)}_{}\underbrace{[f(y) - g(y)]}_{} dy.$$

Pressure at depth   Area of strip at depth
    of $(k - y)$ of $(k - y)$

This is discussed in more detail in the text on pages 305-307.

Now let's try a problem. The face of a dam has a trapezoidal shape, 50 feet wide at the top, 30 feet wide at the bottom, and 15 feet tall. What force will be exerted against the dam by the water when the water's surface is level with the top of the dam?

In order to set up the proper integral, superimpose the face of the dam on a rectangular coordinate system and label appropriately. Go to frame **A** and see how you came out.

A

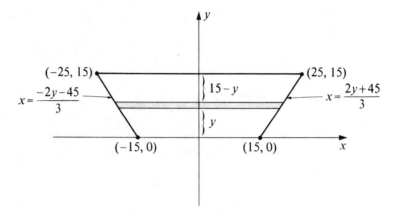

Q226   Now find the force exerted against the dam by the water when the water's surface is level with the top of the dam. How did it go?

Great   Frame **A**   I need help.   Frame **B**

A   **YOUR ANSWER:**   Great.
Very good.

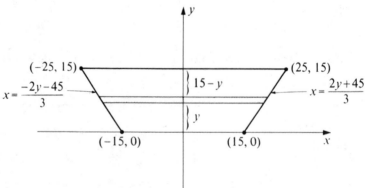

$$F = \int_c^d \rho(k - y)[f(y) - g(y)]\,dy$$

Since the density of water is approximately 62.5 lb/ft^3 and $f(y) - g(y) = (2y + 45)/3 - (-2y - 45)/3 = 4y/3 + 30$,

$$F = \int_0^{15} 62.5(15 - y)\left(4\frac{y}{3} + 30\right)dy$$

$$= 62.5\int_0^{15}\left(-10y - 4\frac{y^2}{3} + 450\right)dy$$

$$= 62.5\left[-5y^2 - 4\frac{y^3}{9} + 450y\right]_0^{15}$$

$$= 62.5(-1125 - 1500 + 6750) = 257{,}812.5 \text{ lb.}$$

B   YOUR ANSWER: I need help.

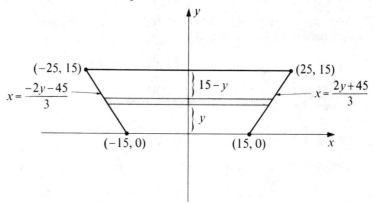

$$F = \int_c^d \rho(k - y)[f(y) - g(y)] \, dy$$

Since the density of water is approximately 62.5 lb/ft³ and $f(y) - g(y) = (2y + 45)/3 - (-2y - 45)/3 = 4y/3 + 30$,

$$F = \int_0^{15} 62.5(15 - y)\left(4\frac{y}{3} + 30\right) dy.$$

Now return to frame **Q226**, complete the problem, and select the other alternative.

6.7   ARC LENGTH

OBJECTIVES

You should be able to find the length of arc between two points on a smooth curve.

Q227   Now let's turn to arc length. If f has a continuous derivative in the closed interval $[a, b]$, then the arc length of the part of the curve $y = f(x)$ between $x = a$ and $x = b$ is

$$\int_a^b \sqrt{1 + [f'(x)]^2} \, dx.$$

This is a formula for finding the arc length of a curve. The rationale for the formula is discussed on pages 311 and 312 of the text.

What is the arc length of the part of the curve $y = x^{3/2}$ between $x = 0$ and $x = 4$?

$$\int_0^4 \sqrt{1 + x^{3/2}} \, dx \qquad \text{Frame A}$$

$$\int_0^4 \sqrt{1 + (9/4)x} \, dx \qquad \text{Frame B}$$

$$\int_0^4 \sqrt{1 + (3/2)x^{1/2}} \, dx \qquad \text{Frame C}$$

A YOUR ANSWER: $\int_0^4 \sqrt{1 + x^{3/2}}\, dx$.

You didn't apply the formula correctly. The arc length of the part of the curve $y = f(x)$ between $x = a$ and $x = b$ is

$$\int_a^b \sqrt{1 + [f'(x)]^2}\, dx.$$

Didn't you use $f(x)$ instead of $[f'(x)]^2$? Now return to frame **Q227** and select the correct answer.

B YOUR ANSWER: $\int_0^4 \sqrt{1 + (9/4)x}\, dx$.

Correct. The arc length of the part of the curve $y = x^{3/2}$ between $x = 0$ and $x = 4$ is

$$\int_0^4 \sqrt{1 + [f'(x)]^2}\, dx = \int_0^4 \sqrt{1 + \frac{9}{4}x}\, dx$$

because $f'(x) = (3/2)x^{1/2}$ and thus $[f'(x)]^2 = (9/4)x$.

C YOUR ANSWER: $\int_0^4 \sqrt{1 + (3/2)x^{1/2}}\, dx$.

You didn't apply the formula correctly. The arc length of the part of the curve $y = f(x)$ between $x = a$ and $x = b$ is

$$\int_a^b \sqrt{1 + [f'(x)]^2}\, dx.$$

Didn't you use $f'(x)$ instead of $[f'(x)]^2$? Now return to frame **Q227** and select the correct answer.

Q228 Find the arc length of the graph of $y = 4 - 2\sqrt{x^3}$ from $A(0, 4)$ to $B(4, -12)$.

$(2/27)(37)^{3/2}$	Frame **A**
$(2/27)[(37)^{3/2} - 1]$	Frame **B**
$16/27$	Frame **C**

A YOUR ANSWER: $(2/27)(37)^{3/2}$.

Be careful. The arc length of the graph of $y = 4 - 2\sqrt{x^3}$ from $A(0, 4)$ to $B(4, -12)$ is

$$\int_0^4 \sqrt{1 + y'^2}\, dx.$$

Now return to frame **Q228**, compute y', complete the integral, and then select the correct answer.

B YOUR ANSWER: $(2/27)[(37)^{3/2} - 1]$.

Correct. We have $y = 4 - 2\sqrt{x^3}$ from $A(0, 4)$ to $B(4, -12)$.

$$y = 4 - 2x^{3/2}$$
$$y' = -3x^{1/2}$$
$$y'^2 = 9x$$

Therefore,

$$\int_a^b \sqrt{1 + y'^2}\, dx = \int_0^4 \sqrt{1 + 9x}\, dx.$$

Let $u = 1 + 9x$. Then $du = 9\,dx$ or $dx = du/9$. Hence,

$$\int_0^4 \sqrt{1 + 9x}\,dx = \frac{1}{9}\int_1^{37} u^{1/2}\,du$$

$$= \frac{2}{27}\left[u^{3/2}\right]_1^{37} = \frac{2}{27}\,[(37)^{3/2} - 1].$$

C **YOUR ANSWER:** 16/27.
No. Evidently you made a mistake in your calculations. Return to frame **Q228**, study the definition of arc length, and then try again.

6.8 OTHER APPLICATIONS

OBJECTIVES

You should be able to solve other "appropriate" applications using the definite integral.

Q229 Several miscellaneous applications are presented in this section. Let's take a look at some of them.
    If the rate of depreciation of a certain piece of equipment is given by $g(t) = 50^{1/2}$, where t is in years and $g(t)$ is in dollars, what is the total depreciation at the end of 4 years?

    $400.00   Frame **A** $100.00   Frame **B** $266.67   Frame **C**

A **YOUR ANSWER:** $400.00.
Sorry, but you made a mistake in your integration. The total depreciation at the end of 4 years is

$$\int_0^4 50t^{1/2}\,dt.$$

Now return to frame **Q229** and try again.

B **YOUR ANSWER:** $100.00.
Didn't you simply evaluate $g(t)$ at $t = 4$? The total depreciation at the end of 4 years is

$$\int_0^4 50t^{1/2}\,dt.$$

Now return to frame **Q229** and try again.

C **YOUR ANSWER:** $266.67.
Of course. The total depreciation after 4 years is

$$\int_0^4 50t^{1/2}\,dt = \left[\frac{100}{3}\,t^{3/2}\right]_0^4 = \frac{100}{3}(8) = \$266.67.$$

Q230 Suppose that the rate of depreciation is given by $g(t) = 50t^{1/2}$ and it takes $200 to overhaul the equipment after t years. When is the best time to overhaul the equipment to minimize the average expense? If you have trouble, study Example 1 on page 317 of the text. After completing the problem, go to frame **A** and see how you did.

A   Let's see how it works out. The average expense $k(t)$ is

$$\left(200 + \int_0^t 50x^{1/2}\, dx\right)/t = \left(200 + \frac{100}{3}t^{3/2}\right)/t.$$

The average expense will have a minimum value if $k(t) = g(t)$ or

$$\left(200 + \frac{100}{3}t^{3/2}\right)/t = 50t^{1/2}$$

$$\frac{50}{3}t^{3/2} = 200$$

$$50t^{3/2} = 600$$

$$t^{3/2} = 12$$

$$t^3 = 144$$

$$t \approx 5.2 \text{ years.}$$

REVIEW TEST

1   Find the area of the region bounded by the graphs of $y = x^3 - 3x - 2$, $y = 0$, $x = -1$, and $x = 2$.

2   Find the area of the region between the graphs of the equations $y = x - 3$ and $y = 3x - x^2$.

3   Find the area of the region **R** in quadrant I bounded by the graphs of $y = 6x$, $3y - 2x = 16$, and $y = (1/2)x^2$.

Sketch the region **R** bounded by the graphs of the given equations and find the volume of the solid generated by revolving **R** about the indicated axis for Exercises 4-7.

4 $y = 2x^2$, $y = 0$, $x = 5$; about the x-axis.

5 $y = 3x^2$, $y = 0$, $x = 3$; about the y-axis.

6 $y = -x^2 - 3x + 6$, $x + y - 3 = 0$; about $x = 3$.

7 $y^2 = 8x$, $x = 2$; about $x = 2$.

8   A solid has a circular base of radius 3 units. Find the volume of the solid if every plane section perpendicular to a fixed diameter is an equilateral triangle.

9   If a given spring of normal length 10 meters requires a force of 25 pounds to stretch it .25 meters, calculate the work done in stretching it from its natural length to 12 meters.

10   Find the length of the arc of $y = (1/24)x^3 + 2x^{-1}$ from $x = 1$ to $x = 3$.

11   Set up, but do not evaluate, the integral for finding the arc length of the graph of $y = x^2/12$ from $A(0, 0)$ to $B(6, 3)$.

12   Use differentials to approximate the arc length of the graph of $y = 2x^3 - 1$ from $A(1, 1)$ to $B(1.1, 1.662)$.

13   If the rate of depreciation of a certain major appliance is given by $g(t) = 1 - 2t^3$, where t is in years and $g(t)$ is in dollars, what is the total depreciation at the end of 5 years?

SAMPLE TEST

1   Find the area of the region bounded by the graphs of $y = x^3$, $y = 0$, $x = 0$, and $x = 4$.

2   Find the area of the region between the graphs of $y = x^2 - 4$ and $y = 4 - x^2$.

3   Find the area of the region bounded by $y^2 = 4x$ and $y = 2x - 4$.

Sketch the region **R** bounded by the graphs of the given equations and find the volume of the solid generated by revolving **R** about the indicated axis for Exercises 4-7.

4   $y^2 = 8x$, $x = 2$; about the y-axis.

5   $y^2 = x^3$, $y = 0$, $x = 2$; about the x-axis.

6   $y = x^3$, $y = 0$, $x = 2$; about $y = 8$.

7   $y = 4x - x^2$, $y = 0$; about $y = 6$.

8   The base of a solid is the first quadrant area bounded by the line $4x + 5y = 20$ and the coordinate axes. Find the volume if every plane section perpendicular to the x-axis is a semicircle.

9   Find the work done in lifting 1000 lb of sand from a ditch 1500 ft deep by means of a cable weighing 2 lb/ft.

10   Find the length of the arc of $y = x^{3/2}$ from $x = 0$ to $x = 5$.

11   Set up, but do not evaluate, the integral for finding the arc length of the graph of $y = 2x^2$ from $A(1, 2)$ to $B(3, 18)$.

12   Use differentials to approximate the arc length of the graph of $y = x^3 - x$ from $A(0, 0)$ to $B(0.1, .099)$.

13   Suppose the net investment flow of a company is approximated by $g(t) = 2\sqrt{t}$, where t is in years and $g(t)$ is in thousands of dollars per year. If $t = 0$ corresponds to the present time, estimate the amount of capital formation over the next 6 years.

CHAPTER 7

Topics in
Analytic
Geometry

7.1 CONIC SECTIONS

In this chapter we will discuss the *conic sections,* or simply *conics.* The geometric figure of the conics can be obtained by intersecting a double-napped right circular cone with a plane. Figure 7.1 on page 325 of the text illustrates the geometric representation of the conic sections.

7.2 PARABOLAS

OBJECTIVES

You should know the definition of the focus and directrix of a parabola and be able to sketch the graph. You should be able to find the equation of a parabola given certain conditions. You should also know the tests for symmetry with respect to an axis.

Q231 A *parabola* is the set of all points in a plane equidistant from a fixed point F and a fixed straight line d. The point F is called the *focus* and the line d is called the *directrix* of the parabola.

The midpoint of the line segment from F to line d is on the parabola because it is equidistant from F and d. This point is called the *vertex.* If we let F have coordinates $(p, 0)$ $p > 0$ and the directrix have equation $x = -p$, then the vertex is at the origin and the equation of the parabola is $y^2 = 4px$.

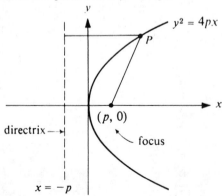

The equation of the parabola is developed in the text on pages 327-328. When we say that $y^2 = 4px$ is the equation of the above parabola, we mean that every point on the parabola has coordinates satisfying $y^2 = 4px$ and every point with coordinates satisfying $y^2 = 4px$ is on the above parabola.

In summary, if the equation of a parabola is $y^2 = 4px$ $(p > 0)$, we know that the parabola opens to the right, the vertex is at the origin, the coordinates of the focus are $(p, 0)$, and the equation of the directrix is $x = -p$.

What are the coordinates of the focus of the parabola $y^2 = 8x$?

(4, 0)   Frame **A**
(2, 0)   Frame **B**
(8, 0)   Frame **C**

A   YOUR ANSWER: (4, 0).
Be careful. If the equation of a parabola is $y^2 = 4px$, then the coordinates of the focus are $(p, 0)$. We have $y^2 = 8x$; therefore, $4p = 8$. Now return to frame **Q231** and select the correct answer.

B   YOUR ANSWER: (2, 0).
Right. If the equation of a parabola is $y^2 = 4px$, then the coordinates of the focus are $(p, 0)$. We have $y^2 = 8x$; therefore, $4p = 8$ and $p = 2$. Therefore, the coordinates of the focus are (2, 0). A sketch of the graph of $y^2 = 8x$ is as follows:

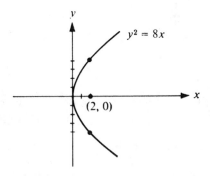

If $p < 0$, then the parabola $y^2 = 4px$ opens to the left and has focus with coordinates $(p, 0)$ where p is negative.

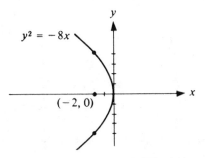

If we started with the focus on the y-axis instead of the x-axis, we obtain the equation $x^2 = 4py$. If $p > 0$, the parabola $x^2 = 4py$ opens upward and has focus with coordinates $(0, p)$.

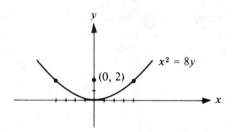

If $p < 0$, then the parabola $x^2 = 4py$ opens downward and has focus with coordinates $(0, p)$ where p is negative.

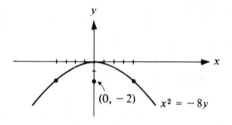

C   YOUR ANSWER: $(8, 0)$.
Be careful. If the equation of a parabola is $y^2 = 4px$, then the coordinates of the focus are $(p, 0)$. We have $y^2 = 8x$; therefore, $4p = 8$. Now return to frame **Q231** and select the correct answer.

Q232   What are the coordinates of the focus of the parabola with equation $x^2 = 12y$?

   $(3, 0)$ Frame **A** $(0, 3)$ Frame **B** $(0, 6)$ Frame **C**

A   YOUR ANSWER: $(3, 0)$.
Be careful. The parabola $x^2 = 4py$ $(p > 0)$ opens upward and has focus with coordinates $(0, p)$. If $x^2 = 12y$, what is p? Return to frame **Q232** and try again.

B   YOUR ANSWER: $(0, 3)$.
Correct. If $x^2 = 12y$, then $p = 3$ and the coordinates of the focus are $(0, 3)$.

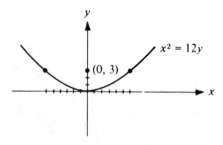

C   YOUR ANSWER: $(0, 6)$.
No. The parabola $x^2 = 4py$ $(p > 0)$ opens upward and has focus with coordinates $(0, p)$. If $x^2 = 12y$, what is p? Return to frame **Q232** and try again.

Q233   Which one of the following is a sketch of the graph of $y^2 = -16x$?

Frame **A**   Frame **B**

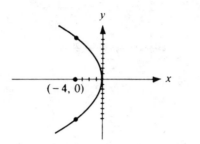   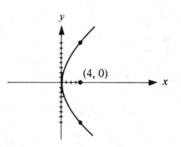

Frame **C**

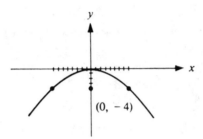

A   **YOUR ANSWER:**

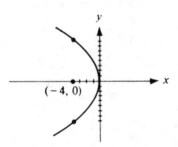

Certainly. This is a sketch of the graph of $y^2 = -16x$. Notice that the focus has coordinates $(-4, 0)$ and it opens to the left.

B   **YOUR ANSWER:**

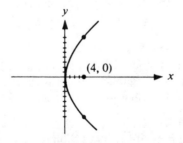

No. If $y^2 = -16x$, then $p < 0$ and the parabola does not open to the right. Return to frame **Q233** and try again.

C YOUR ANSWER:

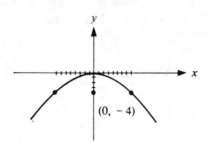

(0, − 4)

No. If $y^2 = -16x$, the axis of the parabola is the x-axis instead of the y-axis. You selected the graph of $x^2 = -16y$. Now return to frame **Q233** and try again.

Q234 What is the equation of a parabola with vertex at the origin and focus with coordinates $(0, -1)$?

$$y^2 = -4x \qquad \text{Frame } \mathbf{A}$$
$$x^2 = -2y \qquad \text{Frame } \mathbf{B}$$
$$x^2 = -4y \qquad \text{Frame } \mathbf{C}$$

A YOUR ANSWER: $y^2 = -4x$.
Watch out. If the focus has coordinates $(0, -1)$, then the axis of the parabola is the y-axis and the equation is of the form $x^2 = 4py$. Now return to frame **Q234** and select the correct answer.

B YOUR ANSWER: $x^2 = -2y$.
Almost, but the coefficient of y is incorrect. If the focus has coordinates $(0, -1)$, then $p = -1$. The form of the desired equation is $x^2 = 4py$. Now return to frame **Q234** and select the correct answer.

C YOUR ANSWER: $x^2 = -4y$.
Good. Since the focus has coordinates $(0, -1)$, the form of the equation is $x^2 = 4py$ where $p = -1$. Therefore, the equation is $x^2 = -4y$.

Q235 Find the equation of the parabola with vertex at the origin, focus on the x-axis, and passing through the point with coordinates $(1, 3)$. Were you successful?

    Yes   Frame **A**   No   Frame **B**

A YOUR ANSWER: Yes.
Excellent. Since the focus is on the x-axis, the form of the equation is $y^2 = 4px$. If the parabola passes through the point with coordinates $(1, 3)$, then $3^2 = 4p(1)$ or $4p = 9$. Therefore, the equation is $y^2 = 9x$.

B YOUR ANSWER: No.
Let's give you a hint. If the focus is on the x-axis, then the form of the equation is $y^2 = 4px$. Now find p when the coordinates $(1, 3)$ satisfy $y^2 = 4px$. After completing the problem, return to frame **Q235** and select the other alternative.

Q236   We may extend our work to the case in which the axis of the parabola is parallel to one of the coordinate axes. The equation

$$(x - h)^2 = 4p(y - k)$$

is called the standard form for the equation of a parabola with vertex at $V(h, k)$ and axis parallel to the y-axis. This is discussed on pages 329 and 330 of the text. Similarly,

$$(y - k)^2 = 4p(x - h)$$

is the equation of a parabola with vertex at $V(h, k)$ and axis parallel to the x-axis.

Using the above standard forms, find the equation of the parabola with vertex $V(2, -3)$ and axis parallel to the x-axis, and which passes through $P(0, -1)$.

$(y + 3)^2 = (-9/8)(x - 2)$	Frame **A**
$(y + 3)^2 = -2(x - 2)$	Frame **B**
$(y - 3)^2 = -8(x - 2)$	Frame **C**
I need some help.	Frame **D**

A   **YOUR ANSWER:** $(y + 3)^2 = (-9/8)(x - 2)$.
Your calculations are off. Since the vertex is $V(2, -3)$ and the axis of the parabola is parallel to the x-axis, the standard form is

$$(y + 3)^2 = 4p(x - 2).$$

Now since the parabola passes through $P(0, -1)$, substitute $x = 0$ and $y = -1$, and solve for p. Return to frame **Q236**, carry out the necessary calculation, and try again.

B   **YOUR ANSWER:** $(y + 3)^2 = -2(x - 2)$.
You are correct. Since the vertex is $V(2, -3)$ and the axis is parallel to the x-axis, the standard form is

$$(y + 3)^2 = 4p(x - 2).$$

Now since the parabola passes through $P(0, -1)$, we have

$$(-1 + 3)^2 = 4p(0 - 2)$$
$$2^2 = 4p(-2)$$
$$p = -\frac{1}{2}.$$

Therefore, the equation is

$$(y + 3)^2 = 4\left(-\frac{1}{2}\right)(x - 2) \quad \text{or} \quad (y + 3)^2 = -2(x - 2).$$

C   **YOUR ANSWER:** $(y - 3)^2 = -8(x - 2)$.
Your calculations are off. Since the vertex is $V(2, -3)$ and the axis of the parabola is parallel to the x-axis, the standard form is

$$(y + 3)^2 = 4p(x - 2).$$

Now since the parabola passes through $P(0, -1)$, substitute $x = 0$ and $y = -1$, and solve for p. Return to frame **Q236**, carry out the necessary calculation, and try again.

D   **YOUR ANSWER:**   I need some help.
Since the vertex is $V(2, -3)$ and the axis of the parabola is parallel to the x-axis, the standard form is

$$(y + 3)^2 = 4p(x - 2).$$

Now since the parabola passes through $P(0, -1)$, substitute $x = 0$ and $y = -1$, and solve for p. Return to frame **Q236,** carry out the necessary calculation, and try again.

Q237   Sketch the graph of $y = 4x^2 - 16x + 10$. How did it go?

      Great   Frame **A**   Terrible   Frame **B**

A   **YOUR ANSWER:**   Great.
Very good.

$$y = 4x^2 - 16x + 10$$
$$y - 10 = 4(x^2 - 4x + \underline{\quad})$$
$$y - 10 + 16 = 4(x^2 - 4x + 4) \quad \text{completing the square by adding}$$
$$\text{16 to both sides}$$
$$y + 6 = 4(x - 2)^2$$

Therefore, the vertex is $V(2, -6)$ and $4p = 1/4$ or $p = 1/16$.

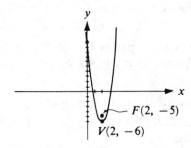

B   **YOUR ANSWER:**   Terrible.
It can't be that bad. Let's see if we can get you started. We have $y = 4x^2 - 16x + 10$. Write this equation in the form

$$y - 10 = 4(x^2 - 4x + \underline{\quad}).$$

Complete the square and express in the form

$$(y - k) = 4(x - h)^2.$$

Now return to frame **Q237,** complete the calculations, sketch the graph, and select the other alternative.

7.3   ELLIPSES

OBJECTIVES

You should know how to find the vertices and foci of an ellipse. You should know how to find an equation for an ellipse satisfying certain given conditions. You should also know how to test for symmetry with respect to the origin.

Q238 An *ellipse* is the set of all points in a plane, the sum of whose distances from two fixed points F_1 and F_2 has a fixed value, greater than the distance between F_1 and F_2. The two fixed points are called *foci* of the ellipse.

If we let the foci lie on the x-axis and have coordinates $(-c, 0)$ and $(c, 0)$, respectively, then the equation of the ellipse has the form

$$\frac{x^2}{a^2} + \frac{y^2}{b^2} = 1,$$

where a and b are as shown in the following sketch of the graph of an ellipse:

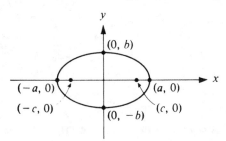

The x-axis is called the major axis. The number a is called the length of the *semimajor axis* and b the length of the *semiminor axis* of the ellipse. The points with coordinates $(a, 0)$ and $(-a, 0)$ are called the *vertices* of the ellipse. The numbers a, b, and c are related by

$$c^2 = a^2 - b^2.$$

Therefore, we can determine from the equation of an ellipse the length of the semimajor axis, the semiminor axis, the coordinates of the vertices, and the coordinates of the foci.

If $x^2/16 + y^2/4 = 1$, what are the coordinates of the vertices?

$(4, 0)$ and $(-4, 0)$	Frame **A**
$(16, 0)$ and $(-16, 0)$	Frame **B**
$(0, 2)$ and $(0, -2)$	Frame **C**

A **YOUR ANSWER:** $(4, 0)$ and $(-4, 0)$.
Right. If

$$\frac{x^2}{16} + \frac{y^2}{4} = 1,$$

then the length of the semimajor axis is $\sqrt{16} = 4$ and the coordinates of the vertices are $(4, 0)$ and $(-4, 0)$. Similarly, the length of the semiminor axis is $\sqrt{4} = 2$ and the coordinates of the endpoints of the minor axis are $(0, 2)$ and $(0, -2)$.

B **YOUR ANSWER:** $(16, 0)$ and $(-16, 0)$.
Be careful. The form of the equation of an ellipse is

$$\frac{x^2}{a^2} + \frac{y^2}{b^2} = 1.$$

The coordinates of the vertices are $(a, 0)$ and $(-a, 0)$. Didn't you use a^2 instead of a? Return to frame **Q238** and try again.

C **YOUR ANSWER:** $(0, 2)$ and $(0, -2)$.
Don't you have the coordinates of the endpoints of the minor axis? We have

$$\frac{x^2}{16} + \frac{y^2}{4} = 1.$$

Since $16 > 4$, the x-axis is the major axis and the endpoints are called the vertices. Now return to frame **Q238** and try again.

Q239

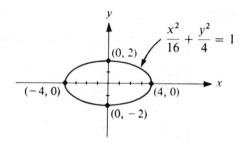

What are the coordinates of the foci of this ellipse?

$(12, 0)$ and $(-12, 0)$	Frame **A**
$(2\sqrt{3}, 0)$ and $(-2\sqrt{3}, 0)$	Frame **B**
$(3, 0)$ and $(-3, 0)$	Frame **C**
I don't know.	Frame **D**

A   YOUR ANSWER: $(12, 0)$ and $(-12, 0)$.
Your calculations are off. The relationship between a, b, and c is $c^2 = a^2 - b^2$. The coordinates of the foci are $(c, 0)$ and $(-c, 0)$. Didn't you use c^2 instead of c? Return to frame **Q239**, calculate c, and then select the correct answer.

B   YOUR ANSWER: $(2\sqrt{3}, 0)$ and $(-2\sqrt{3}, 0)$.
Correct. If

$$\frac{x^2}{16} + \frac{y^2}{4} = 1,$$

then $a^2 = 16$, $b^2 = 4$, and $c^2 = a^2 - b^2 = 16 - 4 = 12$. Therefore, $c = \sqrt{12} = 2\sqrt{3}$. Since the foci are on the x-axis, the coordinates are $(2\sqrt{3}, 0)$ and $(-2\sqrt{3}, 0)$.

C   YOUR ANSWER: $(3, 0)$ and $(-3, 0)$.
Your calculations are off. The relationship between a, b, and c is $c^2 = a^2 - b^2$. The coordinates of the foci are $(c, 0)$ and $(-c, 0)$. Return to frame **Q239**, calculate c, and then select the correct answer.

D   YOUR ANSWER: I don't know.
Since the x-axis is the major axis, the foci are on the x-axis and have coordinates $(c, 0)$ and $(-c, 0)$, where $c^2 = a^2 - b^2$. Now return to frame **Q239**, calculate c, and select the correct answer.

Q240   If the foci are on the y-axis, then the y-axis becomes the major axis and the form of the equation is

$$\frac{x^2}{b^2} + \frac{y^2}{a^2} = 1.$$

What are the coordinates of the vertices of the ellipse

$$\frac{x^2}{4} + \frac{y^2}{25} = 1?$$

(2, 0) and (−2, 0)   Frame **A**
(5, 0) and (−5, 0)   Frame **B**
(0, 5) and (0, −5)   Frame **C**

A   **YOUR ANSWER:**   (2, 0) and (−2, 0).
Watch out. If

$$\frac{x^2}{4} + \frac{y^2}{25} = 1,$$

then the y-axis is the major axis because $25 > 4$. Therefore, the vertices are on the y-axis. You have the coordinates of the endpoints of the minor axis. Return to frame **Q240** and try again.

B   **YOUR ANSWER:**   (5, 0) and (−5, 0).
Watch out. If

$$\frac{x^2}{4} + \frac{y^2}{25} = 1,$$

then the y-axis is the major axis because $25 > 4$. Therefore, the vertices are on the y-axis. Return to frame **Q240** and try again.

C   **YOUR ANSWER:**   (0, 5) and (0, −5).
Of course. If

$$\frac{x^2}{4} + \frac{y^2}{25} = 1,$$

then the y-axis is the major axis because $25 > 4$ and $\sqrt{25} = 5$ is the length of the semimajor axis. Therefore, the coordinates of the vertices are (0, 5) and (0, −5).

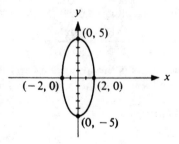

Q241   Which one of the following is a sketch of the graph of $64x^2 + 9y^2 = 576$?

Frame **A**   Frame **B**

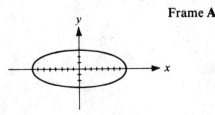

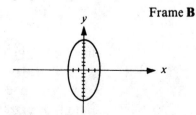

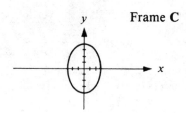

Frame **C**

A   YOUR ANSWER:

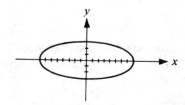

Don't you have the major and minor axes mixed up? Dividing $64x^2 + 9y^2 = 576$ by 576, we obtain

$$\frac{64x^2}{576} + \frac{9y^2}{576} = 1 \quad \text{or} \quad \frac{x^2}{9} + \frac{y^2}{64} = 1.$$

Now return to frame **Q241** and select the correct answer.

B   YOUR ANSWER:

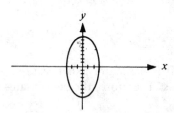

You are correct. Dividing $64x^2 + 9y^2 = 576$, we obtain

$$\frac{64x^2}{576} + \frac{9y^2}{576} = 1 \quad \text{or} \quad \frac{x^2}{9} + \frac{y^2}{64} = 1.$$

Therefore, the y-axis is the major axis and the vertices have coordinates (0, 8) and (0, −8). The endpoints of the minor axis have coordinates (3, 0) and (−3, 0).

C   YOUR ANSWER:

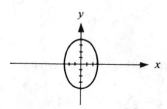

No. Dividing $64x^2 + 9y^2 = 576$ by 576, we obtain

$$\frac{64x^2}{576} + \frac{9y^2}{576} = 1 \quad \text{or} \quad \frac{x^2}{9} + \frac{y^2}{64} = 1.$$

Now return to frame **Q241** and select the correct answer.

Q242 What is the equation of an ellipse given that the coordinates of the vertices are (3, 0) and (−3, 0) and the length of the semiminor axis is 2?

$9x^2 + 4y^2 = 36$ Frame **A**

$4x^2 + 9y^2 = 36$ Frame **B**

$x^2/3 + y^2/2 = 1$ Frame **C**

I need some help. Frame **D**

A **YOUR ANSWER:** $9x^2 + 4y^2 = 36$.

Don't you have the major and minor axes reversed? If the coordinates of the vertices are (3, 0) and (−3, 0) then the x-axis is the major axis and $a = 3$. Since the length of the semiminor axis is 2, $b = 2$. Therefore, the equation of the ellipse is

$$\frac{x^2}{9} + \frac{y^2}{4} = 1.$$

Now return to frame **Q242** and select the correct answer.

B **YOUR ANSWER:** $4x^2 + 9y^2 = 36$.

Very good. Since the coordinates of the vertices are (3, 0) and (−3, 0), the x-axis is the major axis and $a = 3$. Also, since the length of the semiminor axis is 2, $b = 2$. Now, substituting in the equation

$$\frac{x^2}{a^2} + \frac{y^2}{b^2} = 1,$$

we obtain

$$\frac{x^2}{9} + \frac{y^2}{4} = 1,$$

which is $4x^2 + 9y^2 = 36$ after multiplying by 36.

C **YOUR ANSWER:** $x^2/3 + y^2/2 = 1$.

The form of the equation of an ellipse is

$$\frac{x^2}{a^2} + \frac{y^2}{b^2} = 1.$$

Didn't you use a and b instead of a^2 and b^2? Now return to frame **Q242** and try again.

D **YOUR ANSWER:** I need some help.

All right. Since the coordinates of the vertices are (3, 0) and (−3, 0), the x-axis is the major axis and $a = 3$. The form of the equation of the ellipse is

$$\frac{x^2}{a^2} + \frac{y^2}{b^2} = 1.$$

Now return to frame **Q242,** use the appropriate values of a and $b,$ and select the correct answer.

Q243 Can you find the equation of an ellipse given that the foci have coordinates (0, ±4) and vertices have coordinates (0, ±5)?

Yes Frame **A**

No Frame **B**

A   **YOUR ANSWER:**   Yes.

Excellent. Since the foci have coordinates $(0, \pm 4)$ and the vertices have coordinates $(0, \pm 5)$, $c = 4$ and $a = 5$ with the y-axis as major axis. We know that $c^2 = a^2 - b^2$. Therefore, $16 = 25 - b^2$ or $b^2 = 9$, and thus $b = 3$. Substituting $a = 5$ and $b = 3$ in the form

$$\frac{x^2}{b^2} + \frac{y^2}{a^2} = 1,$$

we obtain

$$\frac{x^2}{9} + \frac{y^2}{25} = 1.$$

B   **YOUR ANSWER:**   No.

Sure you can. If the foci have coordinates $(0, \pm 4)$, then $c = 4$. Since the coordinates of the vertices are $(0, \pm 5)$, the major axis is the y-axis and $a = 5$. Now find b from the relationship $c^2 = a^2 - b^2$ and substitute a and b in the equation

$$\frac{x^2}{b^2} + \frac{y^2}{a^2} = 1.$$

After completing the necessary computation, return to frame **Q243** and select the other alternative.

7.4   HYPERBOLAS

OBJECTIVES

You should know how to find the vertices, foci, and asymptotes of a hyperbola. You should also be able to find an equation of a hyperbola satisfying certain given conditions.

Q244   A *hyperbola* is the set of all points in a plane, the difference of whose distances from two fixed points F_1 and F_2 has a fixed value, less than the distance F_1F_2. The two fixed points are called the *foci* of the hyperbola.

     If we let the foci lie on the x-axis and have coordinates $(-c, 0)$ and $(c, 0)$, respectively, then the equation of the hyperbola has the form

$$\frac{x^2}{a^2} - \frac{y^2}{b^2} = 1$$

where a and b are shown in the following sketch of the graph of a hyperbola:

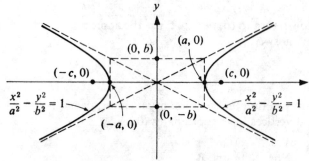

Let's point out a few things about the graph. The points with coordinates $(a, 0)$ and $(-a, 0)$ are called the vertices. The points with coordinates $(0, b)$ and $(0, -b)$ are *not* on the graph; however, they determine the rectangle indicated by dotted lines, which helps to sketch the graph of the hyperbola. The lines $y = (b/a)x$ and $y = -(b/a)x$, indicated by dotted lines, are called the *asymptotes* of the hyperbola and help in sketching the graph because they indicate how wide to open the branches of the hyperbola. The axis passing through the vertices is called the *transverse axis,* while the other one is called the *conjugate axis.* The numbers a, b, and c are related by

$$c^2 = a^2 + b^2.$$

Therefore, as in the case of the ellipse, we can determine from the equation of a hyperbola the coordinates of the vertices, the coordinates of the foci, and sketch the graph.

If $x^2/9 - y^2/4 = 1$, what are the coordinates of the vertices?

$(\pm 3, 0)$ Frame **A** $(\pm 2, 0)$ Frame **B** $(0, \pm 3)$ Frame **C**

A   **YOUR ANSWER:** $(\pm 3, 0)$.
Right. If $x^2/9 - y^2/4 = 1$, then the coordinates of the vertices are $(\pm 3, 0)$.

B   **YOUR ANSWER:** $(\pm 2, 0)$.
Watch out. If $x^2/a^2 - y^2/b^2 = 1$, then the coordinates of the vertices are $(\pm a, 0)$. Now return to frame **Q244,** study the graph of the hyperbola, and then select the correct answer.

C   **YOUR ANSWER:** $(0, \pm 3)$.
Watch out. If $x^2/a^2 - y^2/b^2 = 1$, then the coordinates of the vertices are $(\pm a, 0)$. Now return to frame **Q244,** study the graph of the hyperbola, and then select the correct answer.

Q245   Which one of the following is a sketch of the hyperbola $x^2/9 - y^2/4 = 1$?

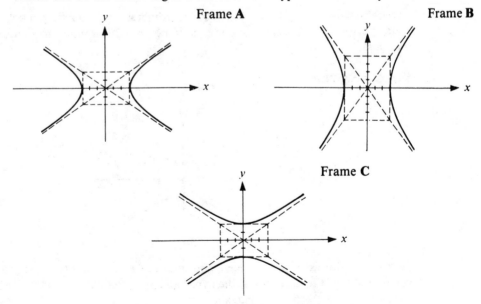

Frame **A**

Frame **B**

Frame **C**

A YOUR ANSWER:

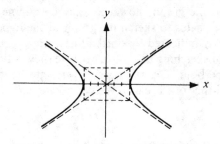

Good. This is a sketch of the graph of the hyperbola

$$\frac{x^2}{9} - \frac{y^2}{4} = 1.$$

Since the vertices are on the x-axis, the x-axis is called the transverse axis. The foci are also on the transverse axis.

B YOUR ANSWER:

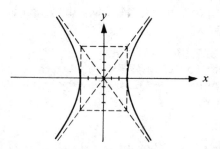

Be careful. If $x^2/9 - y^2/4 = 1$, then the coordinates on the y-axis that determine our rectangle are $(0, \pm 2)$ because in our equation $b^2 = 4$. Now return to frame **Q245** and try again.

C YOUR ANSWER:

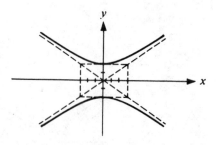

Be careful. Since the vertices have coordinates $(\pm 3, 0)$, the transverse axis is the x-axis, and thus the branches of the hyperbola open to the right and to the left. Now return to frame **Q245** and try again.

Q246

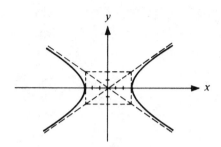

$$\frac{x^2}{9} - \frac{y^2}{4} = 1.$$

What are the coordinates of the foci of the above hyperbola?

$(\pm\sqrt{3}, 0)$	Frame **A**
$(\pm\sqrt{13}, 0)$	Frame **B**
$(\pm 5, 0)$	Frame **C**
I don't know.	Frame **D**

A   YOUR ANSWER: $(\pm\sqrt{3}, 0)$.
Didn't you use the relationship between the numbers a, b, and c for an ellipse instead of a hyperbola? In a hyperbola, $c^2 = a^2 + b^2$. Now return to frame **Q246** and try again.

B   YOUR ANSWER: $(\pm\sqrt{13}, 0)$.
You are correct. In a hyperbola $c^2 = a^2 + b^2$. If $x^2/9 - y^2/4 = 1$, $a = 3$ and $b = 2$. Therefore, $c^2 = 9 + 4 = 13$ or $c = \sqrt{13}$, and hence the coordinates of the foci are $(\pm\sqrt{13}, 0)$.

C   YOUR ANSWER: $(\pm 5, 0)$.
You are off base. In a hyperbola, $c^2 = a^2 + b^2$. Now return to frame **Q246** and try again.

D   YOUR ANSWER: I don't know.
In a hyperbola, $c^2 = a^2 + b^2$. Now return to frame **Q246,** calculate c using the values of a and b, and then select the coordinates of the foci.

Q247   Can you sketch the graph of the hyperbola $9x^2 - 25y^2 = 225$?

Yes	Frame **A**
No	Frame **B**

A   YOUR ANSWER: Yes.
Very good. If $9x^2 - 25y^2 = 225$, then dividing by 225,

$$\frac{x^2}{25} - \frac{y^2}{9} = 1.$$

Therefore, the coordinates of the vertices are $(\pm 5, 0)$ and a sketch of the graph is as follows:

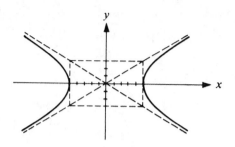

B   YOUR ANSWER: No.

Sure you can. If $9x^2 - 25y^2 = 225$, then dividing by 225, we obtain

$$\frac{x^2}{25} - \frac{y^2}{9} = 1.$$

Now sketch the graph as before and then return to frame **Q247** and select the other alternative.

Q248   If the form of the equation is $y^2/a^2 - x^2/b^2 = 1$, then the coordinates of the vertices are $(0, \pm a)$ and the y-axis is the transverse axis. Let's try one. Sketch the graph of $4y^2 - 9x^2 = 36$. How did it go?

　　　　Great   Frame **A**   Terrible   Frame **B**

A   YOUR ANSWER: Great.

Excellent. If $4y^2 - 9x^2 = 36$, then $y^2/9 - x^2/4 = 1$. The coordinates of the vertices are $(0, \pm 3)$ and the y-axis is the transverse axis.

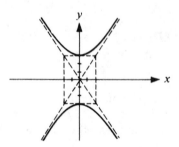

B   YOUR ANSWER: Terrible.

It can't be that bad. If $4y^2 - 9x^2 = 36$, then

$$\frac{y^2}{9} - \frac{x^2}{4} = 1.$$

Therefore, the coordinates of the vertices are $(0, \pm 3)$ and the y-axis is the transverse axis. Now return to frame **Q248**, sketch the graph, and select the other alternative.

Q249   Find the equation of a hyperbola with vertices having coordinates $(0, \pm 3)$ and foci having coordinates $(0, \pm 4)$.

$x^2/9 - y^2/7 = 1$ Frame **A**
$y^2/9 - x^2/16 = 1$ Frame **B**
$y^2/9 - x^2/7 = 1$ Frame **C**

A   **YOUR ANSWER:** $x^2/9 - y^2/7 = 1$.
Don't you have the transverse axis wrong? If the vertices have coordinates $(0, \pm 3)$, then the y-axis is the transverse axis and the equation has the form

$$\frac{y^2}{a^2} - \frac{x^2}{b^2} = 1.$$

Now return to frame **Q249** and try again.

B   **YOUR ANSWER:** $y^2/9 - x^2/16 = 1$.
Your calculations are off. The form is correct, but $b^2 \neq 16$. Return to frame **Q249**, calculate b^2 from $c^2 = a^2 + b^2$, and then select the correct answer.

C   **YOUR ANSWER:** $y^2/9 - x^2/7 = 1$.
Right. If the vertices have coordinates $(0, \pm 3)$, then the form of the equation is

$$\frac{y^2}{9} - \frac{x^2}{b^2} = 1.$$

Since the foci have coordinates $(0, \pm 4)$, $c = 4$, and because $c^2 = a^2 + b^2$, we have $16 = 9 + b^2$ or $b^2 = 7$. Therefore, the equation is

$$\frac{y^2}{9} - \frac{x^2}{7} = 1.$$

Q250   Can you find the equation of a hyperbola with vertices having coordinates $(\pm 2, 0)$ and passing through the point with coordinates $(3, 5)$?

     Yes   Frame **A**   No   Frame **B**

A   **YOUR ANSWER:**   Yes.
Very good. If the vertices have coordinates $(\pm 2, 0)$, then the form of the equation is

$$\frac{x^2}{4} - \frac{y^2}{b^2} = 1.$$

Since the hyperbola passes through the point with coordinates $(3, 5)$,

$$\frac{9}{4} - \frac{25}{b^2} = 1 \quad \text{or} \quad b^2 = 20.$$

Therefore, the desired equation is

$$\frac{x^2}{4} - \frac{y^2}{20} = 1.$$

B   **YOUR ANSWER:**   No.
Sure you can. If the vertices have coordinates $(\pm 2, 0)$ then the form of the equation is

$$\frac{x^2}{4} - \frac{y^2}{b^2} = 1.$$

Now since the hyperbola passes through the point with coordinates $(3, 5)$, we have

$$\frac{9}{4} - \frac{25}{b^2} = 1.$$

Return to frame **Q250**, calculate b^2, and then select the other alternative.

7.5   TRANSLATION OF AXES

OBJECTIVES

You should know what is meant by a translation of axes and how to sketch the graph of an equation after making a suitable translation of axes.

Q251   Sometimes the equation of a curve may be simplified by changing from one coordinate system to another. A change from one coordinate system S to another S' is called a coordinate transformation.

   If the coordinates of a point P in S are (x, y) and the coordinates in S' are (x', y'), then

$$\begin{cases} x' = x - h \\ y' = y - k \end{cases}$$

is called a *translation*.

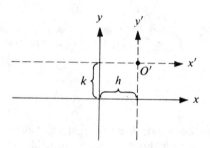

Notice that the coordinates of O' in the S system are (h, k), whereas, the coordinates of O' in the S' system are $(0, 0)$. In other words, we have translated our origin to the point that had coordinates (h, k) in the old system.

   Consider the equation $2x + 3y - 5 = 0$. What is this equation in terms of x' and y' if

$$\begin{cases} x' = x - 2 \\ y' = y + 1 \end{cases} ?$$

$2x' + 3y' - 6 = 0$	Frame **A**	$2x' + 3y' - 4 = 0$	Frame **B**
$2x' + 3y' - 5 = 0$	Frame **C**	I need some help.	Frame **D**

A   **YOUR ANSWER:** $2x' + 3y' - 6 = 0$.
Didn't you make a mistake in signs? If

$$\begin{cases} x' = x - 2 \\ y' = y + 1 \end{cases},$$

then we need to solve for x and y in terms of x' and y' and substitute in the equation $2x + 3y - 5 = 0$. Now return to frame **Q251** and try again.

B   **YOUR ANSWER:** $2x' + 3y' - 4 = 0$.
Right. If

$$\begin{cases} x' = x - 2 \\ y' = y + 1 \end{cases}, \text{ then } \begin{cases} x = x' + 2 \\ y = y' - 1 \end{cases}.$$

Substituting in the equation $2x + 3y - 5 = 0$, we obtain $2(x' + 2) + 3(y' - 1) - 5 = 0$ or $2x' + 3y' - 4 = 0$.

C   YOUR ANSWER: $2x' + 3y' - 5 = 0$.
No. You simply replaced x and y by x' and y'. If

$$\begin{cases} x' = x - 2 \\ y' = y + 1 \end{cases},$$

then we need to solve for x and y in terms of x' and y' and substitute in the equation $2x + 3y - 5 = 0$. Now return to frame **Q251** and try again.

D   YOUR ANSWER: I need some help.

$$\text{If} \begin{cases} x' = x - 2 \\ y' = y + 1 \end{cases}, \text{then} \begin{cases} x = x' + 2 \\ y = y' - 1 \end{cases}.$$

Substitute these values of x and y in terms of x' and y' in the equation $2x + 3y - 5 = 0$ and simplify. Now return to frame **Q251** and try again.

Q252 If we translate the origin to the point with coordinates $(2, -3)$, what are the equations for the translation?

$$\begin{cases} x' = x + 2 \\ y' = y - 3 \end{cases} \quad \text{Frame A} \qquad \begin{cases} x' = x - 2 \\ y' = y + 3 \end{cases} \quad \text{Frame B}$$

A   YOUR ANSWER: $\begin{cases} x' = x + 2 \\ y' = y - 3 \end{cases}$.
Sorry, but you missed the signs. If the origin is translated to the point with coordinates (h, k), then the translation is

$$\begin{cases} x' = x - h \\ y' = y - k \end{cases}.$$

Return to frame **Q252** and select the other alternative.

B   YOUR ANSWER: $\begin{cases} x' = x - 2 \\ y' = y + 3 \end{cases}$.
Good. If the origin is translated to the point with coordinates (h, k), then the translation is

$$\begin{cases} x' = x - h \\ y' = y - k \end{cases}.$$

In our problem $h = 2$ and $k = -3$. Therefore, the translation is

$$\begin{cases} x' = x - 2 \\ y' = y - (-3) \end{cases} \quad \text{or} \quad \begin{cases} x' = x - 2 \\ y' = y + 3 \end{cases}.$$

Q253 Express the equation of $(x - 1)^2/4 + (y - 2)^2/9 = 1$ in terms of x' and y' if the origin is translated to the point with coordinates $(1, 2)$.

$$\frac{(x' + 1)^2}{4} + \frac{(y' + 2)^2}{9} = 1 \quad \text{Frame A} \qquad \frac{(x')^2}{4} + \frac{(y')^2}{9} = 1 \quad \text{Frame B}$$

A   YOUR ANSWER: $\dfrac{(x' + 1)^2}{4} + \dfrac{(y' + 2)^2}{9} = 1$.
Sorry, but if the origin is translated to the point with coordinates $(1, 2)$, then the

198   **CH. 7 TOPICS IN ANALYTIC GEOMETRY**

equations of the translation are

$$\begin{cases} x' = x - 1 \\ y' = y - 2 \end{cases}.$$

Now return to frame **Q253**, think about this, and then select the other alternative.

B YOUR ANSWER: $\dfrac{(x')^2}{4} + \dfrac{(y')^2}{9} = 1.$

Of course. If the origin is translated to the point with coordinates (1, 2), then we have

$$\begin{cases} x' = x - 1 \\ y' = y - 2 \end{cases}.$$

Therefore, $(x - 1)^2/4 + (y - 2)^2/9 = 1$ becomes $(x')^2/4 + (y')^2/9 = 1$. Notice that the latter is the equation of an ellipse in standard form with respect to the x'-axis and the y'-axis. Therefore, we can sketch the graph of

$$\frac{(x - 1)^2}{4} + \frac{(y - 2)^2}{9} = 1$$

by translating the origin to the point with coordinates (1, 2).

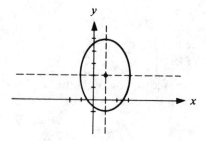

Q254 What translation would simplify the equation $x^2 + 6x + y^2 + 10y = -9$? (*Hint*: Use the technique of completing the square.)

$$\begin{cases} x' = x - 3 \\ y' = y - 5 \end{cases} \quad \text{Frame A}$$

$$\begin{cases} x' = x - 6 \\ y' = y - 10 \end{cases} \quad \text{Frame B}$$

$$\begin{cases} x' = x + 3 \\ y' = y + 5 \end{cases} \quad \text{Frame C}$$

A YOUR ANSWER: $\begin{cases} x' = x - 3 \\ y' = y - 5 \end{cases}.$

Don't you have the signs wrong? Completing the square, we obtain

$$(x^2 + 6x + \underline{}) + (y^2 + 10y + \underline{}) = -9$$
$$(x^2 + 6x + 9) + (y^2 + 10y + 25) = -9 + 9 + 25$$
$$(x + 3)^2 + (y + 5)^2 = 25.$$

Now what is the required translation? Return to frame **Q254** and select the correct answer.

B YOUR ANSWER: $\begin{cases} x' = x - 6 \\ y' = y - 10 \end{cases}.$

Your calculations are off. We have

$$(x^2 + 6x + \underline{\quad}) + (y^2 + 10y + \underline{\quad}) = -9.$$

Now we want to add in the blanks the numbers necessary to make each expression a square. Of course, what we add to one side of the equation must be added to the other. Now return to frame **Q254** and try again.

C YOUR ANSWER: $\begin{cases} x' = x + 3 \\ y' = y + 5 \end{cases}$.

Very good.

$$x^2 + 6x + y^2 + 10y = -9$$
$$(x^2 + 6x + \underline{\quad}) + (y^2 + 10y + \underline{\quad}) = -9$$
$$(x^2 + 6x + 9) + (y^2 + 10y + 25) = -9 + 9 + 25$$
$$(x + 3)^2 + (y + 5)^2 = 25.$$

Therefore, the translation

$$\begin{cases} x' = x + 3 \\ y' = y + 5 \end{cases}$$

reduces the equation to $(x')^2 + (y')^2 = 25$.

Q255 Sketch the graph of $4x^2 - 8x + 9y^2 + 36y + 4 = 0$. How did it go?

Wonderful   Frame **A**   Miserable   Frame **B**

A YOUR ANSWER: Wonderful.
Very good.

$$4x^2 - 8x + 9y^2 + 36y + 4 = 0$$
$$4(x^2 - 2x + \underline{\quad}) + 9(y^2 + 4y + \underline{\quad}) = -4$$
$$4(x^2 - 2x + 1) + 9(y^2 + 4y + 4) = -4 + 4 + 36$$
$$4(x - 1)^2 + 9(y + 2)^2 = 36$$
$$\frac{(x - 1)^2}{9} + \frac{(y + 2)^2}{4} = 1.$$

If we let

$$\begin{cases} x' = x - 1 \\ y' = y + 2 \end{cases},$$

then the equation reduces to the standard form

$$\frac{(x')^2}{9} + \frac{(y')^2}{4} = 1.$$

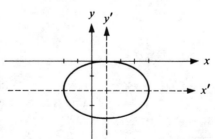

B YOUR ANSWER: Miserable.
Let's see if we can take some of the misery out of it. We have $4x^2 - 8x + 9y^2 + 36y + 4 = 0$. Our immediate task is to complete the square. Therefore, we arrange the

equation in the form

$$4(x^2 - 2x + \underline{\quad}) + 9(y^2 + 4y + \underline{\quad}) = -4.$$

Now we want to add in the blanks the numbers necessary to make each expression a square. Of course, what we add to one side of the equation must be added to the other side. Return to frame **Q255**, study Example 1 on page 349 of the text, complete the calculations, and then select the other alternative.

7.6 ROTATION OF AXES

OBJECTIVES

You should know what is meant by a rotation of axes and the formulas for a rotation of axes through a given angle φ. You should also know how to sketch the graph of an equation after making a suitable rotation.

Q256 There is one other coordinate transformation we wish to consider. If the coordinates of a point P in S are (x, y) and the coordinates in S' are (x', y'), then

$$\begin{cases} x' = x \cos \phi + y \sin \phi \\ y' = -x \sin \phi + y \cos \phi \end{cases}$$

is called a *rotation* of axes through the angle φ.

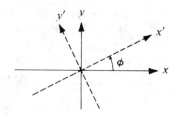

If we solve the above rotation formulas for x and y, we obtain

$$\begin{cases} x = x' \cos \phi - y' \sin \phi \\ y = x' \sin \phi + y' \cos \phi \end{cases}.$$

If we rotate the axes through 30°, what are the rotation formulas for x and y in terms of x' and y'?

$$\begin{cases} x = \dfrac{1}{2}x' - \dfrac{\sqrt{3}}{2}y' \\ y = \dfrac{\sqrt{3}}{2}x' + \dfrac{1}{2}y' \end{cases}$$ Frame **A**

$$\begin{cases} x = \dfrac{\sqrt{3}}{2}x' - \dfrac{1}{2}y' \\ y = \dfrac{1}{2}x' + \dfrac{\sqrt{3}}{2}y' \end{cases}$$ Frame **B**

$$\begin{cases} x = \dfrac{\sqrt{3}}{2}(x' - y') \\ y = \dfrac{1}{2}(x' + y') \end{cases}$$ Frame **C**

A **YOUR ANSWER:** $\begin{cases} x = \dfrac{1}{2}x' - \dfrac{\sqrt{3}}{2}y' \\ y = \dfrac{\sqrt{3}}{2}x' + \dfrac{1}{2}y' \end{cases}$.

Sorry, but you have computed sin 30° and cos 30° incorrectly. Find sin 30° and cos 30° and then return to frame **Q256** and try again.

B **YOUR ANSWER:** $\begin{cases} x = \dfrac{\sqrt{3}}{2}x' - \dfrac{1}{2}y' \\ y = \dfrac{1}{2}x' + \dfrac{\sqrt{3}}{2}y' \end{cases}$.

You are correct. The rotation formulas are

$$\begin{cases} x = x' \cos \phi - y' \sin \phi \\ y = x' \sin \phi + y' \cos \phi \end{cases}.$$

Since sin 30° = 1/2 and cos 30° = $\sqrt{3}/2$, we have

$$\begin{cases} x = \dfrac{\sqrt{3}}{2}x' - \dfrac{1}{2}y' \\ y = \dfrac{1}{2}x' + \dfrac{\sqrt{3}}{2}y' \end{cases}.$$

C **YOUR ANSWER:** $\begin{cases} x = \dfrac{\sqrt{3}}{2}(x' - y') \\ y = \dfrac{1}{2}(x' + y') \end{cases}$.

You are off base. Find sin 30° and cos 30°, substitute in the rotation formulas, and then return to frame **Q256** and try again.

Q257 Now what is the equation of $2x^2 + \sqrt{3}xy + y^2 = 8$ if the axes are rotated through 30°?

$5(x')^2 + (y')^2 = 16$	Frame **A**
$2(x')^2 + (1/2)(y')^2 = 8$	Frame **B**
$(7/4)(x')^2 + (1/2)x'y' + (1/2)(y')^2 = 8$	Frame **C**

A **YOUR ANSWER:** $5(x')^2 + (y')^2 = 16$.
Wonderful. Substituting

$$\begin{cases} x = \dfrac{\sqrt{3}}{2}x' - \dfrac{1}{2}y' \\ y = \dfrac{1}{2}x' + \dfrac{\sqrt{3}}{2}y' \end{cases}$$

in the equation $2x^2 + \sqrt{3}xy + y^2 = 8$, we obtain

$$2\left(\frac{\sqrt{3}}{2}x' - \frac{1}{2}y'\right)^2 + \sqrt{3}\left(\frac{\sqrt{3}}{2}x' - \frac{1}{2}y'\right) \cdot$$
$$\left(\frac{1}{2}x' + \frac{\sqrt{3}}{2}y'\right) + \left(\frac{1}{2}x' + \frac{\sqrt{3}}{2}y'\right)^2 = 8$$

After simplifying, this reduces to $5(x')^2 + (y')^2 = 16$.

B **YOUR ANSWER:** $2(x')^2 + (1/2)(y')^2 = 8$.
Your calculations are off. We want to substitute

$$\begin{cases} x = \dfrac{\sqrt{3}}{2}x' - \dfrac{1}{2}y' \\ y = \dfrac{1}{2}x' + \dfrac{\sqrt{3}}{2}y' \end{cases}$$

in the equation $2x^2 + \sqrt{3}xy + y^2 = 8$. Now return to frame **Q257** and try again.

C YOUR ANSWER: $(7/4)(x')^2 + (1/2)x'y' + (1/2)(y')^2 = 8$.
Your calculations are off. We want to substitute

$$\begin{cases} x = \dfrac{\sqrt{3}}{2}x' - \dfrac{1}{2}y' \\ y = \dfrac{1}{2}x' + \dfrac{\sqrt{3}}{2}y' \end{cases}$$

in the equation $2x^2 + \sqrt{3}xy + y^2 = 8$. Now return to frame **Q257** and try again.

Q258 The general equation of the second degree has the form

$$Ax^2 + Bxy + Cy^2 + Dx + Ey + F = 0.$$

Notice above that the xy term is missing in the equation obtained after rotating. It turns out that we can always rotate the axis in such a manner that the transformed equation has no xy term. In order to eliminate the xy term, we use ϕ where

$$\cot 2\phi = \frac{A - C}{B}, (B \neq 0)$$

in our rotation formulas. This is proved on page 354 of the text. Of course, if $B = 0$, the xy term is missing and we proceed as in the last section. For computational purposes we don't have to actually find ϕ. We only need $\sin \phi$ and $\cos \phi$ in order to obtain the rotation formulas. From our half-angle formulas, we have

$$\sin \phi = \sqrt{\frac{1 - \cos 2\phi}{2}}$$

$$\cos \phi = \sqrt{\frac{1 + \cos 2\phi}{2}}.$$

Therefore, our first problem is to find $\cos 2\phi$ given 2ϕ. Now let's eliminate the xy term in the equation

$$8x^2 - 12xy + 17y^2 - 20 = 0$$

by the proper rotation of ϕ. Since $A = 8$, $B = -12$, and $C = 17$,

$$\cot 2\phi = \frac{8 - 17}{-12} = \frac{3}{4}.$$

What is $\cos 2\phi$?

3/5	Frame **A**	4/5	Frame **B**
−3/5	Frame **C**	I don't know.	Frame **D**

A YOUR ANSWER: 3/5.
Very good. If $\cot 2\phi = 3/4$, then $x = 3$ and $y = 4$. Therefore, $r^2 = x^2 + y^2 = 9 + 16 = 25$ or $r = 5$. Since $\cos 2\phi = x/r$, we have $\cos 2\phi = 3/5$.

B YOUR ANSWER: 4/5.
Don't you have $\sin 2\phi$ instead of $\cos 2\phi$? If $\cot 2\phi = 3/4$, then $x = 3$ and $y = 4$.

Therefore, $r^2 = x^2 + y^2 = 9 + 16 = 25$ or $r = 5$. Doesn't $\cos 2\phi = x/r$? Now return to frame **Q258** and find $\cos 2\phi$.

C   YOUR ANSWER: $-3/5$.
Sorry, but you missed a sign. If $\cot 2\phi = 3/4$, then $x = 3$ and $y = 4$. Therefore, $r^2 = x^2 + y^2 = 9 + 16 = 25$ or $r = 5$. Doesn't $\cos 2\phi = x/r$? Now return to frame **Q258** and find $\cos 2\phi$.

D   YOUR ANSWER: I don't know.
Let's see if we can help. If $\cot 2\phi = 3/4$, then $x = 3$ and $y = 4$. Therefore $r^2 = x^2 + y^2 = 9 + 16 = 25$ or $r = 5$. From our previous work, we know that the cosine is x/r. Now return to frame **Q258** and try again.

Q259   Now we need $\sin \phi$ and $\cos \phi$ to use in our rotation formulas. What is $\sin \phi$? (*Hint:* Use the half-angle formula.)

$\sqrt{5}/5$ Frame **A**   1   Frame **B**   4/5   Frame **C**

A   YOUR ANSWER: $\sqrt{5}/5$.
You are right. Since $\cos 2\phi = 3/5 > 0$, we may choose 2ϕ in the first quadrant and hence $\sin \phi$ will be positive. Therefore,

$$\sin \phi = \sqrt{\frac{1 - \cos 2\phi}{2}} = \sqrt{\frac{1 - 3/5}{2}} = \sqrt{\frac{2}{10}} = \frac{1}{\sqrt{5}} = \frac{\sqrt{5}}{5}.$$

Similarly, $\cos \phi = \sqrt{\dfrac{1 + \cos 2\phi}{2}} = \sqrt{\dfrac{1 + 3/5}{2}} = \sqrt{\dfrac{8}{10}} = \dfrac{2\sqrt{5}}{5}.$

Therefore, the derived rotation formulas are

$$\begin{cases} x = \left(\dfrac{2\sqrt{5}}{5}\right)x' - \left(\dfrac{\sqrt{5}}{5}\right)y \\ y = \left(\dfrac{\sqrt{5}}{5}\right)x' + \left(\dfrac{2\sqrt{5}}{5}\right)y \end{cases}$$

B   YOUR ANSWER: 1.
Your calculations are off. Since $\cos 2\phi = 3/5 > 0$, we may choose 2ϕ in the first quadrant and hence $\sin \phi$ will be positive. Therefore,

$$\sin \phi = \sqrt{\frac{1 - \cos 2\phi}{2}} = \sqrt{\frac{1 - 3/5}{2}}.$$

Return to frame **Q259**, complete the calculations, and try again.

C   YOUR ANSWER: 4/5.
Your calculations are off. Since $\cos 2\phi = 3/5 > 0$, we may choose 2ϕ in the first quadrant and hence $\sin \phi$ will be positive. Therefore,

$$\sin \phi = \sqrt{\frac{1 - \cos 2\phi}{2}} = \sqrt{\frac{1 - 3/5}{2}}.$$

Return to frame **Q259**, complete the calculations, and try again.

Q260   Our equation is $8x^2 - 12xy + 17y^2 - 20 = 0$. The rotation formulas are

$$\begin{cases} x = \left(\dfrac{2\sqrt{5}}{5}\right)x' - \left(\dfrac{\sqrt{5}}{5}\right)y' \\ y = \left(\dfrac{\sqrt{5}}{5}\right)x' + \left(\dfrac{2\sqrt{5}}{5}\right)y'. \end{cases}$$

Which one of the following is the equation after applying the rotation?

$25(x')^2 + 54x'y' + 100(y')^2 = 100$ Frame **A**

$25(x')^2 + 52(y')^2 - 100 = 0$ Frame **B**

$(x')^2 + 4(y')^2 = 4$ Frame **C**

A **YOUR ANSWER:** $25(x')^2 + 54x'y' + 100(y')^2 = 100$.

If your calculations are correct, then there should be no $x'y'$ term. Substitute

$$\begin{cases} x = \left(\dfrac{2\sqrt{5}}{5}\right)x' - \left(\dfrac{\sqrt{5}}{5}\right)y' \\ y = \left(\dfrac{\sqrt{5}}{5}\right)x' + \left(\dfrac{2\sqrt{5}}{5}\right)y' \end{cases}$$

in the equation $8x^2 - 12xy + 17y^2 - 20 = 0$ and simplify. Now return to frame **Q260** and try again.

B **YOUR ANSWER:** $25(x')^2 + 52(y')^2 - 100 = 0$.

Your calculations are off. Substitute

$$\begin{cases} x = \left(\dfrac{2\sqrt{5}}{5}\right)x' - \left(\dfrac{\sqrt{5}}{5}\right)y' \\ y = \left(\dfrac{\sqrt{5}}{5}\right)x' + \left(\dfrac{2\sqrt{5}}{5}\right)y' \end{cases}$$

in the equation $8x^2 - 12xy + 17y^2 - 20 = 0$ and simplify. Now return to frame **Q260** and try again.

C **YOUR ANSWER:** $(x')^2 + 4(y')^2 = 4$.

Wonderful. Substituting

$$\begin{cases} x = \left(\dfrac{2\sqrt{5}}{5}\right)x' - \left(\dfrac{\sqrt{5}}{5}\right)y' \\ y = \left(\dfrac{\sqrt{5}}{5}\right)x' + \left(\dfrac{2\sqrt{5}}{5}\right)y' \end{cases}$$

in the equation $8x^2 - 12xy + 17y^2 - 20 = 0$, we obtain

$$8\left(\frac{4}{5}(x')^2 - \frac{4}{5}x'y' + \frac{1}{5}(y')^2\right) - 12\left(\frac{2}{5}(x')^2 + \frac{3}{5}x'y' - \frac{2}{5}(y')^2\right)$$
$$+ 17\left(\frac{1}{5}(x')^2 + \frac{4}{5}x'y' + \frac{4}{5}(y')^2\right) - 20 = 0.$$

Multiplying through by 5, we have

$$32(x')^2 - 32x'y' + 8(y')^2 - 24(x')^2 - 36x'y' + 24(y')^2$$
$$+ 17(x')^2 + 68x'y' + 68(y')^2 - 100 = 0.$$

Simplifying, we obtain

$$25(x')^2 + 100(y')^2 - 100 = 0 \quad \text{or} \quad (x')^2 + 4(y')^2 = 4.$$

Q261 Let's try one more. Study Example 2 on page 355 of the text and then remove the xy term from

$$3x^2 + 2\sqrt{3}\,xy + y^2 + 4x - 4\sqrt{3}y + 16 = 0$$

by using a suitable rotation of axes. Were you successful?

Yes   Frame **A**   No   Frame **B**

A   YOUR ANSWER: Yes.

Very good. Our equation is

$$3x^2 + 2\sqrt{3}\,xy + y^2 + 4x - 4\sqrt{3}y + 16 = 0.$$

The angle ϕ through which to rotate the axes in order to eliminate the xy term is found from

$$\cot 2\phi = \frac{A - C}{B} = \frac{3 - 1}{2\sqrt{3}} = \frac{\sqrt{3}}{3}.$$

Since $\cot 2\phi$ is positive, we may select 2ϕ in the first quadrant. Now we have $\cos 2\phi = 1/2$, from which

$$\sin \phi = \sqrt{\frac{1 - 1/2}{2}} = \sqrt{\frac{1}{4}} = \frac{1}{2} \quad \text{and}$$

$$\cos \phi = \sqrt{\frac{1 + 1/2}{2}} = \sqrt{\frac{3}{4}} = \frac{\sqrt{3}}{2}.$$

The equations for the required rotation are

$$x = \frac{\sqrt{3}}{2}x' - \frac{1}{2}y'$$

$$y = \frac{1}{2}x' + \frac{\sqrt{3}}{2}y'.$$

These substitutions transform the equation into

$$3\left(\frac{3}{4}(x')^2 - \frac{\sqrt{3}}{2}x'y' + \frac{1}{4}(y')^2\right) + 2\sqrt{3}\left(\frac{\sqrt{3}}{4}(x')^2 + \frac{1}{2}x'y' - \frac{\sqrt{3}}{4}(y')^2\right)$$

$$+ \left(\frac{1}{4}(x')^2 + \frac{\sqrt{3}}{2}x'y' + \frac{3}{4}(y')^2\right) + 4\left(\frac{\sqrt{3}}{2}x' - \frac{1}{2}y'\right)$$

$$- 4\sqrt{3}\left(\frac{1}{2}x' + \frac{\sqrt{3}}{2}y'\right) + 16 = 0.$$

Simplifying, we obtain $4(x')^2 - 8y' + 16 = 0$.

B   YOUR ANSWER: No.

Let's see if we can get you started. The equation is

$$3x^2 + 2\sqrt{3}xy + y^2 + 4x - 4\sqrt{3}y + 16 = 0.$$

The angle ϕ through which to rotate the axes in order to eliminate the xy term is found from $\cot 2\phi = (3 - 1)/2\sqrt{3} = 2/2\sqrt{3} = \sqrt{3}/3$. Now $x = \sqrt{3}$, $y = 3$, and $r^2 = (\sqrt{3})^2 + 3^2 = 12$ or $r = 2\sqrt{3}$. Since $\cos 2\phi = x/r$, we have $\cos 2\phi = \sqrt{3}/2\sqrt{3} = 1/2$. Now find $\sin \phi$ and $\cos \phi$ using the half-angle formulas and then find the desired rotation formulas. Return to frame **Q261**, carry out the necessary computation, and then select the other alternative.

REVIEW TEST

1   Find the vertex of the following and sketch the graph.
   (a) $f(x) = 3x^2 - 2$ (b) $f(x) = -x^2 + 3$

2   Use the technique of completing the square to express $f(x)$ in the form $f(x) = a(x - h)^2 + k$.
   (a) $f(x) = 3x^2 + 6x - 2$ (b) $f(x) = -2x^2 + 3x + 4$

3   Sketch the graphs of the following. Find the vertex by completing the square and the x-intercepts by using the quadratic formula.
    (a) $f(x) = 3x^2 + 2x - 5$ (b) $f(x) = -5x^2 - 8x + 2$

4   Sketch the graph of $x = y^2 - 2y - 3$.

5   Sketch the graph of $16x^2 + 9y^2 = 144$.

6   Sketch the graph of $x^2 - 16y^2 = 16$.

7   Find an equation of an ellipse with center at the origin with x-intercepts ± 6 and passing through the point $(0, 2)$.

8   Find an equation of the tangent line to the ellipse $4x^2 + 3y^2 = 31$ at the point $P(-1, 3)$.

9   A rectangle is inscribed in the ellipse $x^2/400 + y^2/225 = 1$ with its sides parallel to the axes of the ellipse. Find the dimensions of the rectangle of maximum area which can be so inscribed.

10   Find an equation of a hyperbola with foci $(\pm 3, 0)$ and vertices $V(\pm 2, 0)$.

11   Find the volume of the solid obtained by revolving the region bounded by the ellipse $2x^2 + y^2 = 8$ about the x-axis.

12   Sketch the graph of each of the following equations after making a suitable translation of axes.
    (a) $\dfrac{(x + 2)^2}{9} + \dfrac{(y - 4)^2}{16} = 1$ (b) $2x^2 - 8x - 4y^2 + 16y = 12$

13   Given $2x^2 + 3xy + 2y^2 = 7$
    (a)   Find the angle of rotation which will eliminate the xy term.
    (b)   Find the rotation formulas.
    (c)   Transform the given equation using this rotation.
    (d)   Sketch the graph.

SAMPLE TEST

1   Find the vertex of the following and sketch the graph.
    (a) $f(x) = 2x^2 - 5$ (b) $f(x) = -3x^2 + 1$

2   Use the technique of completing the square to express $f(x)$ in the form $f(x) = a(x - h)^2 + k$.
    (a) $f(x) = 2x^2 - 3x + 1$ (b) $f(x) = -4x^2 + 2x + 3$

3   Sketch the graph of the following. Find the vertex by completing the square and the x-intercepts by using the quadratic formula.
    (a) $f(x) = 4x^2 + 7x + 2$ (b) $f(x) = -3x^2 - 6x + 1$

4   Sketch the graph of $x = -3y^2 + 12y + 2$.

5   Sketch the graph of $4x^2 + 9y^2 = 36$.

6   Sketch the graph of $y^2 - 9x^2 = 9$.

7   Find an equation of a hyperbola passing through $(2, 0)$ with asymptotes $y = \pm 2x$.

8   Find an equation of a hyperbola with vertices $V(\pm 2, 0)$ and conjugate axis of length 6.

9   Find an equation of the line tangent to the hyperbola $x^2 - y^2 = 3$ at the point $P(2, 1)$.

10   Find the minimum distance from the point $P(4, 2)$ to the parabola $y^2 = 8x$.

11   Find the volume of the solid obtained by revolving the region bounded by the hyperbola $5x^2 - 4y^2 = 20$ and the line $x = 3$ about the x-axis.

12   Sketch the graph of each of the following equations after making a suitable translation of axes.

(a) $\dfrac{(x - 1)^2}{4} - \dfrac{(y - 2)^2}{16} = 1$ (b) $2x^2 + 8x + y^2 - 4y = 4$

13   Given $13x^2 - 2\sqrt{3}xy + 15y^2 = 192$

(a)   Find the angle of rotation which will eliminate the xy term.

(b)   Find the rotation formulas.

(c)   Transform the given equation using this rotation.

(d)   Sketch the graph.

CHAPTER 8

Exponential
and Logarithmic
Functions

8.1 THE NATURAL LOGARITHMIC FUNCTION

OBJECTIVES

You should know the definition of the natural logarithmic function and how to find the derivative of the natural logarithmic function. You should also be familiar with the laws of logarithms and how to use them.

Q262 The definition of the natural logarithmic function is given on page 360 of the text. If $f(x) = \ln x$ and $x > 0$, then

$$f'(x) = \frac{1}{x}$$

or, in general, if $f(x) = \ln u$ where $u = g(x) > 0$, then

$$f'(x) = \frac{1}{u}D_x u.$$

Notice that $f'(x)$ is $1/u$ times the derivative of u. These formulas are derived in the text.

What is the derivative of $\ln 2x$?

$1/2x$ Frame **A** $2/x$ Frame **B** $1/x$ Frame **C**

A **YOUR ANSWER:** $1/2x$.
No. Use the function of a function formula. The derivative of $\ln 2x$ is $1/2x$ times the derivative of $2x$. Now return to frame **Q262** and try again.

B **YOUR ANSWER:** $2/x$.
No. Use the function of a function formula. The derivative of $\ln 2x$ is $1/2x$ times the derivative of $2x$. Now return to frame **Q262** and try again.

C **YOUR ANSWER:** $1/x$.
Correct. The derivative of $\ln 2x$ is $1/2x$ times the derivative of $2x$ which is

$$\frac{1}{2x} \cdot 2 = \frac{1}{x}.$$

This can also be obtained by writing $\ln 2x$ as $\ln 2 - \ln x$. Now the derivative of $\ln 2$ is 0 since $\ln 2$ is a constant and the derivative of $\ln x$ is $1/x$. Therefore, the derivative of $\ln 2x$ is $1/x$.

Q263   If $y = \ln (3x^2 + 2x + 5)$, what is y'?

$6x + 2$ Frame **A**

$\dfrac{6x + 2}{3x^2 + 2x + 5}$ Frame **B**

$1/x$ Frame **C**

A   **YOUR ANSWER:** $6x + 2$.
Don't you simply have the derivative of $3x^2 + 2x + 5$? Return to frame **Q263** and find the derivative of $\ln (3x^2 + 2x + 5)$.

B   **YOUR ANSWER:** $\dfrac{6x + 2}{3x^2 + 2x + 5}$.
Right. If $y = \ln (3x^2 + 2x + 5)$, then

$$y' = \frac{1}{3x^2 + 2x + 5} D_x(3x^2 + 2x + 5) = \frac{6x + 2}{3x^2 + 2x + 5}.$$

C   **YOUR ANSWER:** $1/x$.
No. You have the derivative of $\ln x$. We want the derivative of $\ln (3x^2 + 2x + 5)$. Using the function of a function formula, the derivative of $\ln (3x^2 + 2x + 5)$ is $1/(3x^2 + 2x + 5)$ times the derivative of $3x^2 + 2x + 5$. Now return to frame **Q263** and try again.

Q264   If $y = x^2 \ln (3x + 2)$, find y'. Were you successful?

Yes   Frame **A**   No   Frame **B**

A   **YOUR ANSWER:**   Yes.
Excellent. If $y = x^2 \ln (3x + 2)$, then

$$y' = x^2 D_x [\ln (3x + 2)] + \ln (3x + 2) D_x(x^2)$$
$$= x^2 \left(\frac{3}{3x + 2}\right) + \ln (3x + 2) \cdot 2x$$
$$= \frac{3x^2}{3x + 2} + 2x \ln (3x + 2).$$

B   **YOUR ANSWER:**   No.
Let's see if we can get you on the right track. If $y = x^2 \ln (3x + 2)$, then we want to use the product formula to find y'. That is,

$$y' = x^2 D_x [\ln (3x + 2)] + \ln (3x + 2) D_x(x^2).$$

Now return to frame **Q264**, try the problem again, and then select the other alternative.

Q265   Let's try one more. Find the derivative of $y = \ln (x + 3)^2$. After completing the problem, go to frame **A** and check your work.

A   Let's see how you did. If $y = \ln (x + 3)^2$, then

$$y' = \frac{1}{(x + 3)^2} D_x(x + 3)^2 = \frac{1}{(x + 3)^2} \cdot 2(x + 3) = \frac{2}{x + 3}.$$

An alternative method would be to use the properties of logarithms before differentiating. That is,

$$y = \ln (x + 3)^2 = 2 \ln (x + 3).$$

Therefore,

$$y' = \frac{2}{x + 3}.$$

8.2   THE NATURAL EXPONENTIAL FUNCTION

OBJECTIVES

You should know the definition of the natural exponential function and the relationship between the natural logarithmic and natural exponential function. You should know how to use the usual laws of exponents. You should also know how to find the derivative of the natural exponential function.

Q266   Now let's consider the exponential function:

$$y = a^x \quad (a > 0).$$

The exponential function is defined for every real number x and is continuous everywhere. The number a is referred to as the base. In our work, we are primarily interested in base e. That is, we are interested in the function $y = e^x$. To five decimal places, $e \approx 2.71828$.

It is shown on page 373 of the text that if $y = e^x$, then $y' = e^x$. That is,

$$D_x(e^x) = e^x.$$

Notice that the derivative of the function is equal to the function itself. This makes this function particularly important. In general, if $y = e^u$, then $y' = e^u D_x u$ where $u = g(x)$.

What is $D_x(e^{8x})$?

e^{8x}	Frame **A**	$8e^x$	Frame **B**
$8e^{8x}$	Frame **C**	I don't know.	Frame **D**

A   **YOUR ANSWER:** e^{8x}.
Didn't you forget to multiply by the derivative of $8x$? Return to frame **Q266** and try again.

B   **YOUR ANSWER:** $8e^x$.
Be careful. We want $D_x(e^{8x})$. That is, if $y = e^{8x}$, we want y'. We need to use the formulas for the derivative of the exponential and the derivative of a function of a function. Now return to frame **Q266** and try again.

C   **YOUR ANSWER:** $8e^{8x}$.
Right.

$$D_x(e^{8x}) = e^{8x}[D_x(8x)] = 8e^{8x}.$$

D   **YOUR ANSWER:**   I don't know.
We want $D_x(e^{8x})$. That is, if $y = e^{8x}$, we want y'. Using the formulas for the derivative of the exponential and the derivative of a function of a function, we obtain

$$y' = e^{8x}[D_x(8x)].$$

Now return to frame **Q266** and try again.

Q267   If $y = e^{2x^3}$, what is y'?

$6x^2e^{2x^3}$ Frame **A** e^{6x^2} Frame **B** e^{2x^3} Frame **C**

A   **YOUR ANSWER:** $6x^2e^{2x^3}$.
You are correct. If $y = e^{2x^3}$, then

$$y' = e^{2x^3}D_x(2x^3) = 6x^2e^{2x^3}.$$

B   **YOUR ANSWER:** e^{6x^2}.
You are off base. You used the derivative of the exponent as the exponent of e. Return to frame **Q267** and try again.

C   **YOUR ANSWER:** e^{2x^3}.
Didn't you forget to multiply by the derivative of the expression $2x^3$? Return to frame **Q267** and try again.

Q268   Let's try another one. Find y' if $y = \sqrt{e^{2x} + x^2}$. How did it go?

Wonderful   Frame **A**   Miserable   Frame **B**

A   **YOUR ANSWER:**   Wonderful.
Excellent. If $y = \sqrt{e^{2x} + x^2} = (e^{2x} + x^2)^{1/2}$, then

$$y' = \frac{1}{2}(e^{2x} + x^2)^{-1/2}D_x(e^{2x} + x^2)$$

$$= \frac{1}{2}(e^{2x} + x^2)^{-1/2}(2e^{2x} + 2x)$$

$$= \frac{e^{2x} + x}{(e^{2x} + x^2)^{1/2}} .$$

B   **YOUR ANSWER:**   Miserable.
We're sorry. Let's see if we can get it straightened out. If $y = \sqrt{e^{2x} + x^2} = (e^{2x} + x^2)^{1/2}$, then y' is $(1/2)(e^{2x} + x^2)^{-1/2}$ times the derivative of the expression $e^{2x} + x^2$. Now return to frame **Q268,** complete the calculations, and select the other alternative.

Q269   Can you find the local extrema for $y = e^{x^2}$?

Yes   Frame **A**   No   Frame **B**

A   **YOUR ANSWER:**   Yes.
Very good. If $y = e^{x^2}$, then $y' = e^{x^2}(2x)$. The critical numbers are the numbers where the first derivative is zero or undefined. When $x = 0$, $y' = 0$ and hence a local

extremum could occur at $x = 0$. Since
$$y'' = e^{x^2}(2) + (2x)e^{x^2}(2x) = 2e^{x^2} + 4x^2e^{x^2},$$
$y''(0) = 2e^0 + 4(0)e^0 = 2$. Therefore, we have a local minimum at $x = 0$ because y'' > 0 when $x = 0$. The actual point on the graph of $y = e^{x^2}$ where the minimum occurs has coordinates $(0, 1)$.

B   **YOUR ANSWER:**   No.
Let's see if we can get you started. The candidates for local extrema are called critical numbers and are the values of x where the first derivative is zero or undefined. Find the critical numbers, determine if they are local extrema, and then return to frame **Q269** and select the other alternative.

8.3   DIFFERENTIATION AND INTEGRATION

OBJECTIVES

You should know the integration formula involving the natural logarithmic function and how to use this formula. You should know the integration formula for the natural exponential function and how to use it. You should also be familiar with the process called logarithmic differentiation.

Q270   Since $D_x(\ln x) = 1/x \ (x > 0)$, we have
$$\int \frac{1}{x} \, dx = \ln x + C \quad (x > 0).$$
It can be shown that if $x \neq 0$, then
$$\int \frac{1}{x} \, dx = \ln |x| + C.$$
Using the above formula, what is $\int (3/x) \, dx$?

$3 \ln |x| + C$	Frame **A**
$1/\ln |x| + C$	Frame **B**
$3/x + C$	Frame **C**

A   **YOUR ANSWER:** $3 \ln |x| + C$.
Of course. Since $\int (1/x) \, dx = \ln |x| + C$, $\int (3/x) \, dx = 3 \ln |x| + C$.

B   **YOUR ANSWER:** $3/\ln |x| + C$.
No. You aren't using the formula correctly. Return to frame **Q270**, study the integration formula, and then try again.

C   **YOUR ANSWER:** $3/x + C$.
You are off base. You aren't using the formula correctly. Return to frame **Q270**, study the integration formula, and then try again.

Q271   What is the area of the region bounded by the curve $y = 3/x$, the x-axis, and the lines $x = 1$ and $x = e$?

$3(e - 1)$ Frame **A**   3   Frame **B** $3e$ Frame **C**

A **YOUR ANSWER:** $3(e - 1)$.
Be careful. The area of the region bounded by the curve $y = 3/x$, the x-axis, and the lines $x = 1$ and $x = e$ is

$$\int_1^e \frac{3}{x} \, dx = 3 \ln |x| \Big]_1^e = 3(\ln e - \ln 1).$$

Did you make an error calculating $\ln e$ and $\ln 1$? Return to frame **Q271** and try again.

B **YOUR ANSWER:** 3.
Very good. The area of the region bounded by the curve $y = 3/x$, the x-axis, and the lines $x = 1$ and $x = e$ is

$$\int_1^e \frac{3}{x} \, dx = 3 \ln |x| \Big]_1^e = 3(\ln e - \ln 1)$$
$$= 3(1 - 0) = 3.$$

C **YOUR ANSWER:** $3e$.
Be careful. The area of the region bounded by the curve $y = 3/x$, the x-axis, and the lines $x = 1$ and $x = e$ is

$$\int_1^e \frac{3}{x} \, dx = 3 \ln |x| \Big]_1^e = 3(\ln e - \ln 1).$$

Did you make an error calculating $\ln e$ and $\ln 1$? Return to frame **Q271** and try again.

Q272 Since the derivative of $\ln |u| = (1/u)D_x u$, we have

$$\int \frac{1}{u} \, du = \ln |u| + C, \text{ where } u = g(x).$$

This is developed in the text on page 377.

What is $\dfrac{x^3 \, dx}{2 + x^4}$?

$\ln (2 + x^4) + C$ Frame **A**
$(1/4) \ln (2 + x^4) + C$ Frame **B**
$(1/2)(2 + x^4)^2 + C$ Frame **C**

A **YOUR ANSWER:** $\ln (2 + x^4) + C$.
You overlooked a constant. We want

$$\int \frac{x^3 \, dx}{2 + x^4} \, .$$

If $u = 2 + x^4$, then $du = 4x^3 \, dx$. The constant 4 is missing in the numerator, but it can be inserted. Therefore,

$$\int \frac{x^3 \, dx}{2 + x^4} = \frac{1}{4} \int \frac{4x^3 \, dx}{2 + x^4} \, .$$

Now return to frame **Q272**, make the proper substitution, and try again.

B **YOUR ANSWER:** $(1/4)\ln (2 + x^4) + C$.
Good.

$$\int \frac{x^3 \, dx}{2 + x^4} = \frac{1}{4} \int \frac{4x^3 \, dx}{2 + x^4} .$$

If $u = 2 + x^4$, then $du = 4x^3 \, dx$. Therefore,

$$\frac{1}{4} \int \frac{4x^3 \, dx}{2 + x^4} = \frac{1}{4} \int \frac{du}{u} = \frac{1}{4} \ln u + C$$

$$= \frac{1}{4} \ln (2 + x^4) + C.$$

C   YOUR ANSWER: $(1/2)(2 + x^4)^2 + C$.
Where did you get this? We want

$$\int \frac{x^3 \, dx}{2 + x^4} .$$

If $u = 2 + x^4$, then $du = 4x^3 \, dx$. The constant 4 is missing in the numerator, but it can be inserted. Therefore,

$$\int \frac{x^3 \, dx}{2 + x^4} = \frac{1}{4} \int \frac{4x^3 \, dx}{2 + x^4} .$$

Now return to frame **Q272**, make the proper substitution, and try again.

Q273   Since $D_x(e^x) = e^x$, we have $\int e^x \, dx = e^x + C$. What is $\int 2e^x \, dx$?

   $2e^x + C$ Frame **A** $e^{2x} + C$ Frame **B** $2e^{2x} + C$ Frame **C**

A   YOUR ANSWER: $2e^x + C$.
Of course, since $\int e^x \, dx = e^x + C$, $\int 2e^x \, dx = 2e^x + C$.

B   YOUR ANSWER: $e^{2x} + C$.
Where did you get this? We have $\int e^x = e^x + C$. Now return to frame **Q273** and find $\int 2e^x \, dx$.

C   YOUR ANSWER: $2e^{2x} + C$.
Where did you get this? We have $\int e^x = e^x + C$. Now return to frame **Q273** and find $\int 2e^x \, dx$.

Q274   Now since $D_x e^u = e^u D_x u$, we have

$$e^u \, du = e^u + C$$

where $u = g(x)$ and $du = g'(x) \, dx$.
   What is $\int 3e^{4x} \, dx$?

   $3e^{4x} + C$ Frame **A**
   $(3/4)e^{4x} + C$ Frame **B**
   $(1/4)e^{4x} + C$ Frame **C**

A   YOUR ANSWER: $3e^{4x} + C$.
Be careful. You must consider the 4 in the exponent. We have $\int 3e^{4x} \, dx = 3\int e^{4x} \, dx$. Return to frame **Q274** and try again.

B   YOUR ANSWER: $(3/4)e^{4x} + C$.
Good. $\int 3e^{4x} \, dx = 3\int e^{4x} \, dx = (3/4)\int e^{4x} 4 \, dx = (3/4)e^{4x} + C$.

C **YOUR ANSWER:** $(1/4)e^{4x} + C$.
Be careful. The derivative of $(1/4)e^{4x}$ is e^{4x}, but we want $\int 3e^{4x}\, dx$. Didn't you over-look the constant 3? Return to frame **Q274** and try again.

Q275 Can you find $\int 4xe^{3x^2}\, dx$?

      Yes   Frame **A**   No   Frame **B**

A **YOUR ANSWER:** Yes.
Great. Our integral is $\int 4xe^{3x^2}\, dx$. If $u = 3x^2$, then $du = 6x\, dx$. Therefore, we need a constant of 6.

$$\int 4xe^{3x^2}\, dx = 4 \cdot \frac{1}{6} \int 6xe^{3x^2}\, dx = \frac{2}{3} \int e^{3x^2}(6x\, dx)$$
$$= \frac{2}{3} \int e^{u}\, du = \frac{2}{3} e^{u} + C = \frac{2}{3} e^{3x^2} + C.$$

B **YOUR ANSWER:** No.
Sure you can. We want $\int 4xe^{3x^2}\, dx$. If $u = 3x^2$, then $du = 6x\, dx$. We have x in the integrand; therefore, we can fix up the integral to have the proper constant. Now return to frame **Q275**, think about the problem again, and then select the other alter-native.

Q276 Find $\int_0^1 xe^{3x^2}\, dx$.

      $(1/6)(e^3 - 1)$ Frame **A**
      $e^3 - 1$ Frame **B**
      $(1/6)(e - 1)$ Frame **C**

A **YOUR ANSWER:** $(1/6)(e^3 - 1)$.
Very good. Our integral is $\int_0^1 xe^{3x^2}\, dx$. If $u = 3x^2$, then $du = 6x\, dx$. Therefore,

$$\int_0^1 xe^{3x^2}\, dx = \frac{1}{6} \int_0^1 e^{3x^2}\, (6x\, dx).$$

When $x = 0$, then $u = 3(0)^2 = 0$, and when $x = 1$, then $u = 3(1)^2 = 3$. Hence,

$$\frac{1}{6}\int_0^1 e^{3x^2}(6x\, dx) = \frac{1}{6} \int_0^3 e^{u}\, du = \frac{1}{6} e^{u}\Big]_0^3 = \frac{1}{6}(e^3 - 1).$$

B **YOUR ANSWER:** $e^3 - 1$.
Your calculations are off. Didn't you forget a constant? Return to frame **Q276** and try again.

C **YOUR ANSWER:** $(1/6)(e - 1)$.
Your calculations are off. Didn't you forget to change the limits of integration? Return to frame **Q276** and try again.

Q277 We can use logarithms in order to find the derivatives of functions that are products, quotients, or powers of functions. The procedure is called *logarithmic differentia-tion*. An example of this technique is presented on page 381 of the text. After study-ing this example, use logarithmic differentiation to find y' if $y = (x^2 + 2)^3(1 - x^3)^4$.

How did it go?

     Good   Frame **A**   Bad   Frame **B**

A   **YOUR ANSWER:**   Good.

Excellent. If $y = (x^2 + 2)^3(1 - x^3)^4$, then

$$\ln y = 3 \ln (x^2 + 2) + 4 \ln (1 - x^3)$$

$$\frac{1}{y}y' = 3\left(\frac{2x}{x^2 + 2}\right) + 4\left(\frac{-3x^2}{1 - x^3}\right)$$

$$y' = y\left(\frac{6x}{x^2 + 2} - \frac{12x^2}{1 - x^3}\right)$$

or $y' = (x^2 + 2)^3(1 - x^3)^4\left(\frac{6x}{x^2 + 2} - \frac{12x^2}{1 - x^3}\right).$

B   **YOUR ANSWER:**   Bad.

It really isn't as bad as it looks. If $y = (x^2 + 2)^3(1 - x^3)^4$, then by considering the logarithm of both sides of the equation, we obtain

$$\ln y = 3 \ln (x^2 + 2) + 4 \ln (1 - x^3).$$

Therefore,

$$\frac{1}{y}y' = 3\left(D_x \ln (x^2 + 2)\right) + 4\left(D_x \ln (1 - x^3)\right).$$

Now return to frame **Q277**, complete the necessary calculations, and then select the other alternative.

Q278   As a review, find the following indefinite and definite integrals:

    1. $\displaystyle\int (1 - x^2)^{1/3}x \, dx.$ 2. $\displaystyle\int \frac{2x \, dx}{(x^2 + 3)}.$

    3. $\displaystyle\int_0^{\sqrt{3}} \sqrt{x^2 + 1}\, x \, dx.$ 4. $\displaystyle\int \frac{e^{1/x}}{x^2} \, dx.$

Go to frame **A** and check your work.

A   Let's see how well you did.

    1. $\int (1 - x^2)^{1/3}x \, dx.$ If $u = 1 - x^2$, then $du = -2x \, dx$. Therefore,

$$\int (1 - x^2)^{1/3}x \, dx = -\frac{1}{2}\int (1 - x^2)^{1/3}(-2x \, dx)$$

$$= -\frac{1}{2}\int u^{1/3} \, du = \frac{(-1/2)u^{4/3}}{4/3} + C$$

$$= -\frac{3}{8}u^{4/3} + C = -\frac{3}{8}(1 - x^2)^{4/3} + C.$$

    2. $\int \dfrac{2x \, dx}{x^2 + 3}.$ If $u = x^2 + 3$, then $du = 2x \, dx$. Therefore,

$$\int \frac{2x \, dx}{x^2 + 3} = \int \frac{du}{u} = \ln u + C = \ln (x^2 + 3) + C.$$

    3. $\int_0^{\sqrt{3}} \sqrt{x^2 + 1}\, x \, dx.$ If $u = x^2 + 1$, then $du = 2x \, dx$. Now when $x = 0$, $u = 1$, and when $x = \sqrt{3}$, $u = 4$. Therefore,

$$\int_0^{\sqrt{3}} \sqrt{x^2 + 1} \, x \, dx = \frac{1}{2}\int_0^{\sqrt{3}} (x^2 + 1)^{1/2}(2x \, dx) = \frac{1}{2}\int_1^4 u^{1/2} \, du$$

$$= \frac{1}{3} u^{3/2}\bigg]_1^4 = \frac{1}{3}(8 - 1) = \frac{7}{3}.$$

4. $\dfrac{e^{1/x}}{x^2} \, dx.$ If $u = 1/x$, then $du = -1/x^2 \, dx$. Therefore,

$$\int \frac{e^{1/x}}{x^2} \, dx = -\int e^{1/x}\left(-\frac{1}{x^2} \, dx\right) = -\int e^u \, du$$

$$= -e^u + C = -e^{1/x} + C.$$

8.4 GENERAL EXPONENTIAL AND LOGARITHMIC FUNCTIONS

OBJECTIVES

You should be able to use the differentiation and integration formulas for the general exponential and logarithmic functions.

Q279 We have considered the exponential function where the base is e. Now we want to consider the general exponential function a^x where a is any positive real number.

If $f(x) = a^x$,
then $f'(x) = a^x \ln a$.

This is proved on page 384 of the text. Notice that if $a = e$, we have $f'(x) = e^x \ln e = e^x$, which agrees with our previous formula. Using the Chain Rule, we find that

if $f(x) = a^u$,
then $f'(x) = a^u(\ln a)D_x u$ where $u = g(x)$.

Let's try a problem. Find y' if $y = 6^{x^2+2}$.

$y' = 6^{x^2+2}$	Frame **A**
$y' = 6^{x^2+2}(\ln 6)(2x)$	Frame **B**
$y' = (\ln 6)6^{x^2}$	Frame **C**

A **YOUR ANSWER:** $y' = 6^{x^2+2}$.
No. You left off a couple of factors. Since the base is 6, we need the factor $\ln 6$ and we also need to multiply by the derivative of the exponent $x^2 + 2$. Now return to frame **Q279** and try again.

B **YOUR ANSWER:** $y' = 6^{x^2+2}(\ln 6)(2x)$.
Correct. If $y = a^u$, then $y' = a^u(\ln a)D_x u$. Therefore,

if $y = 6^{x^2+2}$,
then $y' = 6^{x^2+2}(\ln 6)(2x)$.

C **YOUR ANSWER:** $y' = (\ln 6)6^{x^2}$.
Watch out. You have not applied the formula correctly. Return to frame **Q279**, study the formula, and then try again.

Q280 Since $D_x a^u = a^u(\ln a)D_x u$,

$$\int a^u(\ln a)\, du = a^u + C$$

or since $\ln a$ is a constant,

$$\int a^u\, du = \frac{1}{\ln a}\, a^u + C.$$

What is $\int (2^{1-x} + e^{3x})\, dx$?

$$\left(\frac{-1}{\ln 2}\right) 2^{1-x} + \frac{1}{3}e^{3x} + C \qquad \text{Frame A}$$

$$\left(\frac{1}{\ln 2}\right) 2^{1-x} + \frac{1}{3}e^{3x} + C \qquad \text{Frame B}$$

$$\left(\frac{-1}{\ln 2}\right) 2^{1-x} + e^{3x} + C \qquad \text{Frame C}$$

A YOUR ANSWER: $\left(\dfrac{-1}{\ln 2}\right) 2^{1-x} + \dfrac{1}{3}e^{3x} + C.$

Very good.

$$\int (2^{1-x} + e^{3x})\, dx = \int 2^{1-x}\, dx + \int e^{3x}\, dx$$

$$= -\int 2^{1-x}(-1)\, dx + \frac{1}{3}\int e^{3x}3\, dx$$

$$= \left(\frac{-1}{\ln 2}\right) 2^{1-x} + \frac{1}{3}e^{3x} + C.$$

B YOUR ANSWER: $\left(\dfrac{1}{\ln 2}\right)2^{1-x} + \dfrac{1}{3}e^{3x} + C.$

Sorry, but you missed a sign in the first term. Look carefully at the derivative of the exponent $1 - x$. Now return to frame **Q280** and try again.

C YOUR ANSWER: $\left(\dfrac{-1}{\ln 2}\right)2^{1-x} + e^{3x} + C.$

Didn't you forget to consider the derivative of $3x$ in the expression e^{3x}? Return to frame **Q280,** think about this, and then try again.

Q281 Let's consider the relationship between $\log_a x$ and $\ln x$. It turns out that

$$\log_a x = \frac{\ln x}{\ln a}\ .$$

This means that we can evaluate $\log_a x$ in terms of natural logarithms.

$$D_x(\log_a x) = \frac{1}{\ln a}D_x(\ln x) = \left(\frac{1}{\ln a}\right)\left(\frac{1}{x}\right) = \frac{1}{x \ln a}\ .$$

Using the Chain Rule, we have

$$D_x(\log_a |u|) = \frac{1}{u \ln a}\, D_x u$$

where $u = g(x)$ is differentiable and $g(x) \neq 0$ for all x.
Find $f'(x)$ if $f(x) = \log_2(x^3 + 2x - 1)$.

$$\frac{3x^2 + 2}{x^3 + 2x - 1} \qquad \text{Frame } \mathbf{A}$$

$$\frac{1}{(\ln 2)(x^3 + 2x - 1)} \qquad \text{Frame } \mathbf{B}$$

$$\frac{3x^2 + 2}{(\ln 2)(x^3 + 2x - 1)} \qquad \text{Frame } \mathbf{C}$$

A   YOUR ANSWER: $\dfrac{3x^2 + 2}{x^3 + 2x - 1}$.

Be careful. You have the derivative of $\ln (x^3 + 2x - 1)$. Since we have $\log_2 (x^3 + 2x - 1)$, we need the factor $\ln 2$ in the denominator. Now return to frame **Q281** and select the correct answer.

B   YOUR ANSWER: $\dfrac{1}{(\ln 2)(x^3 + 2x - 1)}$.

Sorry, but you forgot to multiply by the derivative of $g(x)$ where $f(x) = \log_2 g(x)$. Now return to frame **Q281** and try again.

C   YOUR ANSWER: $\dfrac{3x^2 + 2}{(\ln 2)(x^3 + 2x - 1)}$.

You are correct.

$$\text{If } f(x) = \log_2 (x^3 + 2x - 1),$$
$$\text{then } f'(x) = \frac{1}{(\ln 2)(x^3 + 2x - 1)}(3x^2 + 2).$$

Q282   As a review try the following:

1.   Find y' if $y = 7^{4+x^3}$
2.   Find y' if $y = \log_3 \sqrt{x^5 + 2} + e^{x^3+2}$.
3. $\displaystyle\int 2^{x^3+4}x^2 \, dx.$

Go to frame **A** and check your work.

A   How did you come out?

1. $y = 7^{4+x^3}$
   $y' = 7^{4+x^3}(\ln 7)(3x^2).$

2. $y = \log_3 \sqrt{x^5 + 2} + e^{x^3+2}$
   $= \log_3 (x^5 + 2)^{1/2} + e^{x^3+2}$
   $= \dfrac{1}{2}\log_3 (x^5 + 2) + e^{x^3+2}.$

   $y' = \left(\dfrac{1}{2}\right)\dfrac{5x^4}{(\ln 3)(x^5 + 2)} + 3x^2 e^{x^3+2}$

   $= \dfrac{5x^4}{2 \ln 3(x^5 + 2)} + 3x^2 e^{x^3+2}.$

3. $\displaystyle\int 2^{x^3+4}x^2 \, dx = \dfrac{1}{3}\int 2^{x^3+4}(3x^2) \, dx$

   $= \left(\dfrac{1}{\ln 2}\right)\left(\dfrac{1}{3}\right)2^{x^3+4} + C$

   $= \dfrac{1}{3 \ln 2} 2^{x^3+4} + C.$

Q283 Example 6 on page 387 of the text illustrates how to find the derivative when the base is a variable instead of a constant. Let's try one.

Find y' if $y = x^{x^2+3}$. How did it go?

Great   Frame **A**   Not so good   Frame **B**

A **YOUR ANSWER:** Great.

We have $y = x^{x^2+3}$. Taking the natural logarithm of both sides and differentiating implicitly, we obtain

$$\ln y = (x^2 + 3) \ln x$$

$$\frac{y'}{y} = \frac{(x^2 + 3)}{x} + (\ln x)(2x)$$

$$y' = y\left[\frac{x^2 + 3}{x} + (\ln x)(2x)\right] = x^{x^2+3}\left[\frac{x^2 + 3}{x} + (\ln x)(2x)\right].$$

B **YOUR ANSWER:** Not so good.

Probably the easiest way is to take the natural logarithm of both sides and then differentiate implicitly.

$$y = x^{x^2+3}$$

$$\ln y = (x^2 + 3) \ln x.$$

Now differentiate implicitly and then return to frame **Q283** and select the other alternative.

8.5 LAWS OF GROWTH AND DECAY

OBJECTIVES

You should be able to solve problems involving the laws of growth and decay.

Q284 The law of growth or decay of a phenomenon q can sometimes be expressed as a function of time t by the exponential

$$q(t) = q(0)a^{kt}$$

where $q(0)$ is referred to as the initial value of q.

Study the examples in the text and then try the following. The size of the population of the United States was approximately 200 million in 1970. Assuming that the exponential law of growth holds with base e and $k = 2$ percent, what will the size of the population be in the year 2000?

$200e^{60}$ million   Frame **A**   364 million   Frame **B**
200 million   Frame **C**   I need the formula.   Frame **D**

A **YOUR ANSWER:** $200e^{60}$ million.

Be careful. We need to convert 2 per cent to a decimal before using it in the formula. Now return to frame **Q284** and try again.

B **YOUR ANSWER:** 364 million.

You are correct. We want to find the size of the population in the year 2000. The formula is

$$q(t) = q(0)e^{kt}.$$

The initial value $q(0)$ is 200 million and $k = .02$. Therefore,

$$q(t) = 200e^{.02t}.$$

In order to find the size of the population in the year 2000, we use $t = 30$, which is 30 years from the initial year of 1970. Now,

$$q(30) = 200e^{.02(30)} = 200e^{.6}$$
$$= (200)(1.82) = 364 \text{ million.}$$

The value of $e^{.6}$ is found in Table II on page A31 of the text.

C **YOUR ANSWER:** 200 million.
Watch out. The initial value is 200 million. Now return to frame **Q284,** find the formula, and then the population after $t = 30$ years.

D **YOUR ANSWER:** I need the formula.
All right. The formula is

$$q(t) = q(0)e^{kt}.$$

The initial value is 200 million and $k = 2$ percent or $.02$. Therefore, the formula is

$$q(t) = 200e^{.02t}.$$

We want the population after 30 years, that is, from 1970 to 2000. Now return to frame **Q284,** find $q(30)$, and then select the correct answer.

Q285 Let's try one more. A given amount of radium will be half gone after 1600 years. If you start with 150 mg of radium, find the amount left after t years. How did it go?

Good   Frame **A**   Bad   Frame **B**

A **YOUR ANSWER:** Good.
Excellent. Using $a = 1/2$ in the formula and the unit of time a year, we have

$$q(t) = 150\left(\frac{1}{2}\right)^{kt}.$$

Since $q(1600) = 75$ (starting with 150 and half gone in 1600 years),

$$75 = 150\left(\frac{1}{2}\right)^{1600k}$$
$$\frac{1}{2} = \left(\frac{1}{2}\right)^{1600k}.$$

Thus $k = 1/1600$ and we have

$$q(t) = 150\left(\frac{1}{2}\right)^{t/1600}.$$

This is an example of an exponential law of decay.

B **YOUR ANSWER:** Bad.
It really isn't so bad. Using $a = 1/2$ in the formula and the unit of time a year, we have

$$q(t) = 150\left(\frac{1}{2}\right)^{kt}.$$

Now we need to find k. We know that $q(1600) = 75$ because half is gone after 1600 years and we started with 150. Using this information, find k, and then return to frame **Q285** and select the other alternative.

8.6   DERIVATIVES OF INVERSE FUNCTIONS

OBJECTIVES

You should know when a function has an inverse function and, if it does, how to find the derivative of the inverse function.

Q286   If a function f is continuous and increasing (or decreasing) on an interval $[a, b]$, then f has an inverse function f^{-1} which is continuous and increasing (or decreasing) on the interval $[f(a), f(b)]$. This is (8.38) and (8.40) on pages 398 and 399 of the text.
    Which one of the following functions is guaranteed to have an inverse on the given interval by the above theorem?

$f(x) = x^2$ on $[-1, 1]$ Frame **A**
$f(x) = \sqrt{x - 1}$ on $[2, 5]$ Frame **B**
$f(x) = 1 - x^2$ on $[-2, 1]$ Frame **C**

A   **YOUR ANSWER:** $f(x) = x^2$ on $[-1, 1]$.
If $f(x) = x^2$, then $f'(x) = 2x$. The derivative is not the same sign throughout the interval $[-1, 1]$. Therefore, the function is not increasing or decreasing. Notice that if we had an appropriate interval, the function would be either increasing or decreasing. Return to frame **Q286** and try again.

B   **YOUR ANSWER:** $f(x) = \sqrt{x - 1}$ on $[2, 5]$.
You are correct.

$$f(x) = (x - 1)^{1/2}$$
$$f'(x) = \frac{1}{2}(x - 1)^{-1/2} = \frac{1}{2\sqrt{x - 1}}$$

Since $f'(x) > 0$ on $[2, 5]$, f is increasing on $[2, 5]$, and by the theorem it must have an inverse function.

C   **YOUR ANSWER:** $f(x) = 1 - x^2$ on $[-2, 1]$.
No. If $f(x) = 1 - x^2$, then $f'(x) = -2x$. The derivative is not the same sign throughout $[-2, 1]$. Therefore, f is not decreasing or increasing on $[-2, 1]$. If we restricted our interval to $[0, 1]$, then f would be decreasing and f has an inverse on $[0, 1]$. Now return to frame **Q286** and try again.

Q287   The functions $f(x) = 2x^2$ and $g(x) = \sqrt{x/2}$ are inverses on $[0, \infty)$. Verify the formula (8.41),

$$g'(x) = \frac{1}{f'(g(x))},$$

for these particular functions. How did it go?
        Great   Frame **A**   Terrible   Frame **B**

A **YOUR ANSWER:** Great.

Very good. We have

$$f(x) = 2x^2 \qquad g(x) = \left(\frac{x}{2}\right)^{1/2}$$

$$f'(x) = 4x \qquad g'(x) = \left(\frac{1}{2}\right)\left(\frac{x}{2}\right)^{-1/2}\left(\frac{1}{2}\right) = \left(\frac{1}{4}\right)\left(\frac{x}{2}\right)^{-1/2}$$

Now $f'(g(x)) = 4(x/2)^{1/2}$ and thus

$$g'(x) = \left(\frac{1}{4}\right)\left(\frac{x}{2}\right)^{-1/2} = \frac{1}{4(x/2)^{1/2}} = \frac{1}{f'(g(x))}.$$

B **YOUR ANSWER:** Terrible.

Surely it isn't that bad. We have

$$f(x) = 2x^2 \qquad g(x) = \left(\frac{x}{2}\right)^{1/2}$$

$$f'(x) = 4x \qquad g'(x) = \left(\frac{1}{2}\right)\left(\frac{x}{2}\right)^{-1/2}\left(\frac{1}{2}\right) = \left(\frac{1}{4}\right)\left(\frac{x}{2}\right)^{-1/2}$$

Now verify that

$$g'(x) = \frac{1}{f'(g(x))}$$

and return to frame **Q287** and select the other alternative.

REVIEW TEST

In Exercises 1-9, find $f'(x)$.

1 $f(x) = \ln(x^3 + 2)$

2 $f(x) = \ln(2x^2 + x - 1)$

3 $f(x) = x^2 \ln x$

4 $f(x) = \ln\left(\frac{\sqrt{x + 1}}{x^2 + 3}\right)$

5 $f(x) = 3e^{-2x}$

6 $f(x) = \sqrt{1 - e^{3x}}$

7 $f(x) = x^2 e^{-3x}$

8 $f(x) = 3^{2x-1}$

9 $f(x) = \log_{10}(2x^2 - 3)$

10 Find an equation of the line tangent to the graph of $y = x^2 - \ln x$ at $P(1, 1)$.

11 Use implicit differentiation to find y' if $e^y - x^2 + 2y = 5$.

12 Find the local extrema of f where $f(x) = x^2 e^x$.

Evaluate the integrals in Exercises 13-19.

13 $\displaystyle\int \frac{x}{x^2 - 3}\, dx$

14 $\displaystyle\int \frac{5x^2}{x^3 - 1}\, dx$

15 $\displaystyle\int \frac{(1 + \ln x)^2}{2x}\, dx$

16 $\displaystyle\int_1^2 e^{4x}\, dx$

17 $\displaystyle\int e^x(e^x + 3)^3\, dx$

18 $\displaystyle\int \frac{x^2 - 2x + 3}{x}\, dx$

19 $\int 3^{x^3} x^2 \, dx$

20   Find the area of the region bounded by $y = e^x$, $y = e^{-x}$, $x = 0$, and $x = 2$.

21   If $y = \dfrac{(x^2 - 2)^3}{\sqrt{x - 1}}$, find y' by logarithmic differentiation.

22   The number of bacteria in a culture was 2000 at a certain instant and 6000 3 hours later. Assuming that the exponential law of growth holds, how many bacteria are there after t hours?

23   The functions $f(x) = x^2 + 3$ and $g(x) = \sqrt{x - 3}$ are inverse functions on $[3, \infty)$. Verify the relationship

$$g'(x) = \frac{1}{f'(g(x))} \; .$$

SAMPLE TEST

In Exercises 1-9, find $f'(x)$.

1 $f(x) = \ln (\sqrt{x - 3})$

2 $f(x) = \ln (x^3 - 2x - 5)$

3 $f(x) = \ln \left(\dfrac{x^2 - 3}{\sqrt{x - 1}} \right)$

4 $f(x) = e^x \ln (x - 3)$

5 $f(x) = 2e^{x^2}$

6 $f(x) = x^2 - 2xe^x$

7 $f(x) = \dfrac{1 - e^x}{1 + e^x}$

8 $f(x) = 2^{3x+1}$

9 $f(x) = \log_{10} (x^3 - 1)$

10   If $\ln 3.00 \approx 1.099$, use differentials to approximate $\ln 3.01$.

11   Use implicit differentiation to find y' if $\ln y + xy - x^3 = 6$.

12   Find the local extrema of f when $f(x) = x^2 e^{-x}$.

Evaluate the integrals in Exercises 13-19.

13 $\int \dfrac{x^2}{x^3 + 5} \, dx$

14 $\int_1^2 \dfrac{x - 1}{x^2 - 2x + 3} \, dx$

15 $\int \dfrac{(2 + \ln \sqrt{x})^2}{2x} \, dx$

16 $\int_0^1 e^{-3x} \, dx$

17 $\int xe^{x^2} \, dx$

18 $\int \dfrac{3x^2 + 2x - 1}{x} \, dx$

19 $\int \dfrac{3^x}{3^x + 1} \, dx$

20   Find the volume generated by revolving the plane region bounded by $y = e^{-x^2}$, $y = 0$, $x = 0$, and $x = 1$ about the y-axis.

21   If $y = (x - 1)^3 (x - 2)^2 (x + 4)^5$, find y' by logarithmic differentiation.

22   The number of bacteria in a certain culture increases from 3000 to 9000 in 8 hours. Assuming that the exponential law of growth holds, find a formula for the number of bacteria in the culture at any time t.

23   The functions $f(x) = \sqrt{x + 1}$ and $g(x) = x^2 - 1$ are inverse functions on $[-1, \infty)$. Verify the relationship

$$g'(x) = \frac{1}{f'(g(x))} \, .$$

CHAPTER 9

Other
Transcendental
Functions

9.1 LIMITS OF TRIGONOMETRIC FUNCTIONS

OBJECTIVES

You should be able to find the limits of trigonometric functions by using the basic theorems concerning limits of trigonometric functions.

Q288 There are certain limits involving trigonometric functions which are important to the development of the differentiation formulas for the trigonometric functions. Some of these are given below.

$$\lim_{t \to 0} \sin t = 0 \qquad\qquad \lim_{t \to 0} \cos t = 1$$

$$\lim_{t \to 0} \frac{\sin t}{t} = 1 \qquad\qquad \lim_{t \to 0} \frac{1 - \cos t}{t} = 0$$

Now using these limits find $\lim_{t \to 0} \dfrac{\sin (t/3)}{t}$.

$$0 \quad \text{Frame } \mathbf{A} \qquad 1 \quad \text{Frame } \mathbf{B} \qquad 1/3 \quad \text{Frame } \mathbf{C}$$

A YOUR ANSWER: 0.
No. We want

$$\lim_{t \to 0} \frac{\sin (t/3)}{t} .$$

If we divide numerator and denominator by 1/3, we can change the limit to a recognizable form:

$$\lim_{t \to 0} \frac{(1/3) \sin (t/3)}{t/3} = \frac{1}{3} \lim_{t \to 0} \frac{\sin (t/3)}{t/3} .$$

Now return to frame **Q288** and complete the problem.

B YOUR ANSWER: 1.
We know that

$$\lim_{t \to 0} \frac{\sin t}{t} = 1,$$

but we have

$$\lim_{t \to 0} \frac{\sin (t/3)}{t} \, .$$

If we could get $t/3$ in the denominator, then it would be in the proper form. Return to frame **Q288** and try again.

C   YOUR ANSWER: 1/3.
You are correct.

$$\lim_{t \to 0} \frac{\sin (t/3)}{t} = \lim_{t \to 0} \frac{(1/3) \sin (t/3)}{t/3} \quad \text{by dividing numerator}$$
$$\text{and denominator by } 1/3 \, .$$
$$= \frac{1}{3} \lim_{t \to 0} \frac{\sin (t/3)}{t/3}$$
$$= \frac{1}{3}(1) = \frac{1}{3} \, .$$

Q289   Find $\lim_{x \to 0} \dfrac{\sin x - x}{x}$.

0   Frame **A**   1   Frame **B** -1 Frame **C**

A   YOUR ANSWER: 0.
Right.

$$\lim_{x \to 0} \frac{\sin x - x}{x} = \lim_{x \to 0} \frac{\sin x}{x} - \lim_{x \to 0} \frac{x}{x}$$
$$= \lim_{x \to 0} \frac{\sin x}{x} - \lim_{x \to 0} 1$$
$$= 1 - 1 = 0.$$

B   YOUR ANSWER: 1.
Be careful. Let's use the limit of a sum is the sum of the limits. Therefore,

$$\lim_{x \to 0} \frac{\sin x - x}{x} = \lim_{x \to 0} \frac{\sin x}{x} - \lim_{x \to 0} \frac{x}{x}.$$

Now complete the problem, return to frame **Q289,** and select the correct answer.

C   YOUR ANSWER: -1.
You are off base. Return to frame **Q289,** study the limits in the text, and then try again.

9.2   DERIVATIVES OF TRIGONOMETRIC FUNCTIONS

OBJECTIVES

You should be able to find the derivatives of trigonometric functions. You should also be able to use the derivatives of trigonometric functions in applied problems involving derivatives.

Q290   First, let's look at the derivatives of the trigonometric functions sin x and cos x. When we speak of sin x or cos x, the number x is understood to be the radian measure of an angle. Therefore, x simply represents a real number. Some of the basic properties of the trigonometric functions are summarized in Appendix III in the text.

The domain of sin x and cos x is the set of real numbers. Sin x and cos x are periodic functions of period 2π; that is, they have the same functional values every 2π units. The graphs of $y = \sin x$ and $y = \cos x$ for one period are given below.

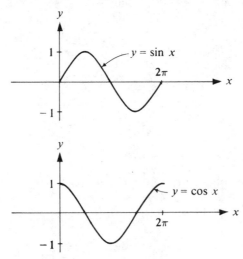

Now if $y = \sin x$, then $y' = \cos x$. This formula for the derivative of sin x is developed in the text on page 412.

What is the slope of $y = \sin x$ at $x = \pi/3$?

1/2	Frame **A**	$\sqrt{3}/2$	Frame **B**
1	Frame **C**	I don't know.	Frame **D**

A   **YOUR ANSWER:** 1/2.
You are correct. If $y = \sin x$, then $y' = \cos x$. Therefore, the slope of $y = \sin x$ at $x = \pi/3$ is cos $(\pi/3) = 1/2$.

B   **YOUR ANSWER:** $\sqrt{3}/2$.
Sorry, but your calculations are wrong. The slope of $y = \sin x$ at $x = \pi/3$ is y' evaluated at $x = \pi/3$. If $y = \sin x$, then $y' = \cos x$. What is cos $(\pi/3)$? If you are having trouble with this, study Appendix III in the text. Now return to frame **Q290** and try again.

C   **YOUR ANSWER:** 1.
Sorry, but your calculations are wrong. The slope of $y = \sin x$ at $x = \pi/3$ is y' evaluated at $x = \pi/3$. If $y = \sin x$, then $y' = \cos x$. What is cos $(\pi/3)$? If you are having trouble with this, study Appendix III in the text. Now return to frame **Q290** and try again.

D   **YOUR ANSWER:** I don't know.
The slope of $y = \sin x$ at $x = \pi/3$ is y' evaluated at $x = \pi/3$. If $y = \sin x$, then $y' = \cos x$. Therefore, we want cos $(\pi/3)$. Now return to frame **Q290**, find cos $(\pi/3)$, and

then select the correct answer.

Q291 By the Chain Rule,

$$D_x \sin u = \cos u \, D_x u \text{ and}$$
$$D_x \cos u = -\sin u \, D_x u,$$

where u is a function of x. For example, if $y = \sin (2x^3)$, then $y' = 6x^2 \cos (2x^3)$. Notice that $6x^2$ is the derivative of $2x^3$.

If $f(x) = \cos (4x)$, what is $f'(x)$?

$4 \cos x$	Frame **A**
$-4 \sin (4x)$	Frame **B**
$-4 \sin x$	Frame **C**

A **YOUR ANSWER:** $4 \cos x$.
No. We know that the derivative of $\cos x$ is $-\sin x$. Therefore, if $f(x) = \cos (4x)$, then $f'(x)$ is $-\sin (4x)$ times the derivative of $4x$. Now return to frame **Q291** and select the correct answer.

B **YOUR ANSWER:** $-4 \sin (4x)$.
Right. If $f(x) = \cos (4x)$, then $f'(x)$ is $-\sin (4x)$ times the derivative of $4x$. Therefore, $f'(x) = (-\sin 4x)(4) = -4 \sin (4x)$.

C **YOUR ANSWER:** $-4 \sin x$.
Didn't you forget to use the function of a function rule? We know that the derivative of $\cos x$ is $-\sin x$. Therefore, if $f(x) = \cos (4x)$, then $f'(x)$ is $-\sin (4x)$ times the derivative of $4x$. Now return to frame **Q291** and select the correct answer.

Q292 If $y = \sin^2 x$, what is y'? (*Hint*: $\sin^2 x = (\sin x)^2$.)

$2 \sin x$	Frame **A**
$2(\sin x)(\cos x)$	Frame **B**
$\cos^2 x$	Frame **C**

A **YOUR ANSWER:** $2 \sin x$.
Didn't you forget to multiply by the derivative of $\sin x$? If $y = (\sin x)^2$, then y' is $2(\sin x)$ times the derivative of $\sin x$. Now return to frame **Q292** and try again.

B **YOUR ANSWER:** $2(\sin x)(\cos x)$.
Correct. If $y = \sin^2 x = (\sin x)^2$, then y' is $2 \sin x$ times the derivative of $\sin x$. Therefore, $y' = 2(\sin x)(\cos x)$.

C **YOUR ANSWER:** $\cos^2 x$.
Sorry, but your calculations are off. If $y = (\sin x)^2$, then y' is $2(\sin x)$ times the derivative of $\sin x$. Now return to frame **Q292** and try again.

Q293 If $y = 3 \cos^2 x + \sin (3x^2)$, find dy/dx.

$-6(\cos x)(\sin x) + 6x \cos (3x^2)$	Frame **A**
$6 \cos x + \sin (6x)$	Frame **B**
$-6(\cos x)(\sin x) + \cos (3x^2)$	Frame **C**
I don't understand.	Frame **D**

A   YOUR ANSWER: $-6(\cos x)(\sin x) + 6x \cos (3x^2)$.

Very good. If $y = 3 \cos^2 x + \sin (3x^2)$, then

$$\frac{dy}{dx} = 6(\cos x)(-\sin x) + \cos (3x^2)(6x)$$

$$= -6(\cos x)(\sin x) + 6x \cos (3x^2).$$

B   YOUR ANSWER: $6 \cos x + \sin (6x)$.

Your calculations are off. The derivative of $3 \cos^2 x$ is $6 \cos x$ times the derivative of $\cos x$ and the derivative of $\sin (3x^2)$ is $\cos (3x^2)$ times the derivative of $3x^2$. Now return to frame **Q293** and try again.

C   YOUR ANSWER: $-6(\cos x)(\sin x) + \cos (3x^2)$.

Your calculations are off. The derivative of $3 \cos^2 x$ is $6 \cos x$ times the derivative of $\cos x$ and the derivative of $\sin (3x^2)$ is $\cos (3x^2)$ times the derivative of $3x^2$. Now return to frame **Q293** and try again.

D   YOUR ANSWER: I don't understand.

The expression dy/dx means the same as the expressions y'. We have $y = 3 \cos^2 x + \sin (3x^2)$. Find the derivatives of $3 \cos^2 x$ and $\sin (3x^2)$ and simply add. Now return to frame **Q293** and try again.

Q294   If $y = \sqrt{\cos^2 x + \sin (2x)}$, find y'. How did it go?

Great	Frame **A**	Bad	Frame **B**	Terrible	Frame **C**

A   YOUR ANSWER: Great.

Wonderful. If $y = \sqrt{\cos^2 x + \sin (2x)} = (\cos^2 x + \sin (2x))^{1/2}$, then

$$y' = \frac{1}{2}(\cos^2 x + \sin (2x))^{-1/2} \text{ times the derivative of } \cos^2 x + \sin (2x)$$

$$= \frac{1}{2}(\cos^2 x + \sin (2x))^{-1/2}[2 \cos x(-\sin x) + 2 \cos (2x)]$$

$$= \frac{-(\sin x)(\cos x) + \cos (2x)}{(\cos^2 x + \sin (2x))^{1/2}} .$$

B   YOUR ANSWER: Bad.

It isn't too bad if you take it a step at a time. Express $\sqrt{\cos^2 x + \sin (2x)}$ as $(\cos^2 x + \sin (2x))^{1/2}$. Now use the power formula and the function of a function formula. Return to frame **Q294**, complete the calculations, and select the "great" alternative.

C   YOUR ANSWER: Terrible.

Nothing is that bad. Express $\sqrt{\cos^2 x + \sin (2x)}$ as $(\cos^2 x + \sin (2x))^{1/2}$. Now if $y = (\cos^2 x + \sin (2x))^{1/2}$, then y' is $1/2(\cos^2 x + \sin (2x))^{-1/2}$ times the derivative of the expression $\cos^2 x + \sin (2x)$. Now return to frame **Q294**, complete the calculations, and select the "great" alternative.

Q295 Let's look at the derivatives of other trigonometric functions. If $u = g(x)$, we have

$$D_x \tan u = \sec^2 u \, D_x u$$
$$D_x \sec u = \sec u \tan u \, D_x u$$
$$D_x \cot u = -\csc^2 u \, D_x u$$
$$D_x \csc u = -\csc u \cot u \, D_x u.$$

You should learn each of these formulas.
   If $f(x) = \sec (x^2 + 2)$, what is $f'(x)$?

$\sec (x^2 + 2) \tan (x^2 + 2)$	Frame **A**
$2x \sec^2 (x^2 + 2)$	Frame **B**
$2x \sec (x^2 + 2) \tan (x^2 + 2)$	Frame **C**

A **YOUR ANSWER:** $\sec (x^2 + 2) \tan (x^2 + 2)$.
Almost, but you forgot to multiply by the derivative of $x^2 + 2$.

$$D_x \sec u = \sec u \tan u \, D_x u.$$

Now return to frame **Q295** and try again.

B **YOUR ANSWER:** $2x \sec^2 (x^2 + 2)$.
Haven't you used the wrong formula? Return to frame **Q295,** study the differentiation formulas, and try again.

C **YOUR ANSWER:** $2x \sec (x^2 + 2) \tan (x^2 + 2)$.
Correct. If $f(x) = \sec u$, then $f'(x) = \sec u \tan u \, D_x u$. Therefore,

$$\text{if } f(x) = \sec (x^2 + 2),$$
$$\text{then } f'(x) = 2x \sec (x^2 + 2) \tan (x^2 + 2)$$

because $D_x(x^2 + 2) = 2x$.

Q296 If $y = \tan^2 (x^3 + 1) + \csc (e^x)$, find y'. Were you successful?

Yes	Frame **A**
No	Frame **B**

A **YOUR ANSWER:** Yes.
Very good.

$$y = \tan^2 (x^3 + 1) + \csc (e^x)$$
$$y' = 2 \tan (x^3 + 1)[D_x \tan (x^3 + 1)] - \csc e^x \cot e^x \, (D_x e^x)$$
$$= 2 \tan (x^3 + 1) \sec^2 (x^3 + 1)(3x^2) - \csc e^x \cot e^x \, (e^x)$$
$$= 6x^2 \tan (x^3 + 1) \sec^2 (x^3 + 1) - e^x \csc e^x \cot e^x.$$

B **YOUR ANSWER:** No.
Let's get you started.

$$\text{If } y = \tan^2 (x^3 + 1) + \csc (e^x),$$
$$\text{then } y' = 2 \tan (x^3 + 1)[D_x \tan (x^3 + 1)] - \csc e^x \cot e^x \, (D_x e^x).$$

Now complete the problem, return to frame **Q296,** and select the other alternative.

Q297 Now let's try an application.
   The position s at time t of a particle moving on a straight line is given by

$s = 3 \sin (4t)$. What is the velocity of the particle at time $t = \pi/12$?

$6\sqrt{3}$	Frame **A**	6	Frame **B**
3/2	Frame **C**	I don't know.	Frame **D**

A   **YOUR ANSWER:** $6\sqrt{3}$.
Didn't you make a mistake in calculating the derivative when $t = \pi/12$? If $s = 3 \sin (4t)$, then the velocity is $s' = 12 \cos (4t)$. Return to frame **Q297**, evaluate s' when $t = \pi/12$, and select the correct answer.

B   **YOUR ANSWER:** 6.
Right. If the position s at a time t of a particle moving on a straight line is given by $s = 3 \sin (4t)$, then the velocity is $s' = 3 \cos (4t) \cdot 4 = 12 \cos (4t)$. Now s' evaluated when $t = \pi/12$ is $12 \cos [4(\pi/12)] = 12 \cos (\pi/3) = 12(1/2) = 6$.

C   **YOUR ANSWER:** 3/2.
Didn't you make a mistake in finding the derivative? If $s = 3 \sin (4t)$, then the velocity is $s' = 12 \cos (4t)$. Return to frame **Q297**, evaluate s' when $t = \pi/12$, and select the correct answer.

D   **YOUR ANSWER:** I don't know.
Let's see if we can help. If the position s at a time t is given by $s = 3 \sin (4t)$, then the velocity at time $t = \pi/12$ is s' evaluated when $t = \pi/12$. Now return to frame **Q297** and try again.

Q298   You should be familiar with the differentiation formulas and how to use them. As a review, find the derivatives of the following functions:

1. $y = \sin (3x) + \cos (2x)$
2. $f(x) = x^2 \sin (4x)$
3. $f(x) = \dfrac{\cos x}{x}$
4. $y = \log (\sin 3x)$
5. $y = x^2 e^{(1/2)x}$
6. $y = x \tan (\sqrt{x + 1})$

Go to frame **A** and check your work.

A   Let's see how well you did.

1.   If $y = \sin (3x) + \cos (2x)$, then $y' = 3 \cos (3x) - 2 \sin (2x)$.

2.   If $f(x) = x^2 \sin (4x)$, then
$$f'(x) = x^2 D_x(\sin 4x) + \sin(4x)D_x(x^2)$$
$$= x^2(4 \cos 4x) + (\sin 4x)(2x)$$
$$= 4x^2 \cos (4x) + 2x \sin (4x).$$

3.   If $f(x) = \dfrac{\cos x}{x}$, then
$$f'(x) = \frac{xD_x(\cos x) - \cos x\, D_x(x)}{x^2}$$
$$= \frac{x(-\sin x) - (\cos x)(1)}{x^2}$$
$$= \frac{-x \sin x - \cos x}{x^2}.$$

4.   If $y = \log (\sin 3x)$, then

$$y' = \frac{1}{\sin 3x} \cdot \frac{d(\sin 3x)}{dx} = \frac{1}{\sin 3x} \cdot 3 \cos 3x$$

$$= 3 \frac{\cos 3x}{\sin 3x} = 3 \cot 3x.$$

5.   If $y = x^2 e^{(1/2)x}$, then

$$y' = x^2 \cdot \frac{d(e^{(1/2)x})}{dx} + e^{(1/2)x} \cdot \frac{d(x^2)}{dx}$$

$$= x^2 \left(\frac{1}{2} e^{(1/2)x} \right) + e^{(1/2)x}(2x)$$

$$= \frac{1}{2} x^2 e^{(1/2)x} + 2x e^{(1/2)x}.$$

6.   If $y = x \tan (\sqrt{x + 1})$, then

$$y' = x D_x[\tan (\sqrt{x + 1})] + \tan (\sqrt{x + 1}) D_x x$$

$$= x \sec^2 (\sqrt{x + 1}) D_x(\sqrt{x + 1}) + \tan (\sqrt{x + 1})$$

$$= x \sec^2 (\sqrt{x + 1}) \frac{1}{2\sqrt{x + 1}} + \tan (\sqrt{x + 1})$$

$$= \frac{x}{2\sqrt{x + 1}} \sec^2 (\sqrt{x + 1}) + \tan (\sqrt{x + 1}).$$

9.3   INTEGRALS OF TRIGONOMETRIC FUNCTIONS

OBJECTIVES

You should be able to evaluate the integrals of trigonometric functions and use the integrals in applied problems.

Q299   We have been considering the differentiating formulas for sin x and cos x. Now let's consider the integration formulas for sin x and cos x:

$$\int \sin x \, dx = -\cos x + C$$

$$\int \cos x \, dx = \sin x + C.$$

Find $\int 2 \sin x \, dx$.

$-2 \cos x + C$	Frame **A**
$2 \cos x + C$	Frame **B**
$2 \sin x + C$	Frame **C**

A   **YOUR ANSWER:** $-2 \cos x + C$.
Of course. $\int 2 \sin x \, dx = 2 \int \sin x \, dx = -2 \cos x + C$. Notice that $2 \int \sin x \, dx$
$= 2[-\cos x + C] = -2 \cos x + 2C$, and since C is an arbitrary constant, so is $2C$.
Therefore, we simply write the result as $-2 \cos x + C$.

B   **YOUR ANSWER:** $2 \cos x + C$.
Be careful. We have $\int \sin x \, dx = -\cos x + C$ and $\int 2 \sin x \, dx = 2 \int \sin x \, dx$. Now return to frame **Q299** and try again.

C   **YOUR ANSWER:** $2 \sin x + C$.
Be careful. We have $\int \sin x \, dx = -\cos x + C$ and $\int 2 \sin x \, dx = 2 \int \sin x \, dx$. Now return to frame **Q299** and try again.

Q300   Let's try a definite integral. Find

$$\int_{\pi/4}^{\pi/2} 3 \cos x \, dx.$$

$-3\sqrt{2}/2$	Frame **A**
$3 - 3\sqrt{2}/2$	Frame **B**
$3\sqrt{2}/2 - 3$	Frame **C**

A   **YOUR ANSWER:** $-3\sqrt{2}/2$.
Sorry, but your calculations are off.

$$\int_{\pi/4}^{\pi/2} 3 \cos x \, dx = 3 \sin x \Big]_{\pi/4}^{\pi/2} = 3\left[\sin \frac{\pi}{2} - \sin \frac{\pi}{4}\right].$$

Now return to frame **Q300,** evaluate the definite integral, and then select the correct answer.

B   **YOUR ANSWER:** $3 - 3\sqrt{2}/2$.
You are correct.

$$\int_{\pi/4}^{\pi/2} 3 \cos x \, dx = 3 \sin x \Big]_{\pi/4}^{\pi/2} = 3\left[\sin \frac{\pi}{2} - \sin \frac{\pi}{4}\right]$$
$$= 3\left(1 - \frac{\sqrt{2}}{2}\right) = 3 - \frac{3\sqrt{2}}{2}.$$

C   **YOUR ANSWER:** $3\sqrt{2}/2 - 3$.
Sorry, but your calculations are off.

$$\int_{\pi/4}^{\pi/2} 3 \cos x \, dx = 3 \sin x \Big]_{\pi/4}^{\pi/2} = 3\left[\sin \frac{\pi}{2} - \sin \frac{\pi}{4}\right].$$

Now return to frame **Q300,** evaluate the definite integral, and then select the correct answer.

Q301   The same technique applies to integrals involving trigonometric functions. For example, consider $\int x \sin (x^2) \, dx$. If $u = x^2$, then $du = 2x \, dx$. Therefore,

$$\int x \sin (x^2) \, dx = \frac{1}{2} \int \sin (x^2)(2x \, dx) = \frac{1}{2} \int \sin u \, du$$
$$= -\frac{1}{2} \cos u + C = -\frac{1}{2} \cos (x^2) + C.$$

Find $\int 3x^2 \cos (3x^3) \, dx$.

$\sin (3x^3) + C$	Frame **A**
$(1/9)\sin (3x^3) + C$	Frame **B**
$(1/3)\sin (3x^3) + C$	Frame **C**

A   **YOUR ANSWER:** $\sin (3x^3) + C$.
No. You ignored the constant. We want $\int 3x^2 \cos (3x^3) \, dx$. If $u = 3x^3$, then $du = 9x^2 \, dx$. Therefore, we need a factor of 9 in the integrand. How do we handle this? Return to frame **Q301**, think about it, and then try again.

B   **YOUR ANSWER:** $(1/9)\sin (3x^3) + C$.
Almost, but you missed the constant. We want $\int 3x^2 \cos (3x^3) \, dx$. If $u = 3x^3$, then $du = 9x^2 \, dx$. Therefore, we need a factor of 9 in the integrand. We already have a factor of 3. How can we obtain 9? Return to frame **Q301**, think about this, and then try again.

C   **YOUR ANSWER:** $(1/3)\sin (3x^3) + C$.
Very good.

$$\int 3x^2 \cos (3x^3) \, dx = \frac{1}{3} \int \cos \ (3x^3)(9x^2 \, dx).$$

If $u = 3x^3$, then $du = 9x^2 \, dx$. Therefore,

$$\frac{1}{3} \int \cos (3x^3)(9x^2 \, dx) = \frac{1}{3} \int \cos u \, du = \frac{1}{3} \sin u + C$$

$$= \frac{1}{3} \sin (3x^3) + C.$$

Q302   If $u = g(x)$ and $du = g'(x) \, dx$, the other integration formulas are as follows.

$$\int \sec^2 u \, du = \tan u + C$$

$$\int \sec u \tan u \, du = \sec u + C$$

$$\int \csc^2 u \, du = -\cot u + C$$

$$\int \csc u \cot u \, du = -\csc u + C$$

What is $\int \csc (2x) \cot (2x) \, dx$?

$(1/2)\csc^2 2x + C$	Frame **A**
$(1/2)\csc (2x) + C$	Frame **B**
$(-1/2)\csc (2x) + C$	Frame **C**

A   **YOUR ANSWER:** $(1/2)\csc^2 2x + C$.
Haven't you used the wrong formula?

$$\int \csc u \cot u \, du = -\csc u + C$$

Now return to frame **Q302** and try again.

B   **YOUR ANSWER:** $(1/2)\csc (2x) + C$.
Almost, but you missed a sign.

$$\int \csc u \cot u \, du = -\csc u + C$$

Now return to frame **Q302** and try again.

C   **YOUR ANSWER:** $(-1/2)\csc (2x) + C$.
Right.

$$\int \csc (2x) \cot (2x) \, dx = \frac{1}{2} \int \csc(2x) \cot (2x)(2) \, dx$$

$$= -\frac{1}{2} \csc (2x) + C.$$

Q303   Find $\int e^x \sec^2 (e^x) \, dx$. How did it go?

       Great   Frame **A**

       I need help.   Frame **B**

A   **YOUR ANSWER:**   Great.
Excellent.

$$\int e^x \sec^2 (e^x) \, dx = \tan (e^x) + C$$

because if $u = e^x$, $du = e^x dx$ and we have

$$\int \sec^2 u \, du = \tan u + C.$$

B   **YOUR ANSWER:**   I need help.
It is really a matter of recognizing the form of the integral. If $u = e^x$, $du = e^x \, dx$ and we obtain

$$\int e^x \sec^2 (e^x) \, dx = \int \sec^2 u \, du.$$

Now complete the problem, return to frame **Q303**, and select the other alternative.

Q304   What is the area of the region bounded by $y = \sin x$, the x-axis, and the lines $x = 0$ and $x = \pi/2$?

      3/2   Frame **A**

      1   Frame **B**

      I need some help.   Frame **C**

A   **YOUR ANSWER:**   3/2.
Watch out. The area of the region bounded by $y = \sin x$, the x-axis, and the lines $x = 0$ and $x = \pi/2$ is

$$\int_0^{\pi/2} \sin x \, dx.$$

Now return to frame **Q304** and calculate the necessary definite integral.

B   **YOUR ANSWER:**   1.
Very good. The area of the region bounded by $y = \sin x$, the x-axis, and the lines $x = 0$ and $x = \pi/2$ is

$$\int_0^{\pi/2} \sin x \, dx = -\cos x \Big]_0^{\pi/2} = -\left[\cos \frac{\pi}{2} - \cos 0\right]$$

$$= -(0 - 1) = 1.$$

C   **YOUR ANSWER:**   I need some help.
All right. The area of the region bounded by $y = \sin x$, the x-axis, and the lines

$x = 0$ and $x = \pi/2$ is

$$\int_0^{\pi/2} \sin x \, dx.$$

Now return to frame **Q304** and calculate the necessary definite integral.

Q305   Now for review, evaluate the following integrals:

1. $\displaystyle\int 2x \sin (2x^2 + 3) \, dx.$

2. $\displaystyle\int_0^{\sqrt{\pi/6}} x \cos (x^2) \, dx$

3. $\displaystyle\int \sec^2 x \tan x \, dx$

4. $\displaystyle\int_0^{\pi/2} \sin^2 x \cos x \, dx$

After you complete the problems, go to frame **A** and see how well you did.

A   Let's check your work.

1. $\displaystyle\int 2x \sin (2x^2 + 3) \, dx.$ If $u = 2x^2 + 3$, then $du = 4x \, dx$. Therefore,

$$\int 2x \sin (2x^2 + 3) \, dx = \frac{1}{2} \int \sin (2x^2 + 3)(4x \, dx)$$

$$= \frac{1}{2} \int \sin u \, du$$

$$= -\frac{1}{2} \cos u + C$$

$$= -\frac{1}{2} \cos (2x^2 + 3) + C.$$

2. $\displaystyle\int_0^{\sqrt{\pi/6}} x \cos (x^2) \, dx.$

If $u = x^2$, then $du = 2x \, dx$. Now when $x = 0$, then $u = 0$, and when $x = \sqrt{\pi/6}$, then $u = \pi/6$. Therefore,

$$\int_0^{\sqrt{\pi/6}} x \cos (x^2) \, dx = \frac{1}{2} \int_0^{\sqrt{\pi/6}} \cos (x^2)(2x \, dx)$$

$$= \frac{1}{2} \int_0^{\pi/6} \cos u \, du = \frac{1}{2} \sin u \Big]_0^{\pi/6}$$

$$= \frac{1}{2} \left(\frac{1}{2} - 0 \right) = \frac{1}{4} \ .$$

3. $\displaystyle\int \sec^2 x \tan x \, dx = \int \sec x (\sec x \tan x) \, dx$

$$= \int u \, du \text{ where } u = \sec x \text{ and } du = \sec x \tan x \, dx$$

$$= \frac{u^2}{2} + C = \sec^2 \frac{x}{2} + C.$$

4. $\displaystyle\int_0^{\pi/2} \sin^2 x \cos x \, dx = \frac{\sin^3 x}{3} \Big]_0^{\pi/2}$ $(\int u^2 \, du \text{ where } u = \sin x \text{ and}$
$du = \cos x \, dx)$

$$= \frac{1}{3} - 0 = \frac{1}{3} \ .$$

9.4   INVERSE TRIGONOMETRIC FUNCTIONS

OBJECTIVES

You should be able to define and evaluate inverse trigonometric functions. You should be able to verify identities using the inverse trigonometric functions. You should also be able to sketch the graphs of the inverse trigonometric functions.

Q306   In this section, we are interested in the inverse of the trigonometric functions. However, the trigonometric functions are not one-to-one and hence do not have inverses. By restricting the domain it is possible to obtain functions that behave in the same way as the trigonometric functions over the restricted domain and that do possess inverse functions. This is discussed on page 427 of the text.

The inverse sine function, denoted by $\sin^{-1}$, is defined by:

$$\sin^{-1} x = y \text{ if and only if } \sin y = x$$

$$\text{where } -1 \leqslant x \leqslant 1 \text{ and } -\frac{\pi}{2} \leqslant y \leqslant \frac{\pi}{2} .$$

This is Definition (9.27) on page 427 of the text.
What is $\sin^{-1}(\sqrt{3}/2)$?

$\pi/3$	Frame **A**	$2\pi/3$	Frame **B**
$\pi/6$	Frame **C**	I don't know.	Frame **D**

A   **YOUR ANSWER:** $\pi/3$.
Right. $\text{Sin}^{-1}(\sqrt{3}/2) = \pi/3$ because $\sin(\pi/3) = \sqrt{3}/2$ and $\pi/3$ is in the interval $[-\pi/2, \pi/2]$.

B   **YOUR ANSWER:** $2\pi/3$.
No. $\text{Sin}(2\pi/3) = \sqrt{3}/2$, but $2\pi/3$ is not in the interval $[-\pi/2, \pi/2]$. Return to frame **Q306** and try again.

C   **YOUR ANSWER:** $\pi/6$.
Sorry, but $\sin(\pi/6) \neq \sqrt{3}/2$. You need a number such that the value of the sine function will be $\sqrt{3}/2$. Return to frame **Q306** and try again.

D   **YOUR ANSWER:**   I don't know.
$\text{Sin}^{-1}(\sqrt{3}/2)$ by definition is a number y in the interval $[-\pi/2, \pi/2]$ such that $\sin y = \sqrt{3}/2$. If you don't remember the values of the trigonometric functions for the special real numbers, they are listed in Appendix III of the text. Now return to frame **Q306** and try again.

Q307   In a similar manner, we arrive at definitions for the inverse cosine function and the inverse tangent function:

$$\cos^{-1} x = y \text{ if and only if } \cos y = x \text{ where } -1 \leqslant x \leqslant 1 \text{ and } 0 \leqslant y \leqslant \pi.$$

$$\tan^{-1} x = y \text{ if and only if } \tan y = x \text{ where } x \text{ is any real number and } -\frac{\pi}{2} < y < \frac{\pi}{2} .$$

It is also customary to refer to the inverse trigonometric functions as arcsine, arccosine, and arctangent and use the notation arcsin x, arccos x, and arctan x in place of $\sin^{-1} x$, $\cos^{-1} x$, and $\tan^{-1} x$.

Notice that the values of the arccos function are in the interval $[0, \pi]$, whereas the values of the arctan function are in the interval $(-\pi/2, \pi/2)$, which is the same as the arcsin function except for the end-points $-\pi/2$ and $\pi/2$.

Which one of the following is arccos $(-\sqrt{2}/2)$?

$-\pi/4$ Frame **A** $\pi/4$ Frame **B** $3\pi/4$ Frame **C**

A **YOUR ANSWER:** $-\pi/4$.
Be careful. Cos $(-\pi/4) = \sqrt{2}/2$ instead of $-\sqrt{2}/2$. Therefore, arccos $(-\sqrt{2}/2) \neq$ $-\pi/4$. Return to frame **Q307** and try again.

B **YOUR ANSWER:** $\pi/4$.
Be careful. Cos $(\pi/4) = \sqrt{2}/2$ instead of $-\sqrt{2}/2$. Therefore, arccos $(-\sqrt{2}/2) \neq \pi/4$. Return to frame **Q307** and try again.

C **YOUR ANSWER:** $3\pi/4$.
Right. Arccos $(-\sqrt{2}/2) = 3\pi/4$ because cos $(3\pi/4) = -\sqrt{2}/2$ and $3\pi/4$ is in the interval $[0, \pi]$.

Q308 Let's try one more. What is $\tan^{-1}(-1)$?

$3\pi/4$ Frame **A** $-\pi/4$ Frame **B** $\pi/4$ Frame **C**

A **YOUR ANSWER:** $3\pi/4$.
Be careful. The values of the arctan function are in the interval $(-\pi/2, \pi/2)$. Tan $(3\pi/4) = -1$, but $3\pi/4 \notin (-\pi/2, \pi/2)$. Return to frame **Q308** and try again.

B **YOUR ANSWER:** $-\pi/4$.
Correct. Tan$^{-1}(-1) = -\pi/4$ because tan $(-\pi/4) = -1$ and $-\pi/4 \notin (-\pi/2, \pi/2)$.

C **YOUR ANSWER:** $\pi/4$.
Sorry, but tan $(\pi/4) \neq -1$. Return to frame **Q308** and try again.

Q309 Evaluate arcsin $[\cos (\pi/6)]$.

$\pi/3$ Frame **A** $\sqrt{3}/2$ Frame **B** $\pi/6$ Frame **C**

A **YOUR ANSWER:** $\pi/3$.
Right. Arcsin $[\cos (\pi/6)] =$ arcsin $(\sqrt{3}/2) = \pi/3$.

B **YOUR ANSWER:** $\sqrt{3}/2$.
Didn't you just find cos $(\pi/6)$? We want to evaluate arcsin $[\cos (\pi/6)]$. Since cos $(\pi/6) = \sqrt{3}/2$, we want arcsin $(\sqrt{3}/2)$. Evaluate this and then return to frame **Q309** and select the correct answer.

C **YOUR ANSWER:** $\pi/6$.
No. Arcsin $[\cos (\pi/6)] \neq \pi/6$. Evaluate cos $(\pi/6)$ first and then determine arcsin $[\cos (\pi/6)]$. Now return to frame **Q309** and try again.

Q310 Examples 2 and 3 on pages 429 and 430 of the text illustrate some of the manipulations that can be carried out with the inverse trigonometric functions. Study these examples.

Now determine, without using tables, sin [2 cos^{-1} ($-3/5$)]. (*Hint*: Let $v = $ cos^{-1} ($-3/5$) and determine sin $2v$.)

24/25	Frame **A**	16/25	Frame **B**
$-24/25$	Frame **C**	I don't understand.	Frame **D**

A   **YOUR ANSWER:**   24/25.
Sorry, but you made a mistake in the sign. Check your work again and then return to frame **Q310** and try again.

B   **YOUR ANSWER:**   16/25.
Your calculations are off. Return to frame **Q310** and try again.

C   **YOUR ANSWER:** $-24/25$.
Excellent. Sin [2 cos^{-1} ($-3/5$)] $= -24/25$. If $v = $ cos^{-1} ($-3/5$), then cos $v = -3/5$ and v is in quadrant II. Now sin^2 $v = 1 - $ cos^2 $v = 1 - 9/25 = 16/25$, and since v is in quadrant II, sin $v = 4/5$. Therefore, sin $2v = 2$ sin v cos $v = 2(4/5)(-3/5) = -24/25$.

D   **YOUR ANSWER:**   I don't understand.
We want to evaluate sin [2 cos^{-1} ($-3/5$)]. Let $v = $ cos^{-1} ($-3/5$). Now we want to evaluate sin $2v$. Since sin $2v = 2$ sin v cos v, we need to determine sin v and cos v. However, since $v = $ cos^{-1} ($-3/5$), we know cos $v = -3/5$ and v is in quadrant II. We can now determine sin v since we know cos v and the quadrant that v is in. See if you can complete the problem and then return to frame **Q310** and try again.

Q311   What does cos [arctan (4/3)] equal?

3/5	Frame A
3/4	Frame **B**
4/5	Frame **C**
I don't know.	Frame **D**

A   **YOUR ANSWER:**   3/5.
Very good. Cos [arctan (4/3)] $= 3/5$. If $v = $ arctan (4/3), then tan $v = 4/3$. Therefore, we want cos v when tan $v = 4/3$. If tan $v = 4/3$, then $y = 4$ and $x = 3$ are coordinates of a point on the terminal side of v and hence $r = \sqrt{4^2 + 3^2} = \sqrt{25} = 5$. Thus, cos $v = x/r = 3/5$.

B   **YOUR ANSWER:**   3/4.
No. Let $v = $ arctan (4/3) and then calculate cos v. Now return to frame **Q311** and try again.

C   **YOUR ANSWER:**   4/5.
Be careful. Let $v = $ arctan (4/3) and then calculate cos v. Now return to frame **Q311** and try again.

D   **YOUR ANSWER:**   I don't know.
We want to evaluate cos [arctan (4/3)]. Let $v = $ arctan (4/3) and then calculate cos v. That is, we want cos v when tan $v = 4/3$. Now return to frame **Q311** and try again.

9.5   DERIVATIVES AND INTEGRALS OF INVERSE TRIGONOMETRIC FUNCTIONS

OBJECTIVES

You should be able to find the derivatives and evaluate integrals involving inverse trigonometric functions. You should also be able to use the derivatives and integrals in applied problems.

Q312   We have

$$D_x \sin^{-1} x = \frac{1}{\sqrt{1 - x^2}} .$$

This is proved on pages 431 and 432 of the text. If $u = g(x)$, where g is differentiable and $|g(x)| < 1$, an application of the Chain Rule gives us

$$D_x \sin^{-1} u = \frac{1}{\sqrt{1 - u^2}} D_x u.$$

If $y = \sin^{-1} (x^2 + 2)$, which one of the following is y'?

$$\frac{1}{\sqrt{1 - (x^2 + 2)^2}} \qquad \text{Frame } \mathbf{A}$$

$$\frac{2x}{\sqrt{1 - x^2}} \qquad \text{Frame } \mathbf{B}$$

$$\frac{2x}{\sqrt{1 - (x^2 + 2)^2}} \qquad \text{Frame } \mathbf{C}$$

A   **YOUR ANSWER:** $\dfrac{1}{\sqrt{1 - (x^2 + 2)^2}}$.

Didn't you forget to multiply by $D_x u$?

$$\text{If } y = \sin^{-1} u, \text{ then } y' = \frac{1}{\sqrt{1 - u^2}} D_x u.$$

Now return to frame **Q312** and try again.

B   **YOUR ANSWER:** $\dfrac{2x}{\sqrt{1 - x^2}}$.

Be careful. You haven't used the formula properly.

$$\text{If } y = \sin^{-1} u, \text{ then } y' = \frac{1}{\sqrt{1 - u^2}} D_x u.$$

Since $y = \sin^{-1} (x^2 + 2)$, $u = x^2 + 2$ in our formula. Now return to frame **Q312** and try again.

C   **YOUR ANSWER:** $\dfrac{2x}{\sqrt{1 - (x^2 + 2)^2}}$.

Good.

$$\text{If } y = \sin^{-1} (x^2 + 2),$$

$$\text{then } y' = \frac{1}{\sqrt{1 - (x^2 + 2)^2}} D_x(x^2 + 2) = \frac{2x}{\sqrt{1 - (x^2 + 2)^2}} .$$

Q313   If $u = g(x)$ where g is differentiable, then

$$D_x \cos^{-1} u = -\frac{1}{\sqrt{1 - u^2}} \, D_x u \quad \text{where } |g(x)| < 1$$

$$D_x \tan^{-1} u = \frac{1}{1 + u^2} \, D_x u$$

$$D_x \sec^{-1} u = \frac{1}{u\sqrt{u^2 - 1}} \, D_x u \quad \text{where } |g(x)| > 1.$$

Now let's find the derivatives of the following inverse trigonometric functions.

1. $y = \cos^{-1} x^3$
2. $f(x) = \tan^{-1} (e^x)$
3. $y = (\ln x) \cos^{-1} (x/2)$
4. $y = \sec^{-1} (\ln x)$
5. $f(t) = t^2 \tan^{-1} t^2$

After completing the problems, go to frame **A** and check your work.

A   1. $y = \cos^{-1} x^3$

$$y' = -\frac{1}{\sqrt{1 - (x^3)^2}} \, D_x x^3 = -\frac{3x^2}{\sqrt{1 - x^6}} \, .$$

2. $f(x) = \tan^{-1} (e^x)$

$$f'(x) = \frac{1}{1 + (e^x)^2} \, D_x e^x = \frac{e^x}{1 + e^{2x}} \, .$$

3. $y = (\ln x) \cos^{-1} (x/2)$

$$y' = (\ln x) D_x \cos^{-1} (x/2) + \cos^{-1} (x/2) D_x (\ln x)$$

$$= \ln x \left(\frac{-1/2}{\sqrt{1 - x^2/4}} \right) + \frac{\cos^{-1} (x/2)}{x} = \frac{-\ln x}{\sqrt{4 - x^2}} + \frac{\cos^{-1} (x/2)}{x} \, .$$

4. $y = \sec^{-1} (\ln x)$

$$y' = \frac{1}{\ln x \sqrt{(\ln x)^2 - 1}} \, D_x(\ln x) = \frac{1}{\ln x \sqrt{(\ln x)^2 - 1}} (1/x)$$

$$= \frac{1}{x \ln x \sqrt{(\ln x)^2 - 1}} \, .$$

5. $f(t) = t^2 \tan^{-1} t^2$

$$f'(t) = t^2 D_t \tan^{-1} t^2 + \tan^{-1} t^2 D_t t^2$$

$$= t^2 \left(\frac{1}{1 + (t^2)^2} \, D_t t^2 \right) + \tan^{-1} t^2 (2t)$$

$$= t^2 \left(\frac{2t}{1 + t^4} \right) + \tan^{-1} t^2 (2t)$$

$$= \frac{2t^3}{1 + t^4} + 2t \tan^{-1} t^2.$$

Q314   Using the derivatives of the inverse trigonometric functions, we can obtain the following integration formulas:

$$\int \frac{1}{\sqrt{1 - u^2}} \, du = \sin^{-1} u + C$$

$$\int \frac{1}{1 + u^2} \, du = \tan^{-1} u + C$$

$$\int \frac{1}{u\sqrt{u^2 - 1}} \, du = \sec^{-1} u + C$$

where u is restricted so that the integrand is defined. Remember, u is a function of x. The important thing in attempting to integrate is to recognize the form. You want to look at the integrand and see if you can arrange it to fit a form which is familiar.

Which one of the following integrals fits one of the forms above?

$$\int \frac{1}{1 + e^{2x}} \, dx \qquad \text{Frame } \mathbf{A}$$

$$\int \frac{x}{\sqrt{1 - x^2}} \, dx \qquad \text{Frame } \mathbf{B}$$

$$\int \frac{2x}{x^2\sqrt{x^4 - 1}} \, dx \qquad \text{Frame } \mathbf{C}$$

A YOUR ANSWER: $\int \dfrac{1}{1 + e^{2x}} \, dx$.

Almost, but it doesn't quite fit. If $u = e^x$, then $du = e^x \, dx$. Don't we need e^x in the numerator? For example,

$$\int \frac{e^x}{1 + e^{2x}} \, dx = \int \frac{1}{1 + u^2} \, du.$$

Now return to frame **Q314** and try again.

B YOUR ANSWER: $\int \dfrac{x}{\sqrt{1 - x^2}} \, dx$.

You don't need the x in the numerator. The form you are thinking about is

$$\int \frac{1}{\sqrt{1 - u^2}} \, du.$$

If $u = x$, then $du = dx$ and we have

$$\int \frac{1}{\sqrt{1 - x^2}} \, dx.$$

Now return to frame **Q314** and try again.

C YOUR ANSWER: $\int \dfrac{2x}{x^2\sqrt{x^4 - 1}} \, dx$.

You are correct. If $u = x^2$, then $du = 2x \, dx$ and we have

$$\int \frac{2x}{x^2\sqrt{x^4 - 1}} \, dx = \int \frac{1}{u\sqrt{u^2 - 1}} \, du.$$

Since

$$\int \frac{1}{u\sqrt{u^2 - 1}} \, du = \sec^{-1} u + C,$$

we have

$$\int \frac{2x}{x^2\sqrt{x^4 - 1}} \, dx = \sec^{-1} x^2 + C.$$

Q315 Evaluate the integral $\int \dfrac{x}{1 + x^4} \, dx$.

$\tan^{-1} x^2 + C$ Frame **A**
$(1/2)\tan^{-1} x^2 + C$ Frame **B**
$(1/2)\tan^{-1} x + C.$ Frame **C**

A   **YOUR ANSWER:** $\tan^{-1} x^2 + C.$
Almost, but you forgot a constant. We want to evaluate

$$\int \frac{x}{1 + x^4}\ dx.$$

If $u = x^2$, then $du = 2x\ dx$. Don't we need a factor of 2 in the numerator in order for the integral to fit the form

$$\int \frac{1}{1 + u^2}\ du?$$

Return to frame **Q315** and try again.

B   **YOUR ANSWER:** $(1/2)\tan^{-1} x^2 + C.$
Right. If we let $u = x^2$, then $du = 2x\ dx$ and we have

$$\int \frac{x}{1 + x^4}\ dx = \frac{1}{2} \int \frac{2x}{1 + x^4}\ dx = \frac{1}{2} \int \frac{1}{1 + u^2}\ du$$

$$= \frac{1}{2}\ \tan^{-1} u + C = \frac{1}{2}\ \tan^{-1} x^2 + C.$$

C   **YOUR ANSWER:** $(1/2)\tan^{-1} x + C.$
You are off base. See if you can get the integral to fit the form

$$\int \frac{1}{1 + u^2}\ du.$$

Now return to frame **Q315** and try again.

Q316   At the top of page 435 of the text, the formulas are extended as follows:

$$\int \frac{1}{\sqrt{a^2 - u^2}}\ du = \sin^{-1} \frac{u}{a} + C$$

$$\int \frac{1}{a^2 + u^2}\ du = \frac{1}{a}\ \tan^{-1} \frac{u}{a} + C$$

$$\int \frac{1}{u\sqrt{u^2 - a^2}}\ du = \frac{1}{a}\ \sec^{-1} \frac{u}{a} + C.$$

Of course, if $a = 1$, we have the previous formulas.
    Try the following problems using these formulas.

1. $\displaystyle\int \frac{x}{\sqrt{4 - x^4}}\ dx$ 2. $\displaystyle\int \frac{e^x}{4 + e^{2x}}\ dx$

3. $\displaystyle\int_0^2 \frac{1}{4 + x^2}\ dx$ 4. $\displaystyle\int \frac{1}{x\sqrt{16 - (\ln x)^2}}\ dx$

Now go to frame **A** and check your work.

A   Let's see how you came out.

1.   If we let $u = x^2$, then $du = 2x\ dx$ and

$$\int \frac{x}{\sqrt{4-x^4}}\ dx = \frac{1}{2}\int \frac{2x}{\sqrt{4-x^4}}\ dx = \frac{1}{2}\int \frac{1}{\sqrt{2^2-u^2}}\ du$$

$$= \frac{1}{2}\ \sin^{-1}\frac{u}{2} + C = \frac{1}{2}\ \sin^{-1}\frac{x^2}{2} + C.$$

2. If we let $u = e^x$, then $du = e^x\ dx$ and

$$\int \frac{e^x}{4+e^{2x}}\ dx = \int \frac{1}{2^2+u^2}\ du$$

$$= \frac{1}{2}\ \tan^{-1}\frac{u}{2} + C = \frac{1}{2}\ \tan^{-1}\frac{e^x}{2} + C.$$

3. If we let $u = x$, then $du = dx$ and

$$\int_0^2 \frac{1}{4+x^2}\ dx = \int_0^2 \frac{1}{2^2+u^2}\ du = \frac{1}{2}\ \tan^{-1}\frac{u}{2}\ \Big]_0^2$$

$$= \frac{1}{2}\ (\tan^{-1}(1) - \tan^{-1}(0))$$

$$= \frac{1}{2}\left(\frac{\pi}{4} - 0\right) = \frac{\pi}{8}\ .$$

4. If we let $u = \ln x$, then $du = (1/x)\ dx$ and

$$\int \frac{1}{x\sqrt{16-(\ln x)^2}}\ dx = \int \frac{1}{\sqrt{4^2-u^2}}\ du$$

$$= \sin^{-1}\frac{u}{4} + C = \sin^{-1}\frac{\ln x}{4} + C.$$

9.6 HYPERBOLIC FUNCTIONS

OBJECTIVES

You should be able to define the hyperbolic functions. You should be able to verify identities involving the hyperbolic functions. You should also be able to find derivatives and evaluate integrals of hyperbolic functions and use them in applied problems.

Q317 The hyperbolic sine function and the hyperbolic cosine function are denoted by

$$\sinh x = \frac{e^x - e^{-x}}{2} \quad \text{and} \quad \cosh x = \frac{e^x + e^{-x}}{2}$$

for all real numbers. These expressions arise in some physical applications.
What is $\sinh(-x)$?

e^x	Frame **A**	$-\sinh x$	Frame **B**
$\cosh x$	Frame **C**	I don't know.	Frame **D**

A   **YOUR ANSWER:** e^x.
No. We have

$$\sinh x = \frac{e^x - e^{-x}}{2}\ .$$

Now substitute $-x$ for x and simplify. After completing the problem, return to frame **Q317** and select the correct answer.

B   **YOUR ANSWER:** $-\sinh x$.
Right.

$$\sinh x = \frac{e^x - e^{-x}}{2}.$$

Therefore,

$$\sinh(-x) = \frac{e^{-x} - e^{-(-x)}}{2} = \frac{e^{-x} - e^x}{2}$$

$$= -\left(\frac{e^x - e^{-x}}{2}\right) = -\sinh x.$$

C   **YOUR ANSWER:** $\cosh x$.
No. We have

$$\sinh x = \frac{e^x - e^{-x}}{2}.$$

Now substitute $-x$ for x and simplify. After completing the problem, return to frame **Q317** and select the correct answer.

D   **YOUR ANSWER:**   I don't know.
Let's get you started.

$$\sinh x = \frac{e^x - e^{-x}}{2}.$$

Therefore,

$$\sinh(-x) = \frac{e^{-x} - e^{-(-x)}}{2}.$$

Now simplify, determine the value, and then return to frame **Q317** and try again.

Q318   The derivatives of the hyperbolic functions are given in the text on page 443.
Find the derivative of $y = \cosh(x^3 + 2)$.

$y' = \sinh(x^3 + 2)$	Frame **A**
$y' = -3x^2 \sinh(x^3 + 2)$	Frame **B**
$y' = 3x^2 \sinh(x^3 + 2)$	Frame **C**

A   **YOUR ANSWER:** $y' = \sinh(x^3 + 2)$.
No. You forgot to multiply by $D_x(x^3 + 2)$. Now return to frame **Q318** and try again.

B   **YOUR ANSWER:** $y' = -3x^2 \sinh(x^3 + 2)$.
No. The sign is different from the differentiation formula for the cosine function

If $y = \cos u$, then $y' = -\sin u\, D_x u$, but
if $y = \cosh u$, then $y' = \sinh u\, D_x u$.

Now return to frame **Q318** and try again.

C   **YOUR ANSWER:** $y' = 3x^2 \sinh(x^3 + 2)$.
Correct.

$$\text{If } y = \cosh(x^3 + 2),$$
$$\text{then } y' = \sinh(x^3 + 2)D_x(x^3 + 2)$$
$$= 3x^2 \sinh(x^3 + 2).$$

Q319 Let's try an integration problem. The formulas are given on page 443 of the text. Find

$$\int x^2 \operatorname{sech}^2(x^3)\, dx.$$

Were you successful?

    Yes   Frame **A**
    No   Frame **B**

A **YOUR ANSWER:** Yes.
Good. If $u = x^3$, then $du = 3x^2\, dx$ and

$$\int x^2 \operatorname{sech}^2(x^3)\, dx = \frac{1}{3}\int \operatorname{sech}^2(x^3)(3x^2)\, dx$$

$$= \frac{1}{3}\int \operatorname{sech}^2 u\, du$$

$$= \frac{1}{3}\tanh u + C$$

$$= \frac{1}{3}\tanh(x^3) + C.$$

B **YOUR ANSWER:** No.
Let's get the integral in the proper form. If $u = x^3$, then $du = 3x^2\, dx$ and we obtain

$$\int x^2 \operatorname{sech}^2(x^3)\, dx = \frac{1}{3}\int \operatorname{sech}^2(x^3)(3x^2)\, dx$$

$$= \frac{1}{3}\int \operatorname{sech}^2 u\, du.$$

Now using the formulas on page 443 of the text, complete the problem, return to frame **Q319,** and select the other alternative.

9.7   INVERSE HYPERBOLIC FUNCTIONS

OBJECTIVES

You should be able to find the derivatives and evaluate integrals of hyperbolic functions.

Q320 The derivatives and integrals of the inverse hyperbolic functions are presented on pages 446 and 447 of the text.
What is $D_x \sinh^{-1}(2x^2)$?

$$\frac{4x}{\sqrt{1 - 4x^4}} \qquad \text{Frame } \mathbf{A}$$

$$\frac{4x}{\sqrt{4x^4 + 1}} \qquad \text{Frame } \mathbf{B}$$

$$\frac{4x}{1 + 4x^4} \qquad \text{Frame } \mathbf{C}$$

A   **YOUR ANSWER:** $\dfrac{4x}{\sqrt{1 - 4x^4}}$.

Wait a minute. Don't you have $\sinh^{-1}(2x^2)$ confused with $\sin^{-1}(2x^2)$?

$$D_x \sinh^{-1} u = \frac{1}{\sqrt{u^2 + 1}} \, D_x u \text{ and}$$

$$D_x \sin^{-1} u = \frac{1}{\sqrt{1 - u^2}} \, D_x u.$$

Now return to frame **Q320** and find $D_x \sinh^{-1}(2x^2)$.

B   **YOUR ANSWER:** $\dfrac{4x}{\sqrt{4x^4 + 1}}$.

You are correct.

$$\text{If } y = \sinh^{-1}(2x^2),$$

$$\text{then } y' = \frac{1}{\sqrt{(2x^2)^2 + 1}} \, D_x(2x^2) = \frac{4x}{\sqrt{4x^4 + 1}} .$$

C   **YOUR ANSWER:** $\dfrac{4x}{1 + 4x^4}$.

You are on the wrong track.

$$D_x \sinh^{-1} u = \frac{1}{\sqrt{u^2 + 1}} \, D_x u.$$

Now return to frame **Q320** and use this formula.

Q321   Find $\displaystyle\int \frac{e^x}{\sqrt{e^{2x} - 4}} \, dx$.

$$\sinh^{-1} \frac{e^x}{2} + C \qquad \text{Frame } \mathbf{A}$$

$$\cosh^{-1} \frac{e^x}{2} + C \qquad \text{Frame } \mathbf{B}$$

$$\frac{1}{2} \cosh^{-1} \frac{e^x}{2} + C \qquad \text{Frame } \mathbf{C}$$

A   **YOUR ANSWER:** $\sinh^{-1} \dfrac{e^x}{2} + C$.

Watch out. Look at (9.53) and (9.56) on pages 446 and 447 of the text. Now return to frame **Q321** and select the correct answer.

B   **YOUR ANSWER:** $\cosh^{-1} \dfrac{e^x}{2} + C$.

Right. If $u = e^x$, then $du = e^x \, dx$ and

$$\int \frac{e^x}{\sqrt{e^{2x} - 4}} \, dx = \int \frac{1}{\sqrt{u^2 - 2^2}} \, du$$

$$= \cosh^{-1} \frac{u}{2} + C = \cosh^{-1} \frac{e^x}{2} + C.$$

C   YOUR ANSWER: $\frac{1}{2} \cosh^{-1} \frac{e^x}{2} + C.$

Where did you get the coefficient 1/2?

$$\int \frac{1}{\sqrt{u^2 - a^2}} \, du = \cosh^{-1} \frac{u}{a} + C.$$

Now return to frame **Q321,** arrange the integral in the proper form, and select the correct answer.

Q322   Evaluate $\int \frac{1}{25 - 9x^2} \, dx.$ How did it go?

Great   Frame **A**   Not so good   Frame **B**

A   YOUR ANSWER: Great.
Very good. If we let $u = 3x,$ then $du = 3 \, dx$ and

$$\int \frac{1}{25 - 9x^2} \, dx = \frac{1}{3} \int \frac{3}{5^2 - (3x)^2} \, dx = \frac{1}{3} \int \frac{1}{5^2 - u^2} \, du$$

$$= \frac{1}{3}\left(\frac{1}{5} \tanh^{-1} \frac{u}{5}\right) + C = \frac{1}{15} \tanh^{-1} \frac{3x}{5} + C.$$

B   YOUR ANSWER: Not so good.
We need the correct form.

$$\int \frac{1}{25 - 9x^2} \, dx = \frac{1}{3} \int \frac{3}{5^2 - (3x)^2} \, dx.$$

Now can you recognize the form? Return to frame **Q322,** study the integrals in the text, complete the problem, and then select the other alternative.

REVIEW TEST

1   Find the following limits.

(a) $\lim\limits_{t \to 0} \frac{\sin^2 3t}{t^2}$ (b) $\lim\limits_{t \to 0} \frac{\sin t - \sin t(\cos t)}{t^2}$

In Exercises 2-12, find $f'(x).$

2 $f(x) = \sin (x/3)$ **3** $f(x) = \sec (x^2 - 1)$

4 $f(x) = (\ln x) \cos (\sqrt{x})$ **5** $f(x) = (x^2 + \tan x)^3$

6 $f(x) = e^{\sin x^2}$ **7** $f(x) = \sin^{-1}(3x^2)$

8 $f(x) = e^x \cos^{-1} (x - 1)$ **9** $f(x) = \frac{\arctan x}{\ln x}$

10 $f(x) = \tan^{-1} \left(\dfrac{e^x}{1 + x^2} \right)$

11 $f(x) = \cosh (x^2 - 1)$

12 $f(x) = \tanh^{-1} (e^x)$

13 Find y' if $e^{\sin xy} + xy = 6$.

14 Find the local extrema of $f(x) = \cos^2 x - \cos x$ in the interval $0 \leqslant x < 2\pi$.

Evaluate the integrals in Exercises 15-22.

15 $\displaystyle\int \cos 5x \, dx$

16 $\displaystyle\int x \tan (2x^2) \sec (2x^2) \, dx$

17 $\displaystyle\int \tan(2x) \sec^2(2x) \, dx$

18 $\displaystyle\int_{\pi/6}^{\pi/3} \dfrac{1 + \cos x}{\sin^2 x} \, dx$

19 $\displaystyle\int_0^3 \dfrac{1}{x^2 + 9} \, dx$

20 $\displaystyle\int \dfrac{x}{\sqrt{1 - x^4}} \, dx$

21 $\displaystyle\int \dfrac{1}{x\sqrt{4x^2 - 9}} \, dx$

22 $\displaystyle\int \dfrac{\sinh (\ln x)}{x} \, dx$

23 Find the area of the region bounded by $y = \tan x$, $x = 0$, and $x = \pi/4$.

24 The region bounded by the graphs of $y = \dfrac{1}{\sqrt{x^2 + 4}}$, $x = 0$, $x = 2$, and $y = 0$ is revolved about the x-axis. Find the volume of the resulting solid.

25 Find the exact value of the following.
  (a) $\sin^{-1} (1/2)$ (b) $\cos^{-1} (-\sqrt{2}/2)$ (c) $\tan^{-1} (1)$ (d) $\sin [\arccos (1/2)]$

26 Rewrite $\cos [\arctan (1 - x)]$ as an algebraic expression in x.

SAMPLE TEST

1 Find the following limits.
  (a) $\displaystyle\lim_{t \to 0} \dfrac{\tan t}{t}$ (b) $\displaystyle\lim_{t \to 0} \dfrac{\sec t - 1}{t \sec t}$

In Exercises 2-12, find $f'(x)$.

2 $f(x) = \cos (4x^2)$

3 $f(x) = \tan (xe^x)$

4 $f(x) = x^2 \sin (\sqrt{x + 1})$

5 $f(x) = (1 + \sec x)^2$

6 $f(x) = \ln (\sin (x^2 + 1))$

7 $f(x) = \cos^{-1} (x^2)$

8 $f(x) = (\ln x)\sin^{-1} x$

9 $f(x) = \dfrac{\arctan x}{x^2}$

10 $f(x) = \sinh (x + 1)$

11 $f(x) = \tanh (2x^3 - 1)$

12 $f(x) = \sinh^{-1} (x^2)$

13 Find y' if $x \sin y + ye^x = 4$.

14 Find the local extrema of $f(x) = (\sin x)(1 + \cos x)$ in the interval $0 \leqslant x < 2\pi$.

Evaluate the integrals in Exercises 15-22.

15 $\displaystyle\int_0^{\pi/2} \sin 6x \, dx$

16 $\displaystyle\int (1 + \sec x)^3 \sec x \tan x \, dx$

17 $\displaystyle\int e^x \sin e^x \cos e^x \, dx$

18 $\displaystyle\int \frac{\sin^2 x}{\cos x} \, dx$

19 $\displaystyle\int \frac{1}{\sqrt{25 - 16x^2}} \, dx$

20 $\displaystyle\int \frac{x}{x^4 + 3} \, dx$

21 $\displaystyle\int \frac{1}{x\sqrt{x^4 - 1}} \, dx$

22 $\displaystyle\int \text{sech } 2x \tanh 2x \, dx$

23 Find the area of the region bounded by $y = x^2\sqrt{4 + x}$, $x = -4$, $y = 0$, and $x = 0$.

24 The region bounded by one arch of $y = \sin 2x$ is revolved about the x-axis. Find the volume of the resulting solid.

25 Find the exact value of the following.
(a) $\arcsin(-1)$ (b) $\cos^{-1}(1/2)$ (c) $\tan^{-1}(-\sqrt{3})$ (d) $\tan[\arcsin(1/2)]$

26 Rewrite $\sin(\arccos x)$ as an algebraic expression in x.

CHAPTER 10

Additional Techniques
and Applications
of Integration

10.1 INTEGRATION BY PARTS

OBJECTIVES

You should be able to evaluate integrals using integration by parts. You should also be able to derive reduction formulas using integration by parts.

Q323 The formula for integration by parts is given by

$$\int f(x)g'(x)\ dx = f(x)g(x) - \int g(x)f'(x)\ dx.$$

This is developed on page 453 of the text. If we let $u = f(x)$ and $v = g(x)$, we have

$$\int \underbrace{f(x)}_{u}\underbrace{g'(x)\ dx}_{dv} = \underbrace{f(x)}_{u}\underbrace{g(x)}_{v} - \int \underbrace{g(x)}_{v}\underbrace{f'(x)\ dx}_{du}.$$

or

$$\int u\ dv = uv - \int v\ du.$$

The trick is to break the integrand into two parts, u and dv, in such a manner that v can be found from dv and the integral of $v\ du$ can be obtained.

If we want to evaluate $\int xe^x\ dx$ by parts, what should we let u be in order to complete the problem?

x Frame **A** e^x Frame **B** xe^x Frame **C**

A   YOUR ANSWER: x.
You are correct. We want to evaluate $\int xe^x\ dx$.

If we let
$$u = x, \quad dv = e^x\ dx.$$

then
$$du = dx, \quad v = \int e^x\ dx = e^x.$$

Therefore,

$$\int xe^x\ dx = xe^x - \int e^x\ dx = xe^x - e^x + C.$$

B YOUR ANSWER: e^x.
This won't help. We want to evaluate $\int xe^x \, dx$.

If we let $$u = e^x, \quad dv = x \, dx,$$

then $$du = e^x \, dx, \quad v = \int x \, dx = \frac{x^2}{2}.$$

This gives us $$\int xe^x \, dx = e^x \frac{x^2}{2} - \int \frac{x^2}{2} e^x \, dx.$$

Notice that the last integral is worse than the one we started with. This isn't so good, is it? Now return to frame **Q323** and try again.

C YOUR ANSWER: xe^x.
This will not work. This choice will produce an integral which is worse than the one we started with. Return to frame **Q323** and try again.

Q324 Evaluate $\int x \sin x \, dx$. How did it come out?

  Good   Frame **A**   I need help.   Frame **B**

A YOUR ANSWER: Good.
Excellent. We want to find $\int x \sin x \, dx$.

If we let $$u = x, \quad dv = \sin x \, dx,$$

then $$du = dx, \quad v = \int \sin x \, dx = -\cos x.$$

Therefore, $$\int x \sin x \, dx = x(-\cos x) - \int (-\cos x) \, dx$$

$$= -x \cos x + \int \cos x \, dx$$

$$= -x \cos x + \sin x + C.$$

B YOUR ANSWER: I need help.
We want to evaluate $\int x \sin x \, dx$. There are two obvious choices for u and dv, namely,

$$(1) \ u = x, \quad dv = \sin x \, dx$$
$$(2) \ u = \sin x, \quad dv = x \, dx.$$

If we choose (2), we have

$$u = \sin x, \ dv = x \, dx$$

$$du = \cos x \, dx, \ v = \int x \, dx = \frac{x^2}{2}$$

and thus $$\int x \sin x \, dx = (\sin x)\left(\frac{x^2}{2}\right) - \int \left(\frac{x^2}{2}\right)(\cos x) \, dx.$$

The latter integral is certainly no easier than the given one. Return to frame **Q324**, choose (1), complete the integration by parts, and then select the other alternative.

Q325 Let's try a few integrals:

1. $\int x \ln x \, dx$

2. $\int \frac{x^3}{\sqrt{1 + x^2}} \, dx$

3. $\int e^x \sin x\, dx$.

Now go to frame **A** and check your results.

A   Let's see how you did.

1. $\int x \ln x\, dx$.

If we let

$$u = \ln x, \quad dv = x\, dx,$$

then

$$du = \frac{1}{x}\, dx, \quad v = \int x\, dx = \frac{x^2}{2}.$$

Therefore,

$$\int x \ln x\, dx = \frac{x^2}{2} \ln x - \int \frac{x^2}{2} \frac{1}{x}\, dx$$

$$= \frac{x^2}{2} \ln x - \int \frac{x}{2}\, dx = \frac{x^2}{2} \ln x - \frac{x^2}{4} + C.$$

2. $\int \frac{x^3}{\sqrt{1 + x^2}}\, dx$.

If we let

$$u = x^2, \quad dv = \frac{x}{\sqrt{1 + x^2}}\, dx,$$

then

$$du = 2x\, dx, \quad v = \int (1 + x^2)^{-1/2} x\, dx = (1 + x^2)^{1/2}.$$

Therefore,

$$\int \frac{x^3}{\sqrt{1 + x^2}}\, dx = x^2 (1 + x^2)^{1/2} - \int (1 + x^2)^{1/2} 2x\, dx$$

$$= x^2 (1 + x^2)^{1/2} - \frac{2}{3}(1 + x^2)^{3/2} + C.$$

3. $\int e^x \sin x\, dx$.

If we let

$$u = e^x, \quad dv = \sin x\, dx,$$

then

$$du = e^x\, dx, \quad v = \int \sin x\, dx = -\cos x.$$

Therefore,

$$\int e^x \sin x\, dx = -e^x \cos x + \int e^x \cos x\, dx.$$

Now use parts again on $\int e^x \cos x\, dx$.

If we let

$$u = e^x, \quad dv = \cos x\, dx,$$

then

$$du = e^x\, dx, \quad v = \int \cos x\, dx = \sin x.$$

Therefore,

$$\int e^x \cos x\, dx = e^x \sin x - \int e^x \sin x\, dx.$$

Putting this all together, we have

$$\int e^x \sin x\, dx = -e^x \cos x + e^x \sin x - \int e^x \sin x\, dx$$

or

$$2\int e^x \sin x\, dx = -e^x \cos x + e^x \sin x$$

$$\int e^x \sin x\, dx = -\frac{1}{2} e^x \cos x + \frac{1}{2} e^x \sin x + C.$$

10.2   TRIGONOMETRIC INTEGRALS

OBJECTIVES

You should be able to evaluate integrals involving trigonometric functions.

Q326   Odd powers of sin x or cos x can be integrated fairly easily. Example 1 on page 460 of the text illustrates the technique. Now find

$$\int \sin^7 x \, dx.$$

Were you successful?

    Yes   Frame **A**   No   Frame **B**

A **YOUR ANSWER:** Yes.
Very good.

$$\int \sin^7 x \, dx = \int \sin^6 x \sin x \, dx$$

$$= \int (\sin^2 x)^3 \sin x \, dx$$

$$= \int (1 - \cos^2 x)^3 \sin x \, dx$$

$$= \int [1 - 3 \cos^2 x + 3 \cos^4 x - \cos^6 x] \sin x \, dx.$$

Now if we let $u = \cos x$, then $du = -\sin x \, dx$ and we have

$$\int \sin^7 x \, dx = \int [-1 + 3 \cos^2 x - 3 \cos^4 x + \cos^6 x](-\sin x) \, dx$$

$$= \int (-1 + 3u^2 - 3u^4 + u^6) \, du$$

$$= -u + u^3 - \frac{3}{5} u^5 + \frac{1}{7} u^7 + C$$

$$= -\cos x + \cos^3 x - \frac{3}{5} \cos^5 x + \frac{1}{7} \cos^7 x + C.$$

B **YOUR ANSWER:** No.
It isn't too bad if you start properly.

$$\int \sin^7 x \, dx = \int \sin^6 x \sin x \, dx = \int (\sin^2 x)^3 \sin x \, dx.$$

Now use $\sin^2 x = 1 - \cos^2 x$, simplify, and obtain a form which is easy to integrate. Think about this and then return to frame **Q326** and try again.

Q327   If the integral is an even power of sin x or cos x, then the half-angle formulas

$$\sin^2 x = \frac{1 - \cos 2x}{2} \quad \text{or} \quad \cos^2 x = \frac{1 + \cos 2x}{2}$$

may be used to simplify the integral. Examples 2 and 3 on page 461 of the text illustrate the procedure. Find

$$\int \sin^2 x \, dx.$$

How did it go?

Great   Frame **A**

I need help.   Frame **B**

A   YOUR ANSWER: Great.

Very good. Using $\sin^2 x = (1 - \cos 2x)/2$, we obtain

$$\int \sin^2 x \, dx = \frac{1}{2} \int (1 - \cos 2x) \, dx = \frac{1}{2}x - \frac{1}{4} \sin 2x + C.$$

B   YOUR ANSWER: I need help.

If the integrand is an even power of sin x, we use

$$\sin^2 x = \frac{1 - \cos 2x}{2}.$$

We have

$$\int \sin^2 x \, dx = \frac{1}{2} \int (1 - \cos 2x) \, dx.$$

Now integrate term by term and return to frame **Q327** and select the other alternative.

Q328   Let's try one where the integrand is a product of powers of sin x and cos x. Find

$$\int \cos^2 x \sin^3 x \, dx.$$

If you have trouble, study Example 4 on page 462 of the text. After completing the problem, go to frame **A** and check your work.

A

$$\int \cos^2 x \sin^3 x \, dx = \int \cos^2 x \sin^2 x \, (\sin x) \, dx$$

$$= \int \cos^2 x (1 - \cos^2 x)(\sin x) \, dx$$

$$= \int (\cos^2 x - \cos^4 x)(\sin x) \, dx$$

If we let $u = \cos x$, then $du = -\sin x \, dx$ and

$$\int \cos^2 x \sin^3 x \, dx = \int (-\cos^2 x + \cos^4 x)(-\sin x) \, dx$$

$$= \int (-u^2 + u^4) \, du$$

$$= -\frac{1}{3}u^3 + \frac{1}{5}u^5 + C$$

$$= -\frac{1}{3} \cos^3 x + \frac{1}{5} \cos^5 x + C.$$

10.3   TRIGONOMETRIC SUBSTITUTIONS

OBJECTIVES

You should be able to evaluate integrals using trigonometric substitutions. You should also be able to evaluate integrals by means of hyperbolic substitutions.

Q329 If an integrand contains the expression $\sqrt{a^2 - x^2}$, where $a > 0$, then the substitution $x = a \sin \theta$ eliminates the radical. Find

$$\int \frac{x}{\sqrt{16 - x^2}} \, dx.$$

Were you successful?

Yes   Frame **A**   No   Frame **B**

A **YOUR ANSWER:** Yes.
Good. We want to find

$$\int \frac{x}{\sqrt{16 - x^2}} \, dx.$$

If we let $x = 4 \sin \theta$, then $dx = 4 \cos \theta \, d\theta$ and we have

$$16 - x^2 = 16 - 16 \sin^2 \theta = 16(1 - \sin^2 \theta) = 16 \cos^2 \theta.$$

Now

$$\int \frac{x}{\sqrt{16 - x^2}} \, dx = \int \frac{4 \sin \theta}{\sqrt{16 \cos^2 \theta}} \, 4 \cos \theta \, d\theta$$

$$= \int \frac{4 \sin \theta}{4 \cos \theta} \, 4 \cos \theta \, d\theta$$

$$= \int 4 \sin \theta \, d\theta$$

$$= -4 \cos \theta + C.$$

If $x = 4 \sin \theta$, we have

and hence $\cos \theta = \sqrt{16 - x^2}/4$. Therefore,

$$\int \frac{x}{\sqrt{16 - x^2}} \, dx = -4 \left(\frac{\sqrt{16 - x^2}}{4} \right) + C = -\sqrt{16 - x^2} + C.$$

B **YOUR ANSWER:** No.
It is a matter of making the proper substitution. Since we want to evaluate

$$\int \frac{x}{\sqrt{16 - x^2}} \, dx,$$

we use the substitution $x = 4 \sin \theta$. This gives us

$$16 - x^2 = 16 - 16 \sin^2 \theta = 16(1 - \sin^2 \theta) = 16 \cos^2 \theta.$$

Therefore, the use of this substitution will eliminate the radical. Now return to frame **Q329** and try again.

Q330 If an integral contains $\sqrt{a^2 + x^2}$, where $a > 0$, then the substitution $x = a \tan \theta$ will eliminate the radical. Example 2 on page 467 of the text illustrates this substitution. Now find

$$\int \sqrt{x^2 + 9} \, dx.$$

How did it go?

    Good   Frame **A**   Bad   Frame **B**

A **YOUR ANSWER:** Good.

All right. Let's check your work. We want to evaluate

$$\int \sqrt{x^2 + 9} \, dx.$$

If we let $x = 3 \tan \theta$, then $dx = 3 \sec^2 \theta \, d\theta$ and we have

$$x^2 + 9 = 9 \tan^2 \theta + 9 = 9(\tan^2 \theta + 1) = 9 \sec^2 \theta.$$

Therefore,

$$\int \sqrt{x^2 + 9} \, dx = \int \sqrt{9 \sec^2 \theta} \, (3 \sec^2 \theta) \, d\theta$$

$$= \int (3 \sec \theta)(3 \sec^2 \theta) \, d\theta$$

$$= 9 \int \sec^3 \theta \, d\theta$$

We need to use parts to integrate $\int \sec^3 \theta \, d\theta$.

If we let $u = \sec \theta$, $dv = \sec^2 \theta \, d\theta$,

then $du = \sec \theta \tan \theta \, d\theta$, $v = \tan \theta$.

Therefore,

$$\int \sec^3 \theta \, d\theta = \sec \theta \tan \theta - \int \sec \theta \tan^2 \theta \, d\theta$$

$$= \sec \theta \tan \theta - \int \sec \theta (\sec^2 \theta - 1) \, d\theta$$

$$= \sec \theta \tan \theta - \int \sec^3 \theta \, d\theta + \int \sec \theta \, d\theta$$

$$= \sec \theta \tan \theta - \int \sec^3 \theta \, d\theta + \ln |\sec \theta + \tan \theta| + C.$$

Combining terms, we have

$$2 \int \sec^3 \theta \, d\theta = \sec \theta \tan \theta + \ln |\sec \theta + \tan \theta| + C$$

or

$$\int \sec^3 \theta \, d\theta = \frac{1}{2} \sec \theta \tan \theta + \frac{1}{2} \ln |\sec \theta + \tan \theta| + C.$$

Therefore,

$$\int \sqrt{x^2 + 9} \, dx = 9 \int \sec^3 \theta \, d\theta = \frac{9}{2} \sec \theta \tan \theta + \frac{9}{2} \ln |\sec \theta + \tan \theta| + C.$$

Since $\tan \theta = x/3$, we have

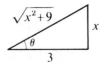

and hence $\sec \theta = \sqrt{x^2 + 9}/3$ and we obtain

$$\int \sqrt{x^2 + 9} \, dx = \frac{9}{2} \left(\frac{\sqrt{x^2 + 9}}{3} \right) \left(\frac{x}{3} \right) + \frac{9}{2} \ln \left| \frac{\sqrt{x^2 + 9}}{3} + \frac{x}{3} \right| + C$$

$$= \frac{x\sqrt{x^2 + 9}}{2} + \frac{9}{2} \ln \left| \frac{\sqrt{x^2 + 9} + x}{3} \right| + C.$$

B   YOUR ANSWER: Bad.
It isn't really as bad as you think. We want to evaluate

$$\int \sqrt{x^2 + 9} \, dx.$$

If we let $x = 3 \tan \theta$, then $dx = 3 \sec^2 \theta \, d\theta$ and we have

$$x^2 + 9 = 9 \tan^2 \theta + 9 = 9(\tan^2 \theta + 1) = 9 \sec^2 \theta.$$

Therefore,

$$\int \sqrt{x^2 + 9} \, dx = \int \sqrt{9 \sec^2 \theta} \, (3 \sec^2 \theta) \, d\theta$$

$$= \int (3 \sec \theta)(3 \sec^2 \theta) \, d\theta$$

$$= 9 \int \sec^3 \theta.$$

This integral can be handled by parts. Now return to frame **Q330**, complete the problem, and then select the other alternative.

Q331   If the integrand contains $\sqrt{x^2 - a^2}$, then the substitution $x = a \sec \theta$ will eliminate the radical. Study Example 3 in the text. Now let's try one. Find

$$\int x \sqrt{x^2 - 16} \, dx.$$

Were you successful?
    Yes   Frame **A**
    No   Frame **B**

A   YOUR ANSWER: Yes.
Very good. If we want to find

$$\int x \sqrt{x^2 - 16} \, dx,$$

let $x = 4 \sec \theta$. Then $dx = 4 \sec \theta \tan \theta \, d\theta$ and

$$x^2 - 16 = 16 \sec^2 \theta - 16 = 16(\sec^2 \theta - 1) = 16 \tan^2 \theta.$$

Therefore,

$$\int x\sqrt{x^2 - 16}\, dx = \int 4 \sec \theta \sqrt{16 \tan^2 \theta}(4 \sec \theta \tan \theta)\, d\theta$$

$$= 64 \int \tan^2 \theta \sec^2 \theta\, d\theta$$

$$= 64 \int u^2\, du, \text{ where } u = \tan \theta \text{ and } du = \sec^2 \theta\, d\theta,$$

$$= \frac{64}{3} u^3 + C$$

$$= \frac{64}{3} \tan^3 \theta + C.$$

Since $\sec \theta = x/4$, we have

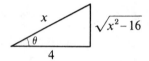

and hence $\tan \theta = \sqrt{x^2 - 16}/4$. Therefore,

$$\int x\sqrt{x^2 - 16}\, dx = \frac{64}{3} \frac{(x^2 - 16)^{3/2}}{64} + C = \frac{1}{3}(x^2 - 16)^{3/2} + C.$$

B   YOUR ANSWER: No.
Simplifying the integral into an integrable form depends on the proper substitution. If we want to evaluate

$$\int x\sqrt{x^2 - 16}\, dx,$$

then we let $x = 4 \sec \theta$. If $x = 4 \sec \theta$, then $dx = 4 \sec \theta \tan \theta\, d\theta$. Now return to frame **Q331**, make these substitutions, evaluate the integral, and then select the other alternative.

Q332   If the integrand contains $\sqrt{a^2 - x^2}$, we let $x = a \sin \theta$.
If the integrand contains $\sqrt{a^2 + x^2}$, we let $x = a \tan \theta$.
If the integrand contains $\sqrt{x^2 - a^2}$, we let $x = a \sec \theta$.

Now as a review, if we want to evaluate

$$\int \frac{x}{\sqrt{x^2 + 16}}\, dx,$$

which substitution do we make?

   $x = 4 \sin \theta$ Frame **A**
   $x = 4 \tan \theta$ Frame **B**
   $x = 4 \sec \theta$ Frame **C**

A   YOUR ANSWER: $x = 4 \sin \theta$.
Be careful. If the integrand contained $\sqrt{16 - x^2}$, then we would use the substitution $x = 4 \sin \theta$. Return to frame **Q332**, study the different substitutions, and then select the correct answer.

B   YOUR ANSWER: $x = 4 \tan \theta$.
You are correct. We want to evaluate

$$\int \frac{x}{\sqrt{x^2 + 16}} \, dx.$$

If $x = 4 \tan \theta$, then $dx = 4 \sec^2 \theta \, d\theta$ and we have

$$x^2 + 16 = 16 \tan^2 \theta + 16 = 16(\tan^2 \theta + 1) = 16 \sec^2 \theta.$$

Therefore,

$$\int \frac{4 \tan \theta}{\sqrt{16 \sec^2 \theta}} \, 4 \sec^2 \theta \, d\theta = 4 \int \frac{\tan \theta}{\sec \theta} \sec^2 \theta \, d\theta$$

$$= 4 \int \tan \theta \sec \theta \, d\theta.$$

Now we have an integral which can be easily evaluated.

C   YOUR ANSWER: $x = 4 \sec \theta$.
Be careful. If the integrand contained $\sqrt{x^2 - 16}$, then we would use the substitution $x = 4 \sec \theta$. Return to frame **Q332**, study the different substitutions, and then select the correct answer.

10.4   PARTIAL FRACTIONS

OBJECTIVES

You should know the definition of a partial fraction and be able to find the partial fraction decomposition of a rational expression. You should be able to evaluate integrals using partial fractions.

Q333   We use the technique referred to as partial fractions when we want the integral of a rational expression $f(x)/g(x)$ where the degree of $f(x)$ is less than the degree of $g(x)$. If this is not the case, then division should be used to obtain such an expression. The technique is discussed on pages 471 and 472 of the text.
Let's find

$$\int \frac{2x^2 - 3x + 1}{x(x + 1)^2} \, dx.$$

First we need the partial fraction decomposition. Which one of the following is the decomposition of

$$\frac{2x^2 - 3x + 1}{x(x + 1)^2} \, ?$$

$$\frac{A}{x} + \frac{B}{x + 1} + \frac{C}{x + 1} \qquad \text{Frame } \mathbf{A}$$

$$\frac{A}{x} + \frac{B}{x + 1} + \frac{C}{(x + 1)^2} \qquad \text{Frame } \mathbf{B}$$

$$\frac{A}{x} + \frac{B}{(x + 1)^2} \qquad \text{Frame } \mathbf{C}$$

A   YOUR ANSWER: $\dfrac{A}{x} + \dfrac{B}{x + 1} + \dfrac{C}{x + 1}$.
No. In the expression

$$\frac{2x^2 - 3x + 1}{x(x + 1)^2} ,$$

we have the factor $(x + 1)^2$ in the denominator; therefore, we must have a fraction in the decomposition for each power of $x + 1$. That is, one for $x + 1$ and one for $(x + 1)^2$. Now return to frame **Q333** and try again.

B YOUR ANSWER: $\dfrac{A}{x} + \dfrac{B}{x + 1} + \dfrac{C}{(x + 1)^2}$.

Right.

$$\frac{2x^2 - 3x + 1}{x(x + 1)^2} = \frac{A}{x} + \frac{B}{x + 1} + \frac{C}{(x + 1)^2} .$$

There must be a fraction for each power of the factor $x + 1$. Now let's find A, B, and C.

$$\frac{A}{x} + \frac{B}{x + 1} + \frac{C}{(x + 1)^2} = \frac{A(x + 1)^2 + Bx(x + 1) + Cx}{x(x + 1)^2}$$

$$= \frac{(A + B)x^2 + (2A + B + C)x + A}{x(x + 1)^2} .$$

Therefore,

$$\begin{cases} A + B & = 2 \\ 2A + B + C & = -3 \\ A & = 1. \end{cases}$$

From these equations, we obtain $A = 1$, $B = 1$, and $C = -6$, and thus

$$\frac{2x^2 - 3x + 1}{x(x + 1)^2} = \frac{1}{x} + \frac{1}{x + 1} - \frac{6}{(x + 1)^2} .$$

C YOUR ANSWER: $\dfrac{A}{x} + \dfrac{B}{(x + 1)^2}$.

No. In the expression

$$\frac{2x^2 - 3x + 1}{x(x + 1)^2}$$

we have the factor $(x + 1)^2$ in the denominator; therefore, we must have a fraction in the decomposition for each power of $x + 1$. That is, one for $x + 1$ and one for $(x + 1)^2$. Now return to frame **Q333** and try again.

Q334 From the above, we have

$$\int \frac{2x^2 - 3x + 1}{x(x + 1)^2} \, dx = \int \frac{1}{x} \, dx + \int \frac{1}{x + 1} \, dx - \int \frac{6}{(x + 1)^2} \, dx.$$

Can you find the value of the integral?

    Of course.   Frame **A**
    I'm not sure.   Frame **B**

A YOUR ANSWER: Of course.
Good.

$$\int \frac{2x^2 - 3x + 1}{x(x + 1)^2} \, dx = \int \frac{1}{x} \, dx + \int \frac{1}{x + 1} \, dx - \int \frac{6}{(x + 1)^2} \, dx$$

$$= \ln x + \ln (x + 1) - \frac{6(x + 1)^{-1}}{-1} + C$$

$$= \ln x(x + 1) + \frac{6}{x + 1} + C.$$

B YOUR ANSWER: I'm not sure.

We have

$$\int \frac{2x^2 - 3x + 1}{x(x + 1)^2} \, dx = \int \frac{1}{x} \, dx + \int \frac{1}{x + 1} \, dx - \int \frac{6}{(x + 1)^2} \, dx.$$

You simply need to evaluate each integral on the right term by term. The first two integrals are in the ln form and the last is in the power form. Now return to frame **Q334** and try again.

Q335 Which one of the following is the partial fractional decomposition of

$$\frac{2x^3 + 6x^2 - x + 1}{(x + 1)(x - 2)^2(x^2 + 3)} \, ?$$

$$\frac{A}{x + 1} + \frac{B}{(x - 2)^2} + \frac{C}{x^2 + 3} \qquad \text{Frame A}$$

$$\frac{A}{x + 1} + \frac{B}{x - 2} + \frac{C}{(x - 2)^2} + \frac{D}{x^2 + 3} \qquad \text{Frame B}$$

$$\frac{A}{x + 1} + \frac{B}{x - 2} + \frac{C}{(x - 2)^2} + \frac{Dx + E}{x^2 + 3} \qquad \text{Frame C}$$

A YOUR ANSWER: $\dfrac{A}{x + 1} + \dfrac{B}{(x - 2)^2} + \dfrac{C}{x^2 + 3}$.

You have two mistakes. We need two partial fractions for the factor $(x - 2)^2$, and the numerator of the partial fraction for the factor $x^2 + 3$ must be a linear factor in x. Now return to frame **Q335**, study the rules for decomposition in the text, and then try again.

B YOUR ANSWER: $\dfrac{A}{x + 1} + \dfrac{B}{x - 2} + \dfrac{C}{(x - 2)^2} + \dfrac{D}{x^2 + 3}$.

Almost, but the numerator of the partial fraction for the factor $x^2 + 3$ must be a linear factor in x. Now return to frame **Q335**, study the rules for decomposition in the text, and then try again.

C YOUR ANSWER: $\dfrac{A}{x + 1} + \dfrac{B}{x - 2} + \dfrac{C}{(x - 2)^2} + \dfrac{Dx + E}{x^2 + 3}$.

You are correct.

$$\frac{2x^3 + 6x^2 - x + 1}{(x + 1)(x - 2)^2(x^2 + 3)} = \frac{A}{x + 1} + \frac{B}{x - 2} + \frac{C}{(x - 2)^2} + \frac{Dx + E}{x^2 + 3}$$

Notice that we have a partial fraction for each power of $(x - 2)$, and the numerator of the partial fraction for the factor $x^2 + 3$ is a linear expression.

Q336 Now let's find the value of an integral using partial fractions. What is the value of

$$\int \frac{x^2 + x + 1}{(2x + 1)(x^2 + 1)} \, dx?$$

After completing the problem, go to frame **A** and check your work.

A   We have

$$\frac{x^2 + x + 1}{(2x + 1)(x^2 + 1)} = \frac{A}{2x + 1} + \frac{Bx + C}{x^2 + 1}.$$

Combining the right side of the equation gives us

$$\frac{x^2 + x + 1}{(2x + 1)(x^2 + 1)} = \frac{(A + 2B)x^2 + (B + 2C)x + (A + C)}{(2x + 1)(x^2 + 1)}.$$

In order for these two fractions to be equal, the numerators must be equal and hence

$$\begin{cases} A + 2B & = 1 \\ B + 2C = 1 \\ A \quad\quad + C = 1. \end{cases}$$

Solving this system, we obtain $A = 3/5$, $B = 1/5$, and $C = 2/5$. Therefore,

$$\int \frac{x^2 + x + 1}{(2x + 1)(x^2 + 1)} \, dx = \frac{3}{5} \int \frac{1}{2x + 1} \, dx + \frac{1}{5} \int \frac{x}{x^2 + 1} \, dx + \frac{2}{5} \int \frac{1}{x^2 + 1} \, dx$$

$$= \frac{3}{5} \left(\frac{1}{2} \ln |2x + 1| \right) + \frac{1}{5} \left(\frac{1}{2} \ln (x^2 + 1) \right) + \frac{2}{5} \tan^{-1} x + C$$

$$= \frac{3}{10} \ln |2x + 1| + \frac{1}{10} \ln (x^2 + 1) + \frac{2}{5} \tan^{-1} x + C.$$

10.5   QUADRATIC EXPRESSIONS

OBJECTIVES

You should be able to evaluate integrals involving quadratic expressions.

Q337   If the integrand contains an irreducible quadratic expression, then completing the square may lead to one of our previous forms. Examples 1, 2, and 3 on pages 478 and 479 of the text illustrate this procedure.
   Let's try one. Find

$$\int \frac{x}{4x^2 + 8x + 13} \, dx.$$

Were you successful?

     Yes   Frame **A**   I need help.   Frame **B**

A   **YOUR ANSWER:**   Yes.
Excellent. We want to find

$$\int \frac{x}{4x^2 + 8x + 13} \, dx.$$

Completing the square, we have $4x^2 + 8x + 13 = 4(x^2 + 2x \quad\quad) + 13 = 4(x^2 + 2x + 1) + 13 - 4 = 4(x + 1)^2 + 9$, and thus

$$\int \frac{x}{4x^2 + 8x + 13}\, dx = \int \frac{x}{4(x+1)^2 + 9}\, dx.$$

If we let $u = x + 1$, then $du = dx$ and

$$\int \frac{x}{4x^2 + 8x + 13}\, dx = \int \frac{u-1}{4u^2 + 9}\, du$$

$$= \int \frac{u}{4u^2 + 9}\, du - \int \frac{1}{4u^2 + 9}\, du$$

$$= \frac{1}{8} \int \frac{8u}{4u^2 + 9}\, du - \frac{1}{4} \int \frac{1}{u^2 + (9/4)}\, du$$

$$= \frac{1}{8} \ln (4u^2 + 9) - \frac{1}{4}\left(\frac{2}{3}\, \tan^{-1} \frac{2u}{3}\right) + C$$

$$= \frac{1}{8} \ln |4x^2 + 8x + 13| - \frac{1}{6}\, \tan^{-1} \frac{2(x+1)}{3} + C.$$

B   YOUR ANSWER: I need help.
Let's see what we can do. Since we want to find

$$\int \frac{x}{4x^2 + 8x + 13}\, dx,$$

the thing to do is complete the square in the denominator. We have

$$4x^2 + 8x + 13 = 4(x^2 + 2x \quad) + 13$$
$$= 4(x^2 + 2x + 1) + 13 - 4$$
$$= 4(x+1)^2 + 9.$$

This gives us

$$\int \frac{x}{4(x+1)^2 + 9}\, dx.$$

Now if we let $u = x + 1$, the integral will fit one of our "nice" forms. Return to frame **Q337**, try this substitution, and then select the other alternative.

10.6 MISCELLANEOUS SUBSTITUTIONS

OBJECTIVES

You should be able to evaluate certain integrals that can be integrated by making an appropriate substitution.

Q338   We have considered several standard types of substitutions. There are other substitutions that will sometimes be useful. Consider

$$\int \frac{\sqrt[4]{1+x}}{x^2}\, dx.$$

What substitution will transform the integral into one that can be dealt with by our previous methods?

$u = 1 + x$ Frame **A** $u = \sqrt[4]{1+x}$ Frame **B** $u = x^2$ Frame **C**

A   **YOUR ANSWER:** $u = 1 + x$.

No. If $u = 1 + x$, then $du = dx$ and

$$\int \frac{\sqrt[4]{1 + x}}{x^2} \, dx = \int \frac{u^{1/4}}{(u - 1)^2} \, du.$$

This doesn't help us any. Now return to frame **Q338** and try a different substitution.

B   **YOUR ANSWER:** $u = \sqrt[4]{1 + x}$.

Right. If $u = \sqrt[4]{1 + x}$, then $u^4 = 1 + x$ (hence $x = u^4 - 1$) and $4u^3 \, du = dx$. Therefore,

$$\int \frac{\sqrt[4]{1 + x}}{x^2} \, dx = \int \frac{u}{(u^4 - 1)^2} \, 4u^3 \, du = 4 \int \frac{u^4}{(u^4 - 1)^2} \, du$$

which can be dealt with by using partial fractions.

C   **YOUR ANSWER:** $u = x^2$.

No. If $u = x^2$, then $du = 2x \, dx$ and

$$\int \frac{\sqrt[4]{1 + x}}{x^2} \, dx = \int \frac{\sqrt[4]{1 + u^{1/2}}}{u} \, \frac{du}{2u^{1/2}} = \frac{1}{2} \int \frac{\sqrt[4]{1 + u^{1/2}}}{u^{3/2}} \, du.$$

This certainly doesn't give us any help. Now return to frame **Q338** and try again.

Q339   Let's try one more. Evaluate

$$\int \frac{1}{\sqrt[4]{x} + \sqrt{x}} \, dx.$$

Were you successful?

    Yes   Frame **A**   No   Frame **B**

A   **YOUR ANSWER:**   Yes.

Good. If we let $u = \sqrt[4]{x}$, then $u^4 = x$ and $4u^3 \, du = dx$ which gives us

$$\int \frac{1}{\sqrt[4]{x} + \sqrt{x}} \, dx = \int \frac{1}{u + u^2} \, 4u^3 \, du = 4 \int \frac{u^3}{u + u^2} \, du = 4 \int \frac{u^2}{1 + u} \, du$$

$$= 4 \int \left(u - 1 + \frac{1}{u + 1} \right) du \quad \left(\frac{u^2}{u + 1} = u - 1 + \frac{1}{u + 1} \right)$$

$$= 4 \left(\frac{u^2}{2} - u + \ln |u + 1| \right) + C$$

$$= \left(4 \frac{\sqrt{x}}{2} - \sqrt[4]{x} + \ln |\sqrt[4]{x} + 1| \right) + C.$$

B   **YOUR ANSWER:**   No.

You just need the right substitution. If we let $u = \sqrt[4]{x}$, then $u^4 = x$ and $4u^3 \, du = dx$ which gives us

$$\int \frac{1}{\sqrt[4]{x} + \sqrt{x}} \, dx = \int \frac{1}{u + u^2} \, 4u^3 \, du \, 4$$

$$= 4 \int \frac{u^3}{u + u^2} \, du = 4 \int \frac{u^2}{1 + u} \, du.$$

Now evaluate this integral, return to frame **Q339**, and then select the other alternative.

10.7   TABLES OF INTEGRALS

OBJECTIVES

You should be able to evaluate integrals by using tables of integrals.

10.8   MOMENTS AND CENTROIDS OF PLANE REGIONS

OBJECTIVES

You should be able to find the moments with respect to the x-axis and y-axis and the center of mass of a system. You should also be able to find the centroid of a region.

Q340   The center of mass or *centroid* of a region in the plane bound by the *x*-axis, $x = a$, $x = b$, and $y = f(x)$ is given by $(\bar{x}, \bar{y})$ where

$$\bar{x} = \frac{\displaystyle\int_a^b xf(x)\,dx}{\displaystyle\int_a^b f(x)\,dx} \; ; \qquad \bar{y} = \frac{\dfrac{1}{2}\displaystyle\int_a^b [f(x)]^2\,dx}{\displaystyle\int_a^b f(x)\,dx} .$$

Find the centroid of the region bounded by $y = \sqrt{x}$, $y = 0$, and $x = 4$. Were you successsful?

Yes   Frame **A**   No   Frame **B**

A   YOUR ANSWER: Yes.
Very good. Since we want the region bounded by $y = \sqrt{x}$, $y = 0$, and $x = 4$, we have $a = 0$, $b = 4$, and $f(x) = \sqrt{x}$.

$$\int_a^b xf(x)\,dx = \int_0^4 x(\sqrt{x})\,dx = \int_0^4 x^{3/2}\,dx$$

$$= \frac{2}{5}x^{5/2}\Big]_0^4 = \frac{2}{5}(32) = \frac{64}{5} \; ;$$

$$\frac{1}{2}\int_a^b [f(x)]^2\,dx = \frac{1}{2}\int_0^4 x\,dx = \frac{1}{4}x^2\Big]_0^4 = 4;$$

and

$$\int_a^b f(x)\,dx = \int_0^4 x^{1/2}\,dx = \frac{2}{3}x^{3/2}\Big]_0^4 = \frac{2}{3}(8) = \frac{16}{3} .$$

Therefore, $\bar{x} = (64/5)/(16/3) = 12/5$ and $\bar{y} = 4/(16/3) = 3/4$, and hence the centroid is the point $(12/5, 3/4)$.

B   YOUR ANSWER: No.
If you are having trouble, study the examples in the text. Since our region is bounded by $y = \sqrt{x}$, $y = 0$, and $x = 4$, we have $a = 0$, $b = 4$, and $f(x) = \sqrt{x}$. Now return to frame **Q340**, substitute in the formulas for the coordinates of the centroid, evaluate, and then select the other alternative.

10.9 CENTROIDS OF SOLIDS OF REVOLUTION

OBJECTIVES

You should be able to find the centroid of a solid of revolution.

Q341 If the region bounded by the x-axis, $x = a$, $x = b$, and $y = f(x)$ is rotated about the
x-axis, the centroid is on the x-axis and the x-coordinate is given by

$$\bar{x} = \frac{\int_a^b x[f(x)]^2 \, dx}{\int_a^b [f(x)]^2 \, dx} \ .$$

If the region bounded by $y = \sqrt{x}$, $y = 0$, and $x = 4$ is rotated about the x-axis, find
the centroid of the solid generated. How did it go?

    Great   Frame **A**   I need help.   Frame **B**

A **YOUR ANSWER:** Great.
Let's check your work. Since the region is bounded by $y = \sqrt{x}$, $y = 0$, and $x = 4$,
we have

$$\int_0^4 x(\sqrt{x})^2 \, dx = \int_0^4 x^2 \, dx = \frac{1}{3} x^3 \Big]_0^4 = 64/3$$

and

$$\int_0^4 (\sqrt{x})^2 \, dx = \int_0^4 x \, dx = \frac{1}{2} x^2 \Big]_0^4 = 8.$$

Therefore, $\bar{x} = (64/3)/8 = 8/3$, and the centroid is the point $(8/3, 0)$.

B **YOUR ANSWER:** I need help.
Since the region is bounded by $y = \sqrt{x}$, $y = 0$, and $x = 4$, we have $a = 0$, $b = 4$,
and $f(x) = \sqrt{x}$. Now in order to find the centroid, we need to evaluate the integrals

$$\int_a^b x[f(x)]^2 \, dx = \int_0^4 x(\sqrt{x})^2 \, dx$$

and

$$\int_a^b [f(x)]^2 \, dx = \int_0^4 (\sqrt{x})^2 \, dx.$$

Return to frame **Q341**, study the formula for the centroid, compute the necessary integrals, and then select the other alternative.

REVIEW TEST

Evaluate the integrals in Exercises 1-17.

1 $\displaystyle\int x \sin 2x \, dx$

2 $\displaystyle\int x^2 e^x \, dx$

3 $\displaystyle\int \cos^3 x \, dx$

4 $\displaystyle\int \tan^3 x \sec^3 x \, dx$

4 $\displaystyle\int \tan^3 x \, \sec^3 x \, dx$

5 $\displaystyle\int \frac{\sqrt{x^2 - 16}}{x} \, dx$

6 $\displaystyle\int \frac{x + 1}{x^3 + x^2 - 6x} \, dx$

7 $\displaystyle\int \frac{2x^3}{(x^2 + 1)^2} \, dx$

8 $\displaystyle\int \frac{1}{x^2 - 4x + 20} \, dx$

9 $\displaystyle\int \frac{1}{\sqrt{x^2 + 6x + 34}} \, dx$

10 $\displaystyle\int \frac{x}{(x + 1)^{1/3}} \, dx$

11 $\displaystyle\int \frac{x^2 + 1}{(x + 1)(x^2 + 2)} \, dx$

12 $\displaystyle\int \frac{\sqrt{9 - x^2}}{x^2} \, dx$

13 $\displaystyle\int \cos^5 x \, \sin^2 x \, dx$

14 $\displaystyle\int x^2 \ln x \, dx$

15 $\displaystyle\int \frac{x + 3}{x^2 + 4x + 13} \, dx$

16 $\displaystyle\int x\sqrt{x^2 - 9} \, dx$

17 $\displaystyle\int \cos^4 x \, dx$

18 The region bounded by the graphs of $y = 25/(x^2 + 25)$, $y = 0$, and $x = 5$ is revolved about the x-axis. Find the volume of the resulting solid.

19 Particles of masses 6, 9, and 2 units are located at the points $P_1(-1, 2)$, $P_2(3, -4)$, and $P_3(5, 1)$, respectively. Find the moments M_x and M_y and the coordinates of the center of mass of the system.

20 Find the centroid of the region bounded by $y = x^2$, $y = 0$, and $x = 2$.

21 If the region bounded by $y = x^2$, $y = 0$, and $x = 2$ is revolved about the x-axis, find the centroid of the solid generated.

SAMPLE TEST

Evaluate the integrals in Exercises 1-17.

1 $\displaystyle\int \sin^3 x \, dx$

2 $\displaystyle\int x^3 e^{2x} \, dx$

3 $\displaystyle\int \frac{x^2}{16 - x^4} \, dx$

4 $\displaystyle\int \frac{1}{\sqrt{9 + x^2}} \, dx$

5 $\displaystyle\int \frac{1}{\sqrt{6 + x - x^2}} \, dx$

6 $\displaystyle\int \frac{x}{(x - 2)^2} \, dx$

7 $\displaystyle\int e^x \sin x \, dx$

8 $\displaystyle\int \cos^{-1}(2x) \, dx$

9 $\displaystyle\int \tan^4 x \, dx$

10 $\displaystyle\int \sin^3 x \, dx$

11 $\displaystyle\int \cos^2 x \, dx$

12 $\displaystyle\int \frac{1}{x^2\sqrt{9 - x^2}} \, dx$

13 $\displaystyle\int \frac{x^2}{(4 - x^2)^{3/2}} \, dx$

14 $\displaystyle\int \frac{1}{x + x^3} \, dx$

15 $\displaystyle\int \frac{1}{\sqrt{x^2 - x + 1}}\, dx$ **16** $\displaystyle\int \frac{1}{x^2\sqrt{4 + x^2}}\, dx$

17 $\displaystyle\int x\sqrt{x + 1}\, dx$

18 The region interior to the circle $x^2 + y^2 = 4$ is revolved about the line $x = 3$. Find the volume of the resulting solid.

19 Particles of masses 4, 3, 5, and 6 units are located at the points $P_1(-2, 5)$, $P_2(0, 1)$, $P_3(1, 2)$, and $P_4(3, 5)$, respectively. Find the moments M_x and M_y and the coordinates of the center of mass of the system.

20 Find the centroid of the region bounded by $y = 1/x$, $y = 0$, $x = 1$, and $x = e$.

21 If the region bounded by $y = 1/x$, $y = 0$, $x = 1$, and $x = e$ is revolved about the x-axis, find the centroid of the solid generated.

Solutions

to

Review Tests

CHAPTER 1

1 (a) If $a - b$ is positive, then $a > b$. $-28 > -78$ because $-28 - (-78) = 50$, which is positive.

(b) $(-1)(-8) = 8$ and $(-7)(5) = -35$. $8 > -35$ because $8 - (-35) = 43$, which is positive. Therefore, $(-1)(-8) > (-7)(5)$.

(c) $3 + (-8) = -5$ and $(7)(-3) = -21$. $-5 > -21$ because $-5 - (-21) = 16$, which is positive. Therefore, $3 + (-8) > (7)(-3)$.

(d) We have $115/4 = 28.75$ and $28.75 > 28.63$. Therefore, $115/4 > 28.63$.

2 (a) $|7 - 10| = |-3| = 3$ (b) $|-4| - |13| = 4 - 13 = -9$

(c) $||-5| - |-8|| = |5 - 8| = |-3| = 3$ (d) $\dfrac{5}{|-5|} = \dfrac{5}{5} = 1$

3 $d(A, B) = |-3 - (-5)| = |-3 + 5| = |2| = 2$

$d(B, C) = |6 - (-3)| = |6 + 3| = |9| = 9$

Therefore, $d(A, B) < d(B, C)$.

4 If $x < 3$, then $x - 3 < 0$. Therefore,
$$|x - 3| = -(x - 3) = 3 - x.$$

5 (a) $-1 < x \leqslant 5$ is equivalent to the interval $(-1, 5]$.

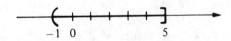

(b) $x \geqslant 6$ is equivalent to the interval $[6, \infty)$.

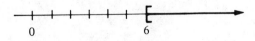

6 (a) $(5, 25]$ can be expressed as $5 < x \leqslant 25$.

(b) $(-\infty, 6)$ can be expressed as $x < 6$.

7 (a) $4x + 2 > 10$

$\qquad 4x > 8$

$\qquad\ \ x > 2$

Hence, the interval solution is $(2, \infty)$.

(b) $6x + 3 \leqslant 5x - 7$
$\qquad x \leqslant -10$

Hence, the interval solution is $(-\infty, -10]$.

(c) Since the numerator is positive, the fraction is positive if and only if $3x - 6 > 0$ or $x > 2$.
Hence, the interval solution is $(2, \infty)$.

8 (a) $|2 - 3x| < 8$ is equivalent to

$$-8 < 2 - 3x < 8$$
$$-10 < -3x < 6$$
$$-6 < 3x < 10$$
$$-2 < x < 10/3$$

The interval solution is $(-2, 10/3)$.

(b) The solutions of $|x - 2| \geqslant 4$ are the solutions of $x - 2 \geqslant 4$ and $x - 2 \leqslant -4$. The inequality $x - 2 \geqslant 4$ is equivalent to $x \geqslant 6$, and $x - 2 \leqslant -4$ is equivalent to $x \leqslant -2$. The interval solution is $(-\infty, -2] \cup [6, \infty)$.

9 $x^2 - x - 2 > 0$ is equivalent to $(x + 1)(x - 2) > 0$. The product $(x + 1)(x - 2)$ is zero if $x = -1$ or 2. These numbers determine the intervals $(-\infty, -1)$, $(-1, 2)$, and $(2, \infty)$.

Interval	Sign of $(x + 1)$	Sign of $(x - 2)$	Sign of product
$(-\infty, -1)$	$-$	$-$	$+$
$(-1, 2)$	$+$	$-$	$-$
$(2, \infty)$	$+$	$+$	$+$

Therefore, the interval solution of $x^2 - x - 2 > 0$ is $(-\infty, -1) \cup (2, \infty)$.

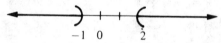

10 In order for a fraction to be negative, the numerator and denominator must be opposite in sign. Therefore, $\dfrac{x - 3}{x^2 - 4} < 0$ is equivalent to $(x - 3)(x^2 - 4) < 0$ or $(x - 3)(x - 2)(x + 2) < 0$.
The product $(x - 3)(x - 2)(x + 2)$ is zero if $x = 3, 2,$ or -2. These numbers determine the intervals $(-\infty, -2)$, $(-2, 2)$, $(2, 3)$, and $(3, \infty)$.

Interval	Sign of $(x - 3)$	Sign of $(x - 2)$	Sign of $(x + 2)$	Sign of product
$(-\infty, -2)$	$-$	$-$	$-$	$-$
$(-2, 2)$	$-$	$-$	$+$	$+$
$(2, 3)$	$-$	$+$	$+$	$-$
$(3, \infty)$	$+$	$+$	$+$	$+$

Therefore, the interval solution of $(x - 3)(x - 2)(x + 2) < 0$ is $(-\infty, -2) \cup (2, 3)$.

11

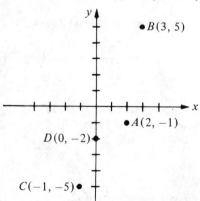

12 The points on a line which bisects the second and fourth quadrants have coordinates that are equal but opposite in sign.

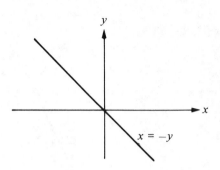

13 (a) $A(5, -2)$, $B(-4, 3)$
$$d(A, B) = \sqrt{(-4 - 5)^2 + (3 - (-2))^2} = \sqrt{(-9)^2 + (5)^2} = \sqrt{106}.$$
The coordinates of the midpoint of the segment AB are
$$\left(\frac{5 + (-4)}{2}, \frac{-2 + 3}{2}\right) = \left(\frac{1}{2}, \frac{1}{2}\right).$$

(b) $A(2, 8)$, $B(-1, -5)$
$$d(A, B) = \sqrt{(-1 - 2)^2 + (-5 - 8)^2} = \sqrt{(-3)^2 + (-13)^2} = \sqrt{178}.$$
The coordinates of the midpoint of the segment AB are
$$\left(\frac{2 + -1}{2}, \frac{8 + (-5)}{2}\right) = \left(\frac{1}{2}, \frac{3}{2}\right).$$

14 By the distance formula, we have
$$d(A, B) = \sqrt{(5 - (-3))^2 + (4 - 1)^2} = \sqrt{73}$$
$$d(A, C) = \sqrt{(0 - (-3))^2 + (-7 - 1)^2} = \sqrt{73}$$
$$d(B, C) = \sqrt{(0 - 5)^2 + (-7 - 4)^2} = \sqrt{146}.$$
Since $[d(A, B)]^2 + [d(A, C)]^2 = 73 + 73 = 146 = [d(B, C)]^2$, the triangle has a right angle at vertex A.

15 We want the distance from P to A to be equal to the distance from P to B. Therefore, we have
$$d(P, A) = d(P, B)$$
$$\sqrt{(x - 2)^2 + (y - 1)^2} = \sqrt{(x - 4)^2 + (y - (-1))^2}$$
$$(x - 2)^2 + (y - 1)^2 = (x - 4)^2 + (y + 1)^2$$
$$x^2 - 4x + 4 + y^2 - 2y + 1 = x^2 - 8x + 16 + y^2 + 2y + 1$$
$$4x - 4y - 12 = 0.$$

16 If $|x| > 1$, then $x > 1$ or $x < -1$, and if $|y - 1| < 1$, then $-1 < y - 1 < 1$ or $0 < y < 2$. Hence, the graph of W consists of all points in the shaded region given below.

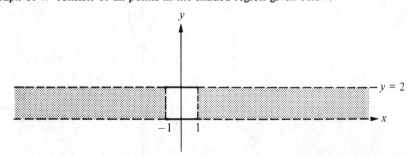

17   (a) Some of the points on the graph of $y = 2x + 3$ are given below.

x	0	1	-1	2
y	3	5	1	7

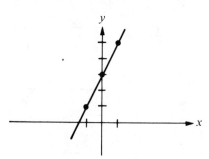

(b) Some of the points on the graph of $y = 2x^2 - 3$ are given below.

x	0	1	2	-1
y	-3	-1	5	-1

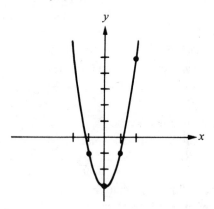

(c) Some of the points on the graph of $y = 1 + x^3$ are given below.

x	0	-1	1	-2	2
y	1	0	2	-7	9

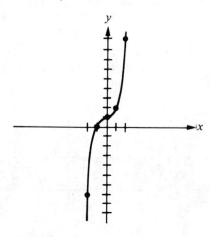

18 (a) $(x - 1)^2 + (y + 3)^2 = 9$

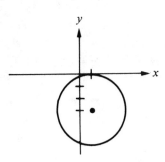

(b) $x^2 + (y - 4)^2 = 4$

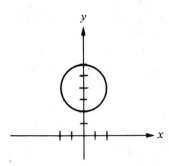

19 (a) The equation of a circle is $(x - h)^2 + (y - k)^2 = r^2$ where (h, k) is the center and r is the radius. Therefore, the desired equation is $(x - 2)^2 + (y - (-3))^2 = 3^2$ or $(x - 2)^2 + (y + 3)^2 = 9$.

(b) If the circle passes through P, then the radius is the distance between the center and P. Therefore,
$$r = \sqrt{(2 - 4)^2 + (-1 - (-2))^2} = \sqrt{(-2)^2 + 1^2} = \sqrt{5}.$$
Now the equation of the desired circle is $(x - 4)^2 + (y - (-2))^2 = (\sqrt{5})^2$ or $(x - 4)^2 + (y + 2)^2 = 5$.

20 (a) $m = \dfrac{10 - 6}{-5 - 2} = \dfrac{4}{-7} = -\dfrac{4}{7}$ (b) $m = \dfrac{7 - 7}{-7 - (-8)} = \dfrac{0}{1} = 0$

(c) $m = \dfrac{\dfrac{7}{3} - \dfrac{2}{3}}{-\dfrac{3}{4} - \dfrac{1}{2}} = \dfrac{\dfrac{5}{3}}{-\dfrac{5}{4}} = -\dfrac{4}{3}$

21 (a) The point-slope form of the line is $y - y_1 = m(x - x_1)$. Therefore, the equation of the line is
$$y - (-3) = \frac{1}{2}(x - 4)$$
$$y + 3 = \frac{1}{2}(x - 4)$$
$$2y + 6 = x - 4$$
$$2y - x + 10 = 0.$$

(b) We can find the slope using the two points $A(-5, 2)$ and $B(4, -3)$.
$$m = \frac{-3 - 2}{4 - (-5)} = -\frac{5}{9}$$
Now using the point-slope form of the line with $A(-5, 2)$ and $m = -5/9$, we have

$$y - 2 = -\frac{5}{9}(x - (-5))$$
$$9y - 18 = -5x - 25$$
$$9y + 5x + 7 = 0.$$

(c) The slope-intercept form of the line is $y = mx + b$ where m is the slope and b is the y-intercept. Therefore, the equation of the desired line is

$$y = \frac{1}{3}x + 2 \ (-3)$$
$$3y = x + 6$$
$$3y - x - 6 = 0.$$

22 Solving $2x - 3y + 1 = 0$ for y, we have $y = (2/3)x + (1/3)$. This is the slope-intercept form and hence the slope is $2/3$, which is also the slope of the line we want. Now we have the slope $m = 2/3$ and a point on the line $A(2, -3)$. Using the point-slope form of the line, we obtain

$$y - (-3) = \frac{2}{3}(x - 2)$$
$$3y + 9 = 2x - 4$$
$$3y - 2x + 13 = 0.$$

23 (a) $f(1) = 1^2 - 2(1) + 3 = 1 - 2 + 3 = 2$

(b) $f(-1) = (-1)^2 - 2(-1) + 3 = 1 + 2 + 3 = 6$

(c) $f(3) = 3^2 - 2(3) + 3 = 9 - 6 + 3 = 6$

(d) $f(a) = a^2 - 2a + 3$

24 (a) $g(a) = \dfrac{a}{(a^2 - 1)}$ 　　　　　(b) $g(a + h) = \dfrac{a + h}{(a + h)^2 - 1}$

(c) $g\left(\dfrac{1}{a}\right) = \dfrac{\dfrac{1}{a}}{\left(\dfrac{1}{a}\right)^2 - 1} = \dfrac{\dfrac{1}{a}}{\dfrac{1 - a^2}{a^2}} = \dfrac{a}{1 - a^2}$ 　　(d) $\dfrac{1}{g(a)} = \dfrac{1}{\dfrac{a}{a^2 - 1}} = \dfrac{a^2 - 1}{a}$

25 (a) Since $x - 1$ cannot be zero, we must exclude $x = 1$ from the domain. Therefore, the domain is the set of real numbers except 1, or $\{x: x \neq 1\}$.

(b) Since the number under the radical cannot be negative, we have $x - 5 \geqslant 0$ or $x \geqslant 5$. Therefore, the domain is the set $\{x: x \geqslant 5\}$.

(c) Since the number under the radical cannot be negative, $2x + 3 \geqslant 0$ or $x \geqslant -3/2$. However, the denominator cannot be zero, so we must exclude $x = 5$. Therefore, the domain is the set $\{x: x \geqslant -3/2, x \neq 5\}$.

26 A function is one-to-one if $a \neq b$ implies $f(a) \neq f(b)$. We have $f(a) = -a + 3$ and $f(b) = -b + 3$. Now if $a \neq b$, then $-a + 3 \neq -b + 3$ or $f(a) \neq f(b)$.

27 We have what is called a step function. The fare goes up a step of 25 cents for each half mile or part thereof. This gives us the following function.

$$f(x) = \begin{cases} .40 \text{ if } 0 \leqslant x \leqslant 1/2 \\ .65 \text{ if } 1/2 < x \leqslant 1 \\ .90 \text{ if } 1 < x \leqslant 3/2 \\ 1.15 \text{ if } 3/2 < x \leqslant 2 \end{cases}$$

28

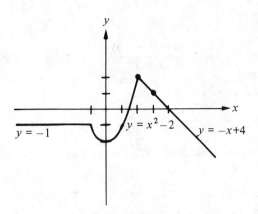

29 (a) $(f \circ g)(x) = f(g(x))$
$\quad\quad = f(x + 3)$
$\quad\quad = 2(x + 3) - 1$
$\quad\quad = 2x + 6 - 1$
$\quad\quad = 2x + 5$

(b) $(f \circ g)(x) = f(g(x))$
$\quad\quad = f(2x - 1)$
$\quad\quad = (2x - 1)^2 + 3$
$\quad\quad = 4x^2 - 4x + 1 + 3$
$\quad\quad = 4x^2 - 4x + 4$

(c) $(f \circ g)(x) = f(g(x))$
$\quad\quad = f(\sqrt{x + 1})$
$\quad\quad = \dfrac{1}{\sqrt{x + 1}}$ $\quad\quad x$ restricted to $(-1, \infty)$.

30 We must show that $(f \circ g)(x) = x$ for $x \geqslant -4$ and $(g \circ f)(x) = x$ for $x \leqslant 0$.

$(f \circ g)(x) = f(g(x))$ $\quad\quad\quad\quad x \geqslant -4$
$\quad\quad = f(-\sqrt{x + 4})$
$\quad\quad = (-\sqrt{x + 4})^2 - 4$
$\quad\quad = x + 4 - 4$
$\quad\quad = x.$

$(g \circ f)(x) = g(f(x))$ $\quad\quad\quad\quad x \leqslant 0$
$\quad\quad = g(x^2 - 4)$
$\quad\quad = -\sqrt{(x^2 - 4) + 4}$
$\quad\quad = -\sqrt{x^2}$
$\quad\quad = -(-x)$ $\quad\quad\quad (\sqrt{x^2} = -x$ if $x \leqslant 0)$
$\quad\quad = x.$

31 If we let $y = 3x^2 + 2$ and solve for x in terms of y, we get

$$x^2 = \frac{y - 2}{3} \quad \text{or} \quad x = \pm\sqrt{\frac{y - 2}{3}}.$$

Since x is nonnegative, we let $g(y) = \sqrt{\dfrac{y - 2}{3}}$ or by interchanging y for x, $g(x) = \sqrt{\dfrac{x - 2}{3}}$.

Checking the two conditions, we have

$(f \circ g)(x) = f(g(x))$ $\quad\quad\quad$ and $\quad\quad (g \circ f)(x) = g(f(x))$
$\quad\quad = f\left(\sqrt{\dfrac{x - 2}{3}}\right)$ $\quad\quad\quad\quad\quad\quad = g(3x^2 + 2)$
$\quad\quad = 3\left(\sqrt{\dfrac{x - 2}{3}}\right)^2 + 2$ $\quad\quad\quad\quad = \sqrt{\dfrac{(3x^2 + 2) - 2}{3}}$
$\quad\quad = x - 2 + 2$ $\quad\quad\quad\quad\quad\quad\quad = \sqrt{x^2}$
$\quad\quad = x$ $\quad\quad\quad\quad\quad\quad\quad\quad\quad\quad = x \quad (\sqrt{x^2} = x$ if $x \geqslant 0)$.

Therefore, $f(x) = 3x^2 + 2$, $x \geqslant 0$ and $g(x) = \sqrt{(x - 2)/3}$, $x \geqslant 2$ are inverse functions of one another.

CHAPTER 2

1 We have $\dfrac{x^2 - 9}{x + 3} = \dfrac{(x + 3)(x - 3)}{x + 3}$. Notice that -3 is not in the domain of $\dfrac{x^2 - 9}{x + 3}$ because $0/0$ is obtained when -3 is substituted for x. Since $x \neq -3$, we can divide numerator and denominator by $x + 3$ and thus

$$\lim_{x \to -3} \left(\frac{x^2 - 9}{x + 3} \right) = \lim_{x \to -3} (x - 3).$$

Therefore, as x gets nearer -3, but not equal to -3, $x - 3$ is nearer $-3 - 3 = -6$ and

$$\lim_{x \to -3} \left(\frac{x^2 - 9}{x + 3} \right) = -6.$$

2 Consider $Q(x, 2x^2 + 1)$. Then m_{PQ}, the slope joining $P(2, 9)$ and Q, is

$$\frac{2x^2 + 1 - 9}{x - 2} = \frac{2x^2 - 8}{x - 2} = \frac{2(x - 2)(x + 2)}{x - 2} .$$

Now the slope at $P(2, 9)$ is

$$\lim_{x \to 2} \frac{2(x - 2)(x + 2)}{x - 2} = \lim_{x \to 2} 2(x + 2) = 8.$$

We want an equation of the line through $P(2, 9)$ with slope $m = 8$. Using the point-slope form of the line, we have

$$y - 9 = 8(x - 2)$$
$$y = 8x - 7.$$

3 (a) In order to prove $\lim_{x \to -1} (3x + 5) = 2$, we must show that for every $\varepsilon > 0$, there exists a $\delta > 0$ such that if $0 < |x - (-1)| < \delta$, then $|(3x + 5) - 2| < \varepsilon$, or if $0 < |x + 1| < \delta$, then $|3x + 3| < \varepsilon$.

   In order to find δ, we examine $|3x + 3| < \varepsilon$.

$$|3x + 3| < \varepsilon$$
$$3|x + 1| < \varepsilon$$
$$|x + 1| < \frac{\varepsilon}{3}$$

This gives us the clue: Let $\delta = \varepsilon/3$. Now

if
$$0 < |x + 1| < \frac{\varepsilon}{3} ,$$

then
$$3|x + 1| < \varepsilon$$
$$|3x + 3| < \varepsilon.$$

(b) In order to prove $\lim_{x \to 2} (x^2 + 3) = 7$, we must show that for every $\varepsilon > 0$, there exists a $\delta > 0$ such that if $0 < |x - 2| < \delta$, then $|(x^2 + 3) - 7| < \varepsilon$ or $|x^2 - 4| < \varepsilon$.

   Restrict x to the interval $(1, 3)$. This is permissible because we are only interested in what happens near 2. This means we are considering values of x which differ from 2 by less than 1, and hence $\delta < 1$. Notice that $|x^2 - 4| = |x - 2||x + 2|$, and since x is restricted to the interval $(1, 3)$, we have $|x + 2| < 5$. Therefore, $|x^2 - 4| = |x - 2||x + 2| < 5|x - 2|$. Now let $\delta = \varepsilon/5$ (or 1 if $1 < \varepsilon/5$).

If
$$0 < |x - 2| < \frac{\varepsilon}{5} ,$$

then
$$5|x - 2| < \varepsilon$$
$$|x + 2||x - 2| < \varepsilon \quad \text{since } |x + 2| < 5$$
$$|x^2 - 4| < \varepsilon.$$

4   Suppose $\lim_{x \to 1} \dfrac{1}{x - 1} = L$. For any $\varepsilon > 0$, it should be possible to find an open interval

$(1 - \delta, 1 + \delta)$ containing 1 such that if $1 - \delta < x < 1 + \delta$, then $\left| \dfrac{1}{x - 1} - L \right| > \varepsilon$. However,

$\dfrac{1}{x - 1}$ can be made as large as desired by choosing x close enough to 1. Therefore,

$\left| \dfrac{1}{x - 1} - L \right|$ can be made larger than ε by choosing x close enough to 1. This says that not

every x in the interval $(1 - \delta, 1 + \delta)$ is such that $\left| \dfrac{1}{x - 1} - L \right| < \varepsilon$. Consequently, our as-

sumption that the limit exists is false.

5   (a) $\lim\limits_{x \to 2} (2x^2 + 3x - 1) = 2(2)^2 + 3(2) - 1 = 13$

     (b) $\lim\limits_{x \to -1} \left(\dfrac{x^2 - 3x + 1}{x - 5} \right) = \dfrac{\lim_{x \to -1} (x^2 - 3x + 1)}{\lim_{x \to -1} (x - 5)} = \dfrac{(-1)^2 - 3(-1) + 1}{(-1) - 5} = -\dfrac{5}{6}$.

     (c) $\lim\limits_{x \to 5} \sqrt{\dfrac{x + 4}{x - 1}} = \sqrt{\lim\limits_{x \to 5} \left(\dfrac{x + 4}{x - 1} \right)} = \sqrt{\dfrac{9}{4}} = \dfrac{3}{2}$.

6   Since $\sqrt{x^2 + 1} \geqslant 1$, $\dfrac{1}{\sqrt{x^2 + 1}} \leqslant 1$ and $\dfrac{|x|}{\sqrt{x^2 + 1}} \leqslant |x|$. Also $0 \leqslant \dfrac{|x|}{\sqrt{x^2 + 1}}$, giving us

$$0 \leqslant \dfrac{|x|}{\sqrt{x^2 + 1}} \leqslant |x|.$$

Now $\lim_{x \to 0} (0) = 0$ and $\lim_{x \to 0} |x| = 0$. Therefore, by the Sandwich Theorem,

$$\lim_{x \to 0} \dfrac{|x|}{\sqrt{x^2 + 1}} = 0.$$

7   (a) $\lim\limits_{x \to 3^+} (\sqrt{x - 3} + x) = \lim\limits_{x \to 3^+} \sqrt{x - 3} + \lim\limits_{x \to 3^+} x = 0 + 3 = 3.$

     (b) $\lim\limits_{x \to -2^-} \left(\dfrac{|x + 2|}{x + 2} \right) = \lim\limits_{x \to -2^-} \left(\dfrac{-(x + 2)}{x + 2} \right)$ since $|x + 2| = -(x + 2)$

                                        when $x + 2 < 0$ or $x < -2$.

              $= \lim\limits_{x \to -2^-} (-1) = -1.$

8   Since $f(x) = \begin{cases} x & \text{if } x \leqslant 0 \\ x + 1 & \text{if } 0 < x \leqslant 1, \\ x^2 + 3 & \text{if } x > 1 \end{cases}$

$$\lim_{x \to 1^-} f(x) = \lim_{x \to 1^-} (x + 1) = 1 + 1 = 2.$$

9   Since $\sqrt{(x - 4)^2} = |x - 4|$, $\dfrac{\sqrt{(x - 4)^2}}{x - 4} = \dfrac{|x - 4|}{x - 4}$, and therefore, $\lim\limits_{x \to 4} \left(\dfrac{\sqrt{(x - 4)^2}}{x - 4} \right) =$

$\lim\limits_{x \to 4} \left(\dfrac{|x - 4|}{x - 4} \right)$.

$$\lim_{x \to 4^-} \left(\dfrac{|x - 4|}{x - 4} \right) = \lim_{x \to 4^-} \left(\dfrac{-(x - 4)}{x - 4} \right) = \lim_{x \to 4^-} (-1) = -1$$

$$\lim_{x \to 4^+} \left(\dfrac{|x - 4|}{x - 4} \right) = \lim_{x \to 4^+} \left(\dfrac{x - 4}{x - 4} \right) = \lim_{x \to 4^+} (1) = 1.$$

Since $\lim\limits_{x \to 4^-} \left(\dfrac{|x - 4|}{x - 4} \right) \neq \lim\limits_{x \to 4^+} \left(\dfrac{|x - 4|}{x - 4} \right)$, the limit does not exist.

10 f is continuous at $a = 2$ provided:

     (1) f is defined in an open interval containing a;

     (2) $\lim\limits_{x \to a} f(x)$ exists;

     (3) $\lim\limits_{x \to a} f(x) = f(a)$.

f is defined everywhere except 0. Therefore, f is defined in an open interval containing 2. For example, consider the open interval $(0, 3)$.

$$\lim_{x \to 2} \left(\frac{x+1}{x^2} \right) = \frac{\lim_{x \to 2} (x+1)}{\lim_{x \to 2} (x^2)} = \frac{3}{4}$$

$$f(2) = \frac{3}{4} \text{ and } \lim_{x \to 2} \left(\frac{x+1}{x^2} \right) = f(2)$$

Therefore, f is continuous at $a = 2$.

11 We must show $\lim_{x \to c} \left(\dfrac{x^2}{x-2} \right) = f(c)$ if $2 < c < 4$ and $\lim_{x \to 4^-} \left(\dfrac{x^2}{x-2} \right) = f(4)$.

$$\lim_{x \to c} \left(\frac{x^2}{x-2} \right) = \frac{\lim_{x \to c} (x^2)}{\lim_{x \to c} (x-2)} = \frac{c^2}{c-2} = f(c) \text{ if } 2 < c < 4$$

$$\lim_{x \to 4^-} \left(\frac{x^2}{x-2} \right) = \frac{\lim_{x \to 4^-} (x^2)}{\lim_{x \to 4^-} (x-2)} = \frac{16}{2} = 8 = f(4)$$

12 f is not continuous at 2 or -2 because f is not defined at 2 or -2.

13 Since $f(x) = \begin{cases} x \text{ if } x \leqslant 1 \\ x^2 \text{ if } 1 < x \leqslant 5, \\ 2x + 3 \text{ if } x > 5 \end{cases}$

$$\lim_{x \to 5^-} f(x) = \lim_{x \to 5^-} (x^2) = 25$$

and

$$\lim_{x \to 5^+} f(x) = \lim_{x \to 5^+} (2x + 3) = 13.$$

Therefore, $\lim_{x \to 5} f(x)$ does not exist, because $\lim_{x \to 5^-} f(x) \neq \lim_{x \to 5^+} f(x)$, and hence, f is not continuous at $x = 5$.

14 The function f where $f(x) = x^2 + 3$ is continuous on $[0, 3]$ and $f(0) = 3$, $f(3) = 12$. If $3 < w < 12$, we must find a number c in the interval $[0, 3]$ such that $f(c) = w$.

$f(c) = c^2 + 3$. Let $c^2 + 3 = w$. Solving for c, we have $c = \sqrt{w-3}$, which is in the interval $[0, 3]$ because if

$$\begin{aligned} 3 &< w & &< 12 \\ 3 - 3 &< w - 3 & &< 12 - 3 \\ 0 &< w - 3 & &< 9 \\ 0 &< \sqrt{w-3} & &< 3. \end{aligned}$$

Checking our work we have

$$f(\sqrt{w-3}) = (\sqrt{w-3})^2 + 3 = w - 3 + 3 = w.$$

CHAPTER 3

1 (a) $f(x) = 3x^2 - x + 2$

$$\begin{aligned} f'(x) &= \lim_{h \to 0} \left(\frac{f(x+h) - f(x)}{h} \right) \\ &= \lim_{h \to 0} \left(\frac{[3(x+h)^2 - (x+h) + 2] - (3x^2 - x + 2)}{h} \right) \\ &= \lim_{h \to 0} \left(\frac{6hx + 3h^2 - h}{h} \right) \\ &= \lim_{h \to 0} (6x + 3h - 1) = 6x - 1 \end{aligned}$$

(b) $f(x) = \dfrac{3}{x}$

$$f'(x) = \lim_{h \to 0} \left(\frac{f(x+h) - f(x)}{h} \right) = \lim_{h \to 0} \left(\frac{\dfrac{3}{x+h} - \dfrac{3}{x}}{h} \right)$$

$$= \lim_{h \to 0} \left(\frac{3x - 3(x+h)}{hx(x+h)} \right) = \lim_{h \to 0} \left(\frac{-3h}{hx(x+h)} \right)$$

$$= \lim_{h \to 0} \left(\frac{-3}{x(x+h)} \right) = -\frac{3}{x^2}$$

2 $f(x) = 4x^3 - 2x^2 + x - 5$

    $f'(x) = 12x^2 - 4x + 1$

3 $g(x) = (x^3 + 5)(2x^2 - 3)$

    $g'(x) = (x^3 + 5)D_x(2x^2 - 3) + (2x^2 - 3)D_x(x^3 + 5)$

        $= (x^3 + 5)(4x) + (2x^2 - 3)(3x^2)$

        $= 4x^4 + 20x + 6x^4 - 9x^2$

        $= 10x^4 - 9x^2 + 20x$

4 $h(s) = \dfrac{4s - 1}{2s + 3}$

    $h'(s) = \dfrac{(2s + 3)D_s(4s - 1) - (4s - 1)D_s(2s + 3)}{(2s + 3)^2}$

       $= \dfrac{(2s + 3)(4) - (4s - 1)(2)}{(2s + 3)^2} = \dfrac{8s + 12 - 8s + 2}{(2s + 3)^2} = \dfrac{14}{(2s + 3)^2}$

5 $f(t) = \dfrac{t^2 + 3t - 1}{t^3 + 1}$

    $f'(t) = \dfrac{(t^3 + 1)D_t(t^2 + 3t - 1) - (t^2 + 3t - 1)D_t(t^3 + 1)}{(t^3 + 1)^2}$

       $= \dfrac{(t^3 + 1)(2t + 3) - (t^2 + 3t - 1)(3t^2)}{(t^3 + 1)^2} = \dfrac{-t^4 - 6t^3 + 3t^2 + 2t + 3}{(t^3 + 1)^2}$

6 $f(x) = (x^3 - x + 1)^4$

    $f'(x) = 4(x^3 - x + 1)^3 D_x(x^3 - x + 1) = 4(x^3 - x + 1)^3(3x^2 - 1)$

7 $h(x) = \dfrac{x^2}{(2x^2 - 1)^3}$

    $h'(x) = \dfrac{(2x^2 - 1)^3 D_x(x^2) - x^2 D_x[(2x^2 - 1)^3]}{[(2x^2 - 1)^3]^2} = \dfrac{(2x^2 - 1)^3(2x) - x^2[3(2x^2 - 1)^2(4x)]}{(2x^2 - 1)^6}$

       $= \dfrac{(2x^2 - 1)(2x) - 12x^3}{(2x^2 - 1)^4} = \dfrac{-8x^3 - 2x}{(2x^2 - 1)^4}$

8 $F(y) = \left(\dfrac{y + 1}{y^2 - 3} \right)^4$

    $F'(y) = 4\left(\dfrac{y + 1}{y^2 - 3} \right)^3 D_y\left(\dfrac{y + 1}{y^2 - 3} \right) = 4\left(\dfrac{y + 1}{y^2 - 3} \right)^3 \left[\dfrac{(y^2 - 3) - (y + 1)(2y)}{(y^2 - 3)^2} \right]$

       $= 4\,\dfrac{(y + 1)^3}{(y^2 - 3)^3}\,\dfrac{(-y^2 - 2y - 3)}{(y^2 - 3)^2} = -\dfrac{4(y + 1)^3(y^2 + 2y + 3)}{(y^2 - 3)^5}$

9 $f(x) = \sqrt{x^2 + 3} = (x^2 + 3)^{1/2}$

    $f'(x) = \dfrac{1}{2}(x^2 + 3)^{-1/2} D_x(x^2 + 3) = \dfrac{1}{2}(x^2 + 3)^{-1/2}(2x) = \dfrac{x}{(x^2 + 3)^{1/2}} = \dfrac{x}{\sqrt{x^2 + 3}}$

10 $h(x) = (x^2 - x + 3)^{-3/5}$

$$h'(x) = -\frac{3}{5}(x^2 - x + 3)^{-8/5}D_x(x^2 - x + 3)$$

$$= -\frac{3}{5}(x^2 - x + 3)^{-8/5}(2x - 1) = -\frac{3(2x - 1)}{5(x^2 - x + 3)^{8/5}}$$

11 $G(x) = \left(\dfrac{2x}{x^3 - 1}\right)^{2/3}$

$$G'(x) = \frac{2}{3}\left(\frac{2x}{x^3 - 1}\right)^{-1/3}D_x\left(\frac{2x}{x^3 - 1}\right) = \frac{2}{3}\left(\frac{2x}{x^3 - 1}\right)^{-1/3}\left[\frac{(x^3 - 1)(2) - 2x(3x^2)}{(x^3 - 1)^2}\right]$$

$$= \frac{2}{3}\left(\frac{x^3 - 1}{2x}\right)^{1/3}\left(\frac{-4x^3 - 2}{(x^3 - 1)^2}\right) = -\frac{4}{3}\left(\frac{x^3 - 1}{2x}\right)^{1/3}\left(\frac{2x^3 + 1}{(x^3 - 1)^2}\right) = -\frac{4(2x^3 + 1)}{3(2x)^{1/3}(x^3 - 1)^{5/3}}$$

12 $f(x) = \sqrt{(x^3 + 1)(3x^2 - 1)^3} = [(x^3 + 1)(3x^2 - 1)^3]^{1/2}$

$$f'(x) = \frac{1}{2}[(x^3 + 1)(3x^2 - 1)^3]^{-1/2}D_x[(x^3 + 1)(3x^2 - 1)^3]$$

$$= \frac{1}{2}[(x^3 + 1)(3x^2 - 1)^3]^{-1/2}[(x^3 + 1)D_x(3x^2 - 1)^3 + (3x^2 - 1)^3D_x(x^3 + 1)]$$

$$= \frac{(x^3 + 1)(3)(3x^2 - 1)^2(6x) + (3x^2 - 1)^3(3x^2)}{2[(x^3 + 1)(3x^2 - 1)^3]^{1/2}}$$

$$= \frac{18x(x^3 + 1)(3x^2 - 1)^2 + 3x^2(3x^2 - 1)^3}{2(x^3 + 1)^{1/2}(3x^2 - 1)^{3/2}}$$

$$= \frac{18x(x^3 + 1)(3x^2 - 1) + 3x^2(3x^2 - 1)^2}{2(x^3 + 1)^{1/2}(3x^2 - 1)^{1/2}}$$

$$= \frac{18x(x^3 + 1)(3x^2 - 1) + 3x^2(3x^2 - 1)^2}{2\sqrt{(x^3 + 1)(3x^2 - 1)}}$$

13 $y = \dfrac{2}{1 - x}$

$$y' = \frac{(1 - x)(0) - 2(-1)}{(1 - x)^2} = \frac{2}{(1 - x)^2}$$

When $x = 0$, $y' = 2$ or $m = 2$. Now we want the line through $P(0, 2)$ with slope 2. Using the point-slope form of the line, we have

$$y - 2 = 2(x - 0)$$
$$y = 2x + 2.$$

14 If $y = 2x^2 - 3x + 1$, $y' = 4x - 3$. The slope of the line $3y - 2x + 1 = 0$ is $2/3$. Therefore, the slope of a line perpendicular to $3y - 2x + 1 = 0$ is $-3/2$. Now we want x such that $4x - 3 = -3/2$. This gives us $x = 3/8$. The y-coordinate of the point on the graph of $y = 2x^2 - 3x + 1$ when $x = 3/8$ is

$$y = 2\left(\frac{3}{8}\right)^2 - 3\left(\frac{3}{8}\right) + 1 = \frac{18}{64} - \frac{9}{8} + 1 = \frac{5}{32}.$$

Hence, we want an equation of a line through $P(3/8, 5/32)$ with slope $-3/2$. Using the point-slope form of the line, we have

$$y - \frac{5}{32} = -\frac{3}{2}\left(x - \frac{3}{8}\right)$$

$$y - \frac{5}{32} = -\frac{3}{2}x + \frac{9}{16}$$

$$32y - 5 = -48x + 18$$

$$32y + 48x - 23 = 0$$

15 $y = 3x^2 - x + 5$, $x = 3$, and $\Delta x = 0.1$

$$\Delta y = f(x + \Delta x) - f(x) = f(3.1) - f(3)$$
$$= [3(3.1)^2 - (3.1) + 5] - [3(3^2) - 3 + 5] = 30.73 - 29 = 1.73$$

$dy = y'dx$. Since $y' = 6x - 1$, $dy = (6x - 1)dx$. When $x = 3$ and $dx = 0.1$, we have

$$dy = (6(3) - 1)(.1) = (17)(.1) = 1.7.$$

16 Let $y = \sqrt{x}$, $x = 25$, and $dx = 1$. $y' = \dfrac{1}{2\sqrt{x}}$.

$$\begin{aligned} dy &= y'dx \\ &= \frac{1}{2\sqrt{x}}\,dx \\ &= \frac{1}{2\sqrt{25}}(1) \quad \text{when } x = 25 \text{ and } dx = 1 \\ &= .1 \end{aligned}$$

Since $\sqrt{25} = 5$, $\sqrt{26} \approx 5.1$.

17 The volume is given by $V = x^3$ and the possible error by dV. Since $V' = 3x^2$, $dV = 3x^2 dx$. If we let $x = 3$ and $dx = \pm.05$, then

$$dV = 3(3)^2(\pm.05) = 27(\pm.05) = \pm1.35.$$

Hence, the possible error in the volume is ±1.35 cm^3.

18 $4x^3 + 3x^2y + 2y^2 = 6$.

Differentiating with respect to x, we have

$$\begin{aligned} D_x(4x^3) + D_x(3x^2y) + D_x(2y^2) &= D_x(6) \\ 12x^2 + 3[x^2D_xy + yD_x(x^2)] + 2D_xy^2 &= 0 \\ 12x^2 + 3[x^2y' + y(2x)] + 2(2yy') &= 0 \\ 12x^2 + 3x^2y' + 6xy + 4yy' &= 0 \\ (3x^2 + 4y)y' &= -12x^2 - 6xy \\ y' &= -\frac{12x^2 + 6xy}{3x^2 + 4y} \end{aligned}$$

19 Differentiating $x + x^2y^2 - y = 1$ with respect to x, we have

$$\begin{aligned} x + [x^2D_x(y^2) + y^2(2x)] - D_xy &= 0 \\ x + x^2(2yy') + 2xy^2 - y' &= 0 \\ x + 2x^2yy' + 2xy^2 - y' &= 0 \\ (2x^2y - 1)y' &= -x - 2xy^2 \\ y' &= -\frac{x + 2xy^2}{2x^2y - 1} \end{aligned}$$

Evaluating y' at $P(1, 1)$ gives us the slope m at $P(1, 1)$. Therefore,

$$m = -\frac{1 + 2(1)(1)^2}{2(1)^2(1) - 1} = -3.$$

Using the point-slope form of the line, we have

$$\begin{aligned} y - 1 &= -3(x - 1) \\ y - 1 &= -3x + 3 \\ y + 3x - 4 &= 0. \end{aligned}$$

20 (a) $f(x) = 3x^3 - 4x^2 + x - 5$
$f'(x) = 9x^2 - 8x + 1$
$f''(x) = 18x - 8$

(b) $h(y) = (\sqrt{2y + 1})^3 = (2y + 1)^{3/2}$

$h'(y) = \dfrac{3}{2}(2y + 1)^{1/2}(2) = 3(2y + 1)^{1/2}$

$h''(y) = \dfrac{3}{2}(2y + 1)^{-1/2}(2) = 3(2y + 1)^{-1/2} = \dfrac{3}{(2y + 1)^{1/2}} = \dfrac{3}{\sqrt{2y + 1}}$

21
$$xy - x^2 - y = 0$$
$$xy' + y - 2x - y' = 0$$
$$(x - 1)y' = 2x - y$$
$$y' = \frac{2x - y}{x - 1}$$
$$y'' = \frac{(x - 1)(2 - y') - (2x - y)(1)}{(x - 1)^2}$$
$$= \frac{(x - 1)\left[2 - \dfrac{2x - y}{x - 1}\right] - (2x - y)(1)}{(x - 1)^2}$$
$$= \frac{2(x - 1) - (x - 1)(2x - y) - (2x - y)}{(x - 1)^2}$$
$$= \frac{2x - 2 - 2x^2 + xy + 2x - y - 2x + y}{(x - 1)^2}$$
$$= \frac{-2x^2 + 2x + xy - 2}{(x - 1)^2}$$

22
$$f(x) = (ax + b)^{-1}$$
$$f'(x) = (-1)(ax + b)^{-2}(a) = (-a)(ax + b)^{-2}$$
$$f^{(2)}(x) = (-2)(-a)(ax + b)^{-3}(a) = 2(-a)^2(ax + b)^{-3}$$
$$f^{(3)}(x) = (-3)2a^2(ax + b)^{-4}(a) = 6(-a)^3(ax + b)^{-4}$$
$$\vdots$$
$$f^{(n)}(x) = n!(-a)^n(ax + b)^{-(n+1)}$$

CHAPTER 4

1 $f(x) = x^3 + 6x^2 + 12x$ on $[-4, 4]$
$f'(x) = 3x^2 + 12x + 12$

Since the derivative exists everywhere, the only critical numbers are those for which the derivative is zero.

$$3x^2 + 12x + 12 = 0$$
$$x^2 + 4x + 4 = 0$$
$$(x + 2)^2 = 0$$

Therefore, the only critical number is -2. Now calculating $f(-2)$, $f(-4)$, and $f(4)$, we obtain

$$f(-2) = (-2)^3 + 6(-2)^2 + 12(-2) = -8;$$
$$f(-4) = (-4)^3 + 6(-4)^2 + 12(-4) = -16; \text{ and}$$
$$f(4) = (4)^3 + 6(4)^2 + 12(4) = 208.$$

Hence, the maximum value is 208 and the minimum value is -16.

2 (a) $f(x) = 2x^3 - 9x^2 + 12x + 7$
$f'(x) = 6x^2 - 18x + 12 = 6(x^2 - 3x + 2) = 6(x - 1)(x - 2)$.

Hence, $f'(x) = 0$ if $x = 1$ or $x = 2$, and since $f'(x)$ exists everywhere, these are the only critical numbers.

(b) $f(x) = x^2 - 5x + 3$
$f'(x) = 2x - 5$

Hence, $f'(x) = 0$ if $x = 5/2$ and since $f'(x)$ exists everywhere, this is the only critical number.

(c) $f(x) = \dfrac{1}{1 - x^2}$

$$f'(x) = \frac{(1 - x^2)(0) - 1(-2x)}{(1 - x^2)^2} = \frac{2x}{(1 - x^2)^2}$$

Hence, $f'(x) = 0$ if $x = 0$. The derivative does not exist if $x = 1$ or $x = -1$. Therefore, the critical numbers are 0, 1, and -1.

3   If $f(x) = ax^4$, then $f'(x) = 4ax^3$ and the only critical number is $x = 0$. Therefore, f can have, at most, one local extremum.

Let $a < 0$. If $x > 0$ or $x < 0$, then $x^4 > 0$ and hence $f(x) = ax^4 < 0$. Now since $f(0) = 0$ and $f(x) < f(0)$ when $x > 0$ or $x < 0$, $f(0)$ is a local maximum occuring at $x = 0$.

Let $a > 0$. If $x > 0$ or $x < 0$, then $x^4 > 0$ and hence $f(x) = ax^4 > 0$. Now since $f(0) = 0$ and $f(x) > f(0)$ when $x > 0$ or $x < 0$, $f(0)$ is a local minimum occurring at $x = 0$.

4   $f(x) = 3x^{2/3} + 1$

$f(-1) = 3(-1)^{2/3} + 1 = 4$ and $f(1) = 3(1)^{2/3} + 1 = 4$; therefore, $f(-1) = f(1)$. Now $f'(x) = 2/x^{1/3}$ and hence there is no number c in the interval $(-1, 1)$ such that $f'(c) = 0$. Now since f is not differentiable at $x = 0$, f does not meet the conditions of Rolle's Theorem on $[-1, 1]$; namely, f is not differentiable on $(-1, 1)$. Since f does not meet the hypothesis of Rolle's Theorem, there is no contradiction.

5   If $f(x) = 3x^2 - 2x + 6$, then $f'(x) = 6x - 2$. Notice f is continuous on the interval $[0, 3]$ and f' exists on $(0, 3)$. Therefore, f meets the conditions of the Mean Value Theorem. We want to find c such that

$$f'(c) = \frac{f(3) - f(0)}{3 - 0} \ .$$

Now $f(3) = 3(3)^2 - 2(3) + 6 = 27$ and $f(0) = 3(0)^2 - 2(0) + 6 = 6$. Substituting c in f' we have

$$6c - 2 = \frac{27 - 6}{3 - 0}$$
$$6c - 2 = 7$$
$$6c = 9$$
$$c = \frac{3}{2} \ .$$

6   (a) $f(x) = 2x^3 + 3x^2 - 12x + 5$
$f'(x) = 6x^2 + 6x - 12$

Since $6x^2 + 6x - 12 = 6(x - 1)(x + 2)$, 1 and -2 are critical numbers. Consider the following intervals.

Interval	$(x - 1)$	$(x + 2)$	$f'(x)$	f
$(-\infty, -2)$	$-$	$-$	$+$	increasing
$(-2, 1)$	$-$	$+$	$-$	decreasing
$(1, \infty)$	$+$	$+$	$+$	increasing

Now f is increasing to the left of -2 and decreasing to the right of -2; therefore, f has a local maximum at -2. This local maximum is $f(-2) = 2(-2)^3 + 3(-2)^2 - 12(-2) + 5 = 25$.

Similarly, since f decreases to the left of 1 and increases to the right of 1, f has a local minimum at 1. This local minimum is $f(1) = 2(1)^3 + 3(1) - 12(1) + 5 = -2$.

(b) $f(x) = \dfrac{2}{3}x^3 + \dfrac{2}{x}$

$$f'(x) = 2x^2 - \frac{2}{x^2} = \frac{2x^4 - 2}{x^2} = \frac{2(x^2 + 1)(x - 1)(x + 1)}{x^2} \ .$$

Since f' is zero if $x = 1$ or $x = -1$ and f' is undefined at 0, the critical numbers are $-1, 0$, and 1. Now since $2(x^2 + 1)/x^2$ is positive regardless of x, the sign of $f(x)$ is determined by $(x - 1)(x + 1)$. Now consider the following intervals.

Interval	$(x - 1)$	$(x + 1)$	$f'(x)$	f
$(-\infty, -1)$	$-$	$-$	$+$	increasing
$(-1, 0)$	$-$	$+$	$-$	decreasing
$(0, 1)$	$-$	$+$	$-$	decreasing
$(1, \infty)$	$+$	$+$	$+$	increasing

Since f is increasing to the left of -1 and decreasing to the right of -1, f has a local maximum at -1. Since f is decreasing on both sides of 0, f does not have a local extremum at 0. Since f is decreasing to the left of 1 and increasing to the right of 1, f has a local minimum at 1. The local maximum is $f(-1) = \dfrac{2}{3}(-1)^3 + \dfrac{2}{(-1)} = -2\dfrac{2}{3}$ and the local minimum is $f(1) = \dfrac{2}{3}(1)^3 + \dfrac{2}{1} = 2\dfrac{2}{3}$.

7   We found in Problem 6(a) that f has a local minimum at 1 and the value is -2. Now consider the end-points. We have $f(0) = 5$ and $f(3) = 2(3)^3 + 3(3)^2 - 12(3) + 5 = 50$. Therefore, the absolute minimum is -2 and occurs at 1, and the absolute maximum is 50 and occurs at the end-point 3.

8   The graph of y is concave upward on any interval where $y'' > 0$. We have

$$y = 3x^3 + 4x^2 - 6x + 5$$
$$y' = 9x^2 + 8x - 6$$
$$y'' = 18x + 8.$$

Therefore, the graph of $y = 3x^3 + 4x^2 - 6x + 5$ is concave upward when $x > -4/9$ because if $18x + 8 > 0$, then $x > -4/9$.

9 $y = \dfrac{x}{x - 1}$

$y' = \dfrac{(x - 1)(1) - x(1)}{(x - 1)^2} = -\dfrac{1}{(x - 1)^2}$

$y'' = \dfrac{2}{(x - 1)^3}$

Since $y' < 0$ for all $x \neq 1$, the graph is decreasing for all $x \neq 1$. If $x < 1$, then $y'' < 0$ and the graph is concave downward, and if $x > 1$, then $y'' > 0$ and the graph is concave upward.

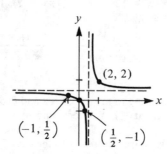

Notice, the graph has no inflection points, but does have a critical point at $x = 1$ because the graph fails to have a tangent at $x = 1$.

10   (a) If $f(x) = 2x^3 - x^2 - 4x - 5$, then
    $f'(x) = 6x^2 - 2x - 4$; and
    $f''(x) = 12x - 2.$

If $f'(x) = 6x^2 - 2x - 4 = 2(3x + 2)(x - 1) = 0$, then $x = -2/3$ or $x = 1$. These are the values of x for which f may have an extremum. Since $f''(-2/3) = 12(-2/3) - 2 = -10 < 0$, f has a local maximum at $x = -2/3$. Since $f''(1) = 12(1) - 2 = 10 > 0$, f has a local minimum at $x = 1$.

Now if $f''(x) = 12x - 2 = 0$, $x = 1/6$. This is the only value for which f may have a point of inflection.

Interval	$f''(x) = 12x - 2$	Concavity
$(-\infty, 1/6)$	$-$	downward
$(1/6, \infty)$	$+$	upward

Since the concavity changes, f has an inflection point at $x = 1/6$.

(b) If $f(x) = \dfrac{1}{x^2 + 3}$, then

$$f'(x) = \frac{-2x}{(x^2 + 3)^2} \text{ ; and}$$

$$f''(x) = \frac{6(x^2 - 1)}{(x^2 + 3)^3} \text{ .}$$

If $f'(x) = 0$, then $x = 0$. Therefore, this is the only value of x for which f may have an extremum. Since $f''(0) = -2/9 < 0$, f has a local maximum at $x = 0$.

Now if $f''(x) = 0$, $x = 1$ or $x = -1$. These are the only values for which f may have a point of inflection.

Interval	$f''(x) = \dfrac{6(x^2 - 1)}{(x^2 + 3)^3}$	Concavity
$(-\infty, -1)$	$+$	upward
$(-1, 1)$	$-$	downward
$(1, \infty)$	$+$	upward

Since the concavity changes from upward to downward around -1 and downward to upward around 1, f has inflection points at both $x = -1$ and $x = 1$.

11   If $f(x) = ax^2 + bx + c$, then
$$f'(x) = 2ax + b; \text{ and}$$
$$f''(x) = 2a.$$

Now since $f''(x)$ is continuous and cannot be zero for any value of x, f cannot have an inflection point.

12   (a) $\displaystyle\lim_{x \to \infty} \frac{2x^3 + x^2 - 5}{5x^3 - 2x + 1} = \lim_{x \to \infty} \frac{2 + \dfrac{1}{x} - \dfrac{5}{x^3}}{5 - \dfrac{2}{x^2} + \dfrac{1}{x^3}}$ dividing numerator and denominator by x^3

$$= \frac{2 + 0 - 0}{5 - 0 + 0}$$

$$= \frac{2}{5}$$

(b) $\displaystyle\lim_{x \to \infty} \frac{\sqrt{x^2 - 1}}{x + 2} = \lim_{x \to \infty} \frac{\sqrt{1 - \dfrac{1}{x^2}}}{1 + \dfrac{2}{x}}$ dividing numerator and denominator by x

$$= \frac{\sqrt{1 - 0}}{1 + 0}$$

$$= 1$$

(c) $\displaystyle\lim_{x \to 2^+} \frac{3}{x - 2} = \infty$

The expression $x - 2$ approaches 0 through positive numbers as x approaches 2 from the right, and since the numerator is positive, the fraction gets numerically larger.

(d) $\displaystyle\lim_{x \to -1^-} \frac{2x}{(x + 1)^3} = \lim_{x \to -1^-} (2x) \cdot \lim_{x \to -1^-} \frac{1}{(x + 1)^3} = \infty$

$\displaystyle\lim_{x \to -1^-} (2x) = -2$ and $\displaystyle\lim_{x \to -1^-} \frac{1}{(x + 1)^3} = -\infty$

Therefore, the product of the limits is ∞ by Theorem (4.27).

13 (a) In order to find the horizontal asymptotes, we want the limit of $f(x)$ as $x \to \pm\infty$.

$$\lim_{x \to \pm\infty} \frac{x^2}{x^2 + x - 6} = \lim_{x \to \pm\infty} \frac{1}{1 + \dfrac{1}{x} - \dfrac{6}{x^2}} = \frac{1}{1 + 0 - 0} = 1.$$

Therefore, $y = 1$ is a horizontal asymptote. Factoring the denominator, we have

$$f(x) = \frac{x^2}{x^2 + x - 6} = \frac{x^2}{(x - 2)(x + 3)} \, .$$

Therefore, $x = 2$ and $x = -3$ are likely candidates for vertical asymptotes.

$$\lim_{x \to 2^-} \frac{x^2}{(x - 2)(x + 3)} = \lim_{x \to 2^-} \left(\frac{1}{x - 2} \right) \cdot \lim_{x \to 2^-} \left(\frac{x^2}{x + 3} \right).$$

Since $\displaystyle\lim_{x \to 2^-} \left(\frac{1}{x - 2} \right) = -\infty$ and $\displaystyle\lim_{x \to 2^-} \left(\frac{x^2}{x + 3} \right) = \frac{4}{5}$,

$$\lim_{x \to 2^-} \frac{x^2}{(x - 2)(x + 3)} = -\infty \text{ by Theorem (4.27).}$$

Similarly,

$$\lim_{x \to 2^+} \frac{x^2}{(x - 2)(x + 3)} = \lim_{x \to 2^+} \left(\frac{1}{x - 2} \right) \cdot \lim_{x \to 2^+} \left(\frac{x^2}{x + 3} \right).$$

Since $\displaystyle\lim_{x \to 2^+} \left(\frac{1}{x - 2} \right) = \infty$ and $\displaystyle\lim_{x \to 2^+} \left(\frac{x^2}{x + 3} \right) = \frac{4}{5}$,

$$\lim_{x \to 2^+} \frac{x^2}{(x - 2)(x + 3)} = \infty \text{ by Theorem (4.27).}$$

In like manner,

$$\lim_{x \to -3^-} \frac{x^2}{(x - 2)(x + 3)} = \lim_{x \to -3^-} \left(\frac{x^2}{x - 2} \right) \cdot \lim_{x \to -3^-} \left(\frac{1}{x + 3} \right).$$

Since $\displaystyle\lim_{x \to -3^-} \left(\frac{x^2}{x - 2} \right) = -\frac{9}{5}$ and $\displaystyle\lim_{x \to -3^-} \left(\frac{1}{x + 3} \right) = -\infty$,

$$\lim_{x \to -3^-} \frac{x^2}{(x - 2)(x + 3)} = \infty \text{ by Theorem (4.27).}$$

Similarly,

$$\lim_{x \to -3^+} \frac{x^2}{(x - 2)(x + 3)} = \lim_{x \to -3^+} \left(\frac{x^2}{x - 2} \right) \cdot \lim_{x \to -3^+} \left(\frac{1}{x + 3} \right).$$

Since $\displaystyle\lim_{x \to -3^+} \left(\frac{x^2}{x - 2} \right) = -\frac{9}{5}$ and $\displaystyle\lim_{x \to -3^+} \left(\frac{1}{x + 3} \right) = \infty$,

$$\lim_{x \to -3^+} \frac{x^2}{(x - 2)(x + 3)} = -\infty \text{ by Theorem (4.27).}$$

Therefore, $x = 2$ and $x = -3$ are vertical asymptotes.

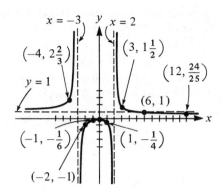

(b) In order to find the horizontal asymptotes, we want the limit of $f(x)$ as $x \to \pm\infty$.

$$\lim_{x \to \pm\infty} \frac{-2x}{(x-3)^2} = \lim_{x \to \pm\infty} \frac{-2x}{x^2 - 6x + 9}$$

$$= \lim_{x \to \pm\infty} \frac{-\dfrac{2}{x}}{1 - \dfrac{6}{x} + \dfrac{9}{x^2}} = \frac{0}{1 - 0 + 0} = 0$$

Therefore, $y = 0$ is a horizontal asymptote.

Now
$$\lim_{x \to 3^-} \frac{-2x}{(x-3)^2} = \lim_{x \to 3^-} (-2x) \cdot \lim_{x \to 3^-} \frac{1}{(x-3)^2} \; .$$

Since $\lim_{x \to 3^-} (-2x) = -6$ and $\lim_{x \to 3^-} \dfrac{1}{(x-3)^2} = \infty$,

$$\lim_{x \to 3^-} \frac{-2x}{(x-3)^2} = -\infty \text{ by Theorem (4.27).}$$

Similarly,

$$\lim_{x \to 3^+} \frac{-2x}{(x-3)^2} = \lim_{x \to 3^+} (-2x) \cdot \lim_{x \to 3^+} \frac{1}{(x-3)^2} \; .$$

Since $\lim_{x \to 3^+} (-2x) = -6$ and $\lim_{x \to 3^+} \dfrac{1}{(x-3)^2} = \infty$,

$$\lim_{x \to 3^+} \frac{-2x}{(x-3)^2} = -\infty \text{ by Theorem (4.27).}$$

Therefore, $x = 3$ is a vertical asymptote.

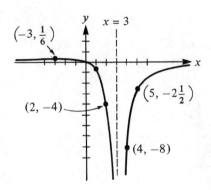

14   If x is the number of new trees planted per acre, then there are $20 + x$ trees per acre having an average yield of $320 - 8x$ peaches per tree. Hence, the total yield of peaches per acre is given by

$$f(x) = (20 + x)(320 - 8x) = 6400 + 160x - 8x^2.$$

Since $f'(x) = 160 - 16x$, $f'(x) = 0$ if $x = 10$. Hence, an additional 10 trees per acre will give the largest crop. Then there will be 30 trees per acre, each yielding an average of 240 peaches.

15   If $T(t) = 1 + t^2 - \dfrac{1}{1 + t}$, then the rate of change is given by $T'(t)$.

$$T'(t) = 2t + \frac{1}{(1 + t)^2}$$

Therefore, the rate of change at $t = 8$ minutes is

$$T'(8) = 2(8) + \frac{1}{(1 + 8)^2} = 16\frac{1}{81} \text{ degrees Celsius per minute.}$$

16 $s(t) = 20 - 5t + t^3$
$s'(t) = v(t) = -5 + 3t^2$
$s''(t) = a(t) = 6t$
Therefore, when $t = 5$, $v = -5 + 3(5)^2 = 70$ cm/sec and $a = 6(5) = 30$ cm/sec².

17   The volume of a sphere is $V = \dfrac{4}{3}\pi r^3$. Therefore,

$$\frac{dV}{dt} = 4\pi r^2 \frac{dr}{dt} \; .$$

Now in order to find $\dfrac{dV}{dt}$ when $r = 8$, we need to find $\dfrac{dr}{dt}$. Since the radius decreases 4 inches in 30 minutes and $\dfrac{dr}{dt}$ is constant, $\dfrac{dr}{dt} = -\dfrac{4}{30} = -\dfrac{2}{15}$. Thus, when $r = 8$,

$$\frac{dV}{dt} = 4\pi(8)^2 \left(-\frac{2}{15}\right) = -\frac{512\pi}{5} \text{ inches}^3/\text{minute.}$$

18   If $y = 2x^2 - x + 1$, $\dfrac{dy}{dt} = 4x\dfrac{dx}{dt} - \dfrac{dx}{dt}$. When $\dfrac{dx}{dt} = 3$ and $x = 1$, $\dfrac{dy}{dt} = 4(1)(3) - (3) = 9$ units per second.

19   (a) $f(x) = 3x - 5$

$$F(x) = \frac{3}{2}x^2 - 5x + C$$

(b) $f(x) = x^2 - 2x + 3$

$$F(x) = \frac{1}{3}x^3 - \frac{2}{2}x^2 + 3x + C = \frac{1}{3}x^3 - x^2 + 3x + C$$

(c) $f(x) = \sqrt{x} + x^{2/3} - 1 = x^{1/2} + x^{2/3} - 1$

$$F(x) = \frac{1}{3/2}x^{3/2} + \frac{1}{5/3}x^{5/3} - x + C = \frac{2}{3}x^{3/2} + \frac{3}{5}x^{5/3} - x + C$$

(d) $f(x) = (2x - 3)(x + 5) = 2x^2 + 7x - 15$

$$F(x) = \frac{2}{3}x^3 + \frac{7}{2}x^2 - 15x + C$$

20   The most general antiderivative is

$$f(x) = \frac{1}{2}x^4 - \frac{1}{2}x^2 + 5x + C.$$

Now since $f(1) = 2$, we have

$$2 = \frac{1}{2}(1)^4 - \frac{1}{2}(1)^2 + 5(1) + C \quad \text{or} \quad 2 = 5 + C.$$

Hence, $C = -3$ and $f(x) = (1/2)x^4 - (1/2)x^2 + 5x - 3$.

21 If $a(t) = 2t^2 - t + 3$, $v(t) = (2/3)t^3 - (1/2)t^2 + 3t + C$. Since $v(0) = 2$, we have $C = 2$ and hence,

$$v(t) = \frac{2}{3}t^3 - \frac{1}{2}t^2 + 3t + 2.$$

Now

$$s(t) = \frac{(2/3)}{4}t^4 - \frac{(1/2)}{3}t^3 + \frac{3}{2}t^2 + 2t + K$$

$$= \frac{1}{6}t^4 - \frac{1}{6}t^3 + \frac{3}{2}t^2 + 2t + K.$$

Since $s(0) = 4$, we have $K = 4$ and hence,

$$s(t) = \frac{1}{6}t^4 - \frac{1}{6}t^3 + \frac{3}{2}t^2 + 2t + 4.$$

22 (a) $C(x) = 100 + 0.03x + 0.001x^2$
$C(300) = 100 + 0.03(300) + 0.001(300)^2 = 100 + 9 + 90 = 199$

(b) The average cost of producing x units is given by

$$C(x) = \frac{C(x)}{x} = \frac{100}{x} + 0.03 + 0.001x$$

$$C(300) = \frac{100}{300} + 0.03 + 0.001(300)$$

$$\approx .333 + 0.03 + 0.3 = .663.$$

(c) The marginal cost is given by $C'(x)$. If

$$C(x) = 100 + 0.03x + 0.001x^2, \text{ then}$$
$$C'(x) = 0.03 + 0.002x, \text{ and hence,}$$
$$C'(300) = 0.03 + 0.002(300) = 0.03 + 0.6 = .63.$$

CHAPTER 5

1 (a) $\sum_{i=1}^{4} (i - 1) = (1 - 1) + (2 - 1) + (3 - 1) + (4 - 1)$
$= 0 + 1 + 2 + 3 = 6$

(b) $\sum_{i=1}^{5} (i^2 + 1) = (1^2 + 1) + (2^2 + 1) + (3^2 + 1) + (4^2 + 1) + (5^2 + 1)$
$= 2 + 5 + 10 + 17 + 26 = 60$

(c) $\sum_{i=1}^{3} i(i^2 + 1) = 1(1^2 + 1) + 2(2^2 + 1) + 3(3^2 + 1)$
$= 1(2) + 2(5) + 3(10) = 2 + 10 + 30 = 42$

2 $\sum_{i=1}^{n} (2i^2 + i + 3) = 2\sum_{i=1}^{n} i^2 + \sum_{i=1}^{n} i + \sum_{i=1}^{n} 3$

$$= 2\left[\frac{n(n + 1)(2n + 1)}{6}\right] + \frac{n(n + 1)}{2} + 3n$$

$$= \frac{2n(n + 1)(2n + 1) + 3n(n + 1) + 18n}{6}$$

$$= \frac{4n^3 + 6n^2 + 2n + 3n^2 + 3n + 18n}{6}$$

$$= \frac{4n^3 + 9n^2 + 23n}{6}$$

3

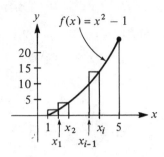

If we subdivide the interval $[1, 5]$ into n equal parts, the length of each subinterval is

$$\Delta x = \frac{(5 - 1)}{n} = \frac{4}{n} \; .$$

Therefore,

$$x_1 = 1 + \frac{4}{n}$$

$$x_2 = 1 + 2\left(\frac{4}{n}\right)$$

$$\vdots$$

$$x_i = 1 + i\left(\frac{4}{n}\right).$$

Since f is increasing, the right end-point of each subinterval produces the number in each subinterval at which f takes on its maximum value. The area of the ith circumscribed rectangle is

$$f(x_i)\Delta x = f\left(1 + i\left(\frac{4}{n}\right)\right)\left(\frac{4}{n}\right)$$

$$= \left[\left(1 + i\left(\frac{4}{n}\right)\right)^2 - 1\right]\left(\frac{4}{n}\right)$$

$$= \left(1 + \frac{8}{n}i + \frac{16}{n^2}i^2 - 1\right)\left(\frac{4}{n}\right)$$

$$= \frac{32}{n^2}i + \frac{64}{n^3}i^2.$$

Now the area is

$$A = \lim_{n \to \infty} \Sigma_{i=1}^n f(x_i)\Delta x \qquad \text{as } \Delta x \to 0, n \to \infty$$

$$= \lim_{n \to \infty} \Sigma_{i=1}^n \left(\frac{32}{n^2}i + \frac{64}{n^3}i^2\right)$$

$$= \lim_{n \to \infty} \left(\frac{32}{n^2} \Sigma_{i=1}^n i + \frac{64}{n^3} \Sigma_{i=1}^n i^2\right) \qquad \begin{array}{l}\text{limit of the sum is} \\ \text{the sum of the limits}\end{array}$$

$$= \lim_{n \to \infty} \left[\frac{32}{n^2}\left(\frac{n(n + 1)}{2}\right) + \frac{64}{n^3}\left(\frac{n(n + 1)(2n + 1)}{6}\right)\right] \qquad \text{using 5.9 \& 5.10}$$

$$= \lim_{n \to \infty} \left[\frac{16(n + 1)}{n} + \frac{32(n + 1)(2n + 1)}{3n^2}\right]$$

$$= \lim_{n \to \infty} \left(\frac{16n + 16}{n} + \frac{64n^2 + 96n + 32}{3n^2}\right)$$

$$= \lim_{n \to \infty} \left(16 + \frac{16}{n} + \frac{64}{3} + \frac{32}{n} + \frac{32}{3n^2}\right)$$

$$= \lim_{n \to \infty} \left(\frac{112}{3} + \frac{48}{n} + \frac{32}{3n^2}\right) = \frac{112}{3} = 37\frac{1}{3} \; .$$

4 (a)

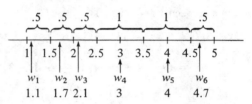

$$R_P = \Sigma_i f(w_i)\triangle x_i \text{ where } f(x) = x^2 - 1$$
$$= f(1.1)(.5) + f(2)(1) + f(3)(1.5) + f(4.5)(1)$$
$$= (.21)(.5) + (3)(1) + (8)(1.5) + (19.25)(1)$$
$$= .105 + 3 + 12.0 + 19.25$$
$$= 34.355$$

(b)

$$R_P = \Sigma_i f(w_i)\triangle x_i \text{ where } f(x) = x^2 - 1$$
$$= f(1.1)(.5) + f(1.7)(.5) + f(2.1)(.5) + f(3)(1) + f(4)(1) + f(4.7)(.5)$$
$$= (.21)(.5) + (1.89)(.5) + (3.41)(.5) + (8)(1) + (15)(1) + (21.09)(.5)$$
$$= .105 + .945 + 1.705 + 8 + 15 + 10.545$$
$$= 36.3$$

Notice that as we increase the number of subintervals, the Riemann sum gets closer to the value obtained for the area in Problem 3.

5 Since $\int_c^d f(x)dx = -\int_d^c f(x)dx$ when $c < d$, we have

$$\int_1^3 (2x^3 - 1)dx = -\int_3^1 (2x^3 - 1)dx.$$

If $\int_1^3 (2x^3 - 1)dx = 78$, then

$$78 = -\int_3^1 (2x^3 - 1)dx \quad \text{or} \quad \int_3^1 (2x^3 - 1)dx = -78.$$

6 $\int_0^3 \dfrac{x^2}{x - 4}dx$ exists because $f(x) = \dfrac{x^2}{x - 4}$ is continuous on [0, 3].

Since $f(x) = \dfrac{1}{x - 1}$ is not continuous at 1, we have no guarantee that $\int_0^1 \dfrac{1}{x - 1}dx$ exists.

Similarly, since $f(x) = \dfrac{1}{x^2 - 4}$ is not continuous at 2, we have no guarantee that $\int_0^3 \dfrac{1}{x^2 - 4}dx$

exists.

7 If x is in the interval [1, 4],

$$x^3 < 2x^3 \quad \text{and} \quad x < 5.$$

Therefore,

$$x^3 + x < 2x^3 + 5 \quad \text{or} \quad x(x^2 + 1) < 2x^3 + 5.$$

By Corollary (5.28), since $x(x^2 + 1) < 2x^3 + 5$ for all x in [1, 4],

$$\int_1^4 x(x^2 + 1)dx < \int_1^4 (2x^3 + 5)dx.$$

8 $\int_a^b f(x)dx + \int_b^c f(x)dx + \int_c^d f(x)dx$
$$= [\int_a^b f(x)dx + \int_b^c f(x)dx] + \int_c^d f(x)dx$$
$$= \int_a^c f(x)dx + \int_c^d f(x)dx \qquad \text{by Theorem (5.26)}$$
$$= \int_a^d f(x)dx \qquad \text{by Theorem (5.26)}$$

9   According to the Mean Value Theorem for Definite Integrals, there is a number z between 1 and 3 such that

$$\frac{58}{3} = (2z^2 + 1)(3 - 1).$$

Solving for z, we have

$$\frac{58}{3} = (2z^2 + 1)(2)$$
$$58 = (2z^2 + 1)(6)$$
$$58 = 12z^2 + 6$$
$$12z^2 = 52$$
$$z^2 = 4.33$$
$$z \approx \pm 2.08.$$

The only value between 1 and 3 is 2.08.

10   $\displaystyle\int_{-1}^{3} (x^2 - 2x + 3)dx = \left[\frac{1}{3}x^3 - x^2 + 3x\right]_{-1}^{3}$

$$= (9 - 9 + 9) - \left(-\frac{1}{3} - 1 - 3\right)$$
$$= 9 - \left(-\frac{13}{3}\right) = \frac{40}{3}$$

11   $\displaystyle\int_{1}^{2} \frac{t - 6}{t^3}dt = \int_{1}^{2} \left(\frac{1}{t^2} - \frac{6}{t^3}\right)dt = \int_{1}^{2} (t^{-2} - 6t^{-3})dt$

$$= \left[-\frac{1}{t} + \frac{3}{t^2}\right]_{1}^{2} = \left(-\frac{1}{2} + \frac{3}{4}\right) - (-1 + 3)$$
$$= \frac{1}{4} - 2 = -\frac{7}{4}$$

12   $\displaystyle\int_{-1}^{1} (1 + x^2)^2 dx = \int_{-1}^{1} (1 + 2x^2 + x^4)dx$

$$= \left[x + \frac{2}{3}x^3 + \frac{1}{5}x^5\right]_{-1}^{1}$$
$$= \left(1 + \frac{2}{3} + \frac{1}{5}\right) - \left(-1 - \frac{2}{3} - \frac{1}{5}\right)$$
$$= \frac{28}{15} - \left(-\frac{28}{15}\right) = \frac{56}{15}$$

13   $|x - 2| = \begin{cases} x - 2 \text{ if } x \geq 2 \\ 2 - x \text{ if } x < 2 \end{cases}$

Therefore,

$$\int_{0}^{4} |x - 2|dx = \int_{0}^{2} (2 - x)dx + \int_{2}^{4} (x - 2)dx$$
$$= \left[2x - \frac{1}{2}x^2\right]_{0}^{2} + \left[\frac{1}{2}x^2 - 2x\right]_{2}^{4}$$
$$= [(4 - 2) - (0)] + [(8 - 8) - (2 - 4)]$$
$$= 2 + 2 = 4$$

14   $\int_{2}^{3} \sqrt[3]{x - 1}\, dx = \int_{2}^{3} (x - 1)^{1/3}\, dx$

If $u = x - 1$, then $du = dx$. Now if $x = 2$, then $u = 2 - 1 = 1$, and if $x = 3$, then $u = 3 - 1 = 2$. Therefore,

$$\int_{2}^{3} (x - 1)^{1/3}\, dx = \int_{1}^{2} u^{1/3}\, du = \left[\frac{3}{4}u^{4/3}\right]_{1}^{2}$$
$$= \left(\frac{3}{4}2\sqrt[3]{2}\right) - \left(\frac{3}{4}\right) = \frac{3}{4}(2\sqrt[3]{2} - 1).$$

15   If $u = y^2 + 1$, then $du = 2y\,dy$. If $y = 0$, then $u = 0 + 1 = 1$, and if $y = \sqrt{3}$, then $u = 3 + 1 = 4$. Therefore,

$$\int_0^{\sqrt{3}} \frac{y}{\sqrt{y^2 + 1}}\, dy = \int_0^{\sqrt{3}} (y^2 + 1)^{-1/2} y\, dy$$

$$= \frac{1}{2} \int_0^{\sqrt{3}} (y^2 + 1)^{-1/2} 2y\, dy$$

$$= \frac{1}{2} \int_1^4 u^{-1/2}\, du = \frac{1}{2} \left[2u^{1/2} \right]_1^4$$

$$= \frac{1}{2} [4 - 2] = 1.$$

16   If we let $u = 2x - 1$, then $du = 2\,dx$. Therefore,

$$\int (2x - 1)^5\, dx = \frac{1}{2} \int (2x - 1)^5 (2)\, dx$$

$$= \frac{1}{2} \int u^5\, du = \frac{1}{2} \left(\frac{1}{6} u^6 \right) + C$$

$$= \frac{1}{12} u^6 + C = \frac{1}{12} (2x - 1)^6 + C.$$

17   If we let $u = 8 - y^2$, then $du = -2y\,dy$. Therefore,

$$\int \sqrt{8 - y^2}\, y\, dy = -\frac{1}{2} \int (8 - y^2)^{1/2} (-2y)\, dy$$

$$= -\frac{1}{2} \int u^{1/2}\, du = -\frac{1}{2} \left(\frac{2}{3} u^{3/2} \right) + C$$

$$= -\frac{1}{3} u^{3/2} + C = -\frac{1}{3} (8 - y^2)^{3/2} + C.$$

18   If we let $u = v^3 + 1$, then $du = 3v^2\,dv$. Therefore,

$$\int \frac{v^2}{(v^3 + 1)^2}\, dv = \frac{1}{3} \int (v^3 + 1)^{-2} (3v^2)\, dv$$

$$= \frac{1}{3} \int u^{-2}\, du = \frac{1}{3} (-u^{-1}) + C$$

$$= -\frac{1}{3u} + C = -\frac{1}{3(v^3 + 1)} + C.$$

19   If we let $u = 1 - 4t$, then $du = -4\,dt$. Therefore,

$$\int \frac{3}{\sqrt{1 - 4t}}\, dt = -\frac{1}{4} \int 3(1 - 4t)^{-1/2} (-4)\, dt$$

$$= -\frac{1}{4} \int 3u^{-1/2}\, du = -\frac{1}{4} \left(\frac{3u^{1/2}}{1/2} \right) + C$$

$$= -\frac{3}{2} u^{1/2} + C = -\frac{3}{2} \sqrt{1 - 4t} + C.$$

20   If we let $u = \sqrt{x} + 1$, then $du = \frac{1}{2\sqrt{x}}\, dx$. Therefore,

$$\int \frac{(\sqrt{x} + 1)^2}{\sqrt{x}}\, dx = 2 \int (\sqrt{x} + 1)^2 \left(\frac{1}{2\sqrt{x}} \right) dx$$

$$= 2 \int u^2\, du = \frac{2}{3} u^3 + C = \frac{2}{3} (\sqrt{x} + 1)^3 + C.$$

21   The area is indicated by

$$\int_1^3 (2x^2 - 1)\, dx.$$

Therefore, the desired area is

$$\int_1^3 (2x^2 - 1)\, dx = \left[\frac{2}{3}x^3 - x\right]_1^3 = (18 - 3) - \left(\frac{2}{3} - 1\right) = 15 + \frac{1}{3} = \frac{46}{3}.$$

22 (a) The integral is

$$\int_0^4 \frac{1}{1 + x^2}\, dx.$$

i	x_i	$f(x_i)$	m	$mf(x_i)$
0	0.0	1.0000	1	1.0000
1	0.4	.8621	2	1.7242
2	0.8	.6098	2	1.2196
3	1.2	.4098	2	.8196
4	1.6	.2809	2	.5618
5	2.0	.2000	2	.4000
6	2.4	.1479	2	.2958
7	2.8	.1131	2	.2262
8	3.2	.0890	2	.1780
9	3.6	.0716	2	.1432
10	4.0	.0588	1	.0588
				6.6272

Since $(b - a)/2n = (4 - 0)/20 = .2$, we have by the Trapezoidal Rule

$$\int_0^4 \frac{1}{1 + x^2}\, dx \approx (.2)(6.6272) = 1.3254.$$

(b)

i	x_i	$f(x_i)$	m	$mf(x_i)$
0	0.0	1.0000	1	1.0000
1	0.4	.8621	4	3.4484
2	0.8	.6098	2	1.2196
3	1.2	.4098	4	1.6392
4	1.6	.2809	2	.5618
5	2.0	.2000	4	.8000
6	2.4	.1479	2	.2958
7	2.8	.1131	4	.4524
8	3.2	.0890	2	.1780
9	3.6	.0716	4	.2864
10	4.0	.0588	1	.0588
				9.9404

Since $(b - a)/3n = (4 - 0)/30 \approx .1333$, we have by Simpson's Rule

$$\int_0^4 \frac{1}{1 + x^2}\, dx \approx (.1333)(9.9404) \approx 1.3251.$$

CHAPTER 6

1

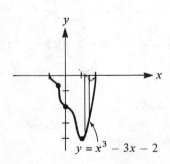

$y = x^3 - 3x - 2$

If we consider vertical rectangles, we let the width be dx and the height is the value of y of the upper boundary of the region minus the value of y of the lower boundary, which is

$$0 - (x^3 - 3x - 2) = -x^3 + 3x + 2.$$

Therefore, the area is

$$\int_{-1}^{2} (-x^3 + 3x + 2)\, dx = \left[-\frac{x^4}{4} + \frac{3x^2}{2} + 2x \right]_{-1}^{2}$$

$$= (-4 + 6 + 4) - \left(-\frac{1}{4} + \frac{3}{2} - 2 \right)$$

$$= \frac{27}{4} \text{ square units.}$$

2 The graphs will intersect in those points whose coordinates are the simultaneous solutions of the given equations. Eliminating y, we have

$$x - 3 = 3x - x^2$$
$$x^2 - 2x - 3 = 0$$
$$(x + 1)(x - 3) = 0.$$

Thus $x = -1$ or $x = 3$ and the common points of the two graphs are $(-1, -4)$ and $(3, 0)$.

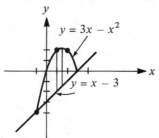

Considering vertical rectangles, the upper boundary of this region has equation

$$y = 3x - x^2 \quad \text{for} \quad -1 \le x \le 3$$

and the lower boundary has equation

$$y = x - 3 \quad \text{for} -1 \le x \le 3.$$

Therefore, the area is

$$\int_{-1}^{3} [(3x - x^2) - (x - 3)]\, dx = \int_{-1}^{3} (-x^2 + 2x + 3)\, dx$$

$$= \left[-\frac{x^3}{3} + x^2 + 3x \right]_{-1}^{3}$$

$$= (-9 + 9 + 9) - \left(\frac{1}{3} + 1 - 3 \right)$$

$$= \frac{32}{3} \text{ square units.}$$

3

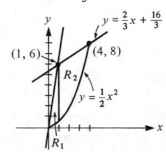

The region must be divided into two subregions, R_1 and R_2; then we can determine the area of each and add them together.

For region R_1, the upper and lower boundaries are $y = 6x$ and $y = \frac{1}{2}x^2$ for $0 \le x \le 1$, respectively, and hence the area of R_1 is

$$\int_0^1 \left(6x - \frac{1}{2}x^2\right) dx = \left[3x^2 - \frac{x^3}{6}\right]_0^1 = 3 - \frac{1}{6} = \frac{17}{6}.$$

For region R_2, the upper and lower boundaries are $y = \frac{2}{3}x + \frac{16}{3}$ and $y = \frac{1}{2}x^2$ for $1 \le x \le 4$, respectively, and hence the area of R_2 is

$$\int_1^4 \left[\left(\frac{2}{3}x + \frac{16}{3}\right) - \frac{1}{2}x^2\right] dx = \int_1^4 \left(\frac{2}{3}x + \frac{16}{3} - \frac{x^2}{2}\right) dx$$
$$= \left[\frac{x^2}{3} + \frac{16}{3}x - \frac{x^3}{6}\right]_1^4$$
$$= \left(\frac{16}{3} + \frac{64}{3} - \frac{32}{3}\right) - \left(\frac{1}{3} + \frac{16}{3} - \frac{1}{6}\right)$$
$$= \frac{48}{3} - \frac{33}{6} = \frac{63}{6}.$$

Therefore, the area is $\frac{17}{6} + \frac{63}{6} = \frac{40}{3}$ square units.

4

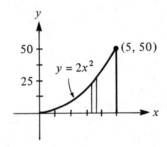

We want to revolve the above region about the x-axis. Since the radius of a generated disk is $2x^2$, the volume of a typical disk is $\pi(2x^2)^2\,dx = \pi(4x^4)\,dx$. Therefore,

$$V = \pi \int_0^5 4x^4\,dx = \pi\left[\frac{4}{5}x^5\right]_0^5$$
$$= 2500\pi \text{ cubic units.}$$

5

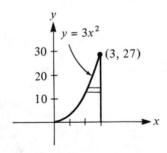

We want to revolve the above region about the y-axis. When a horizontal rectangle is revolved about the y-axis, a washer is generated. The outer radius is 3 and the inner radius is $\sqrt{\frac{y}{3}}$. Therefore, the volume of one washer is

$$\pi\left[3^2 - \left(\sqrt{\frac{y}{3}}\right)^2\right]dy = \pi\left(9 - \frac{y}{3}\right) dy$$

and thus,

$$V = \pi \int_0^{27} \left(9 - \frac{y}{3}\right) dy = \pi \left[9y - \frac{y^2}{6}\right]_0^{27}$$
$$= \pi \left[243 - \frac{729}{6}\right]$$
$$= \frac{729}{6}\pi \text{ cubic units.}$$

6

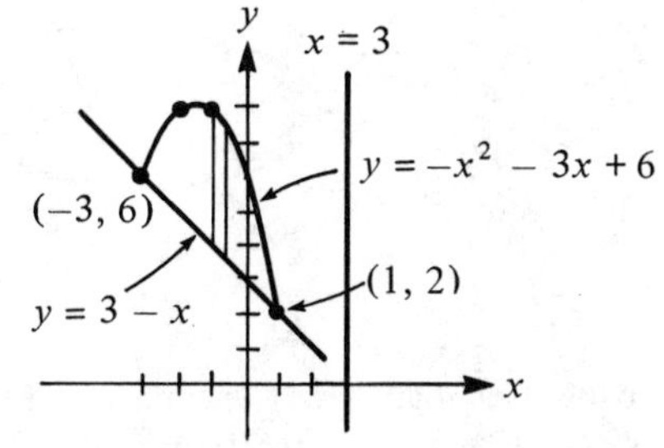

A typical vertical rectangle in the above region rotated about the line $x = 3$ generates a cylindrical shell. The altitude of a typical shell is $(-x^2 - 3x + 6) - (3 - x) = -x^2 - 2x + 3$; the radius is $3 - x$; and the thickness is dx. Therefore, the volume is

$$V = 2\pi \int_{-3}^{1} (-x^2 - 2x + 3)(3 - x) \, dx$$
$$= 2\pi \int_{-3}^{1} (x^3 - x^2 - 9x + 9) \, dx$$
$$= 2\pi \left[\frac{x^4}{4} - \frac{x^3}{3} - \frac{9x^2}{2} + 9x\right]_{-3}^{1}$$
$$= 2\pi \left[\left(\frac{1}{4} - \frac{1}{3} - \frac{9}{2} + 9\right) - \left(\frac{81}{4} + 9 - \frac{81}{2} - 27\right)\right]$$
$$= 2\pi \left[\frac{53}{12} - \left(-\frac{153}{4}\right)\right] = \frac{256}{3}\pi \text{ cubic units.}$$

7

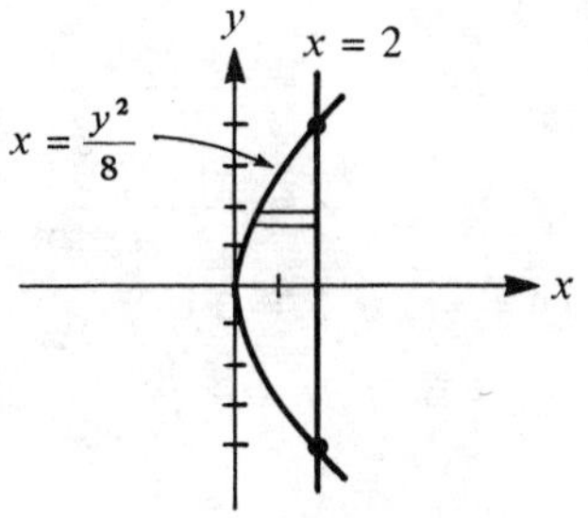

When a horizontal rectangle is revolved about the line $x = 2$, a disk is generated with radius $2 - (y^2/8)$. Therefore, the volume is

$$V = \pi \int_{-4}^{4} \left(2 - \frac{y^2}{8}\right)^2 dy$$

or, since the region is symmetrical about the x-axis,

$$V = 2\pi \int_0^4 \left(2 - \frac{y^2}{8}\right)^2 dy = 2\pi \int_0^4 \left(4 - \frac{y^2}{2} + \frac{y^4}{64}\right) dy$$

$$= 2\pi \left[4y - \frac{y^3}{6} + \frac{y^5}{320}\right]_0^4 = 2\pi \left(16 - \frac{64}{6} + \frac{1024}{320}\right) = \frac{256}{15}\pi.$$

8

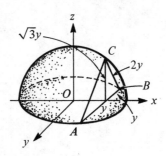

Let the x-axis be the fixed diameter. The equation of the circle is $x^2 + y^2 = 9$. The cross section ABC of the solid is an equilateral triangle of side $2y$ and altitude $\sqrt{3}y$, and thus $A(x) = \frac{1}{2}(2y)(\sqrt{3}y) = \sqrt{3}y^2 = \sqrt{3}(9 - {}'x^2)$. Therefore,

$$V = 2\sqrt{3}\int_0^3 (9 - x^2)\, dx = 2\sqrt{3}\left[9x - \frac{x^3}{3}\right]_0^3$$
$$= 2\sqrt{3}(27 - 9) = 36\sqrt{3} \text{ cubic units.}$$

9 By Hooke's Law, $f(x) = kx$, where $f(x)$ is the force and x is the stretch. When $x = .25$, $f(x) = 25$. Hence, $25 = .25k$ or $k = 100$, and $f(x) = 100x$. The work corresponding to a stretch dx is $100x\, dx$ and the required work is given by

$$W = \int_0^2 100x\, dx = [50x^2]_0^2 = 200 \text{ m-lb.}$$

10 If $y = \frac{1}{24}x^3 + 2x^{-1}$, then $y' = \frac{1}{8}x^2 - \frac{2}{x^2} = \frac{x^4 - 16}{8x^2}$ and

$$1 + (y')^2 = 1 + \left(\frac{x^4 - 16}{8x^2}\right)^2$$
$$= 1 + \frac{x^8 - 32x^4 + 256}{64x^4}$$
$$= \frac{64x^4 + x^8 - 32x^4 + 256}{64x^4}$$
$$= \frac{x^8 + 32x^4 + 256}{64x^4} = \frac{(x^4 + 16)^2}{64x^4}.$$

The arc length from $x = 1$ to $x = 3$ is

$$\int_1^3 \sqrt{1 + (y')^2}\, dx = \int_1^3 \sqrt{\frac{(x^4 + 16)^2}{64x^4}}\, dx = \int_1^3 \frac{x^4 + 16}{8x^2}\, dx$$
$$= \frac{1}{8}\int_1^3 (x^2 + 16x^{-2})\, dx = \frac{1}{8}\left[\frac{x^3}{3} - \frac{16}{x}\right]_1^3$$
$$= \frac{1}{8}\left[\left(9 - \frac{16}{3}\right) - \left(\frac{1}{3} - 16\right)\right] = \frac{29}{12}.$$

11 If $y = x^2/12$, then $y' = x/6$ and $1 + (y')^2 = 1 + (x^2/36) = (36 + x^2)/36$. Therefore, the arc length is

$$\frac{1}{6}\int_0^6 \sqrt{36 + x^2}\, dx.$$

12 If we let $f(x) = 2x^3 - 1$, then $f'(x) = 6x^2$ and

$$ds = \sqrt{1 + 36x^4}\, dx.$$

We obtain an approximation by letting $x = 1$ and $dx = 0.1$. Therefore,

$$ds = \sqrt{1 + 36}(0.1) = \sqrt{37}(0.1) \approx .608.$$

13 The total depreciation after 5 years is

$$\int_0^5 (1 - 2t^3)\, dt = \left[t - \frac{t^4}{2} \right]_0^5 = 5 - \frac{625}{2} = \$307.50.$$

CHAPTER 7

1 (a) If $f(x) = ax^2 + c$, then the graph is a parabola with vertex at the point $(0, c)$. Therefore, the vertex is at the point $(0, -2)$ and since $a = 3 > 0$, the parabola opens upward.

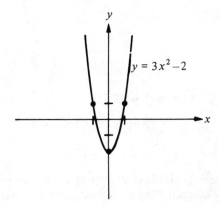

$y = 3x^2 - 2$

(b) The vertex is at the point $(0, 3)$ and since $a = -1 < 0$, the parabola opens downward.

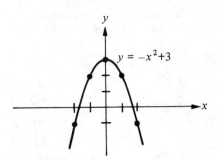

$y = -x^2 + 3$

2 (a) $f(x) = 3(x^2 + 2x + \underline{}) - 2 = 3(x^2 + 2x + 1) - 2 - 3 = 3(x + 1)^2 - 5$

(b) $f(x) = -2(x^2 - \dfrac{3}{2}x + \underline{}) + 4 = -2\left(x^2 - \dfrac{3}{2}x + \dfrac{9}{16}\right) + 4 + \dfrac{9}{8}$

$$= -2\left(x - \dfrac{3}{4}\right)^2 + \dfrac{41}{8}$$

3 (a) Completing the square, we have

$$f(x) = 3\left(x^2 + \frac{2}{3}x + \underline{}\right) - 5 = 3\left(x^2 + \frac{2}{3}x + \frac{1}{9}\right) - 5 - \frac{1}{3}$$

$$= 3\left(x + \frac{1}{3}\right)^2 - \frac{16}{3}.$$

Therefore, the vertex is the point $(-1/3, -16/3)$. Now we solve $3x^2 + 2x - 5 = 0$ using the quadratic formula to find the x-intercepts.

$$x = \frac{-2 \pm \sqrt{2^2 - 4(3)(-5)}}{2(3)} = \frac{-2 \pm \sqrt{64}}{6} = \frac{-2 \pm 8}{6}$$

Therefore, the x-intercepts are $(-2 + 8)/6 = 1$ and $(-2 - 8)/6 = -5/3$. Since $a = 3 > 0$, the parabola opens upward.

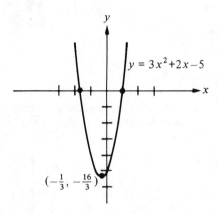

(b) Completing the square, we have

$$f(x) = -5\left(x^2 + \frac{8}{5}x + \underline{\quad}\right) + 2 = -5\left(x^2 + \frac{8}{5}x + \frac{16}{25}\right) + 2 + \frac{16}{5}$$

$$= -5\left(x + \frac{4}{5}\right)^2 + \frac{26}{5}.$$

Therefore, the vertex is at the point $(-4/5, 26/5)$. Now we solve $-5x^2 - 8x + 2 = 0$ using the quadratic formula to find the x-intercepts.

$$x = \frac{8 \pm \sqrt{(-8)^2 - 4(-5)(2)}}{2(-5)} = \frac{8 \pm \sqrt{104}}{-10} \approx \frac{8 \pm 10.2}{-10}$$

Therefore, the x-intercepts are approximately $(8 + 10.2)/(-10) = -1.82$ and $(8 - 10.2)/(-10) = .22$. Since $a = -5 < 0$, the parabola opens downward.

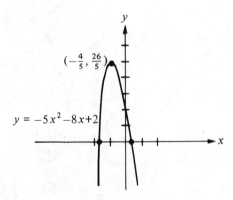

4 Completing the square in y, we obtain

$$x = (y^2 - 2y + \underline{\quad}) - 3 = (y^2 - 2y + 1) - 3 - 1$$
$$= (y - 1)^2 - 4 \quad \text{or} \quad x + 4 = (y - 1)^2.$$

The vertex is the point $(-4, 1)$ and since $a = 1 > 0$, the parabola opens to the right. To find the y-intercepts of the graph we solve the quadratic $y^2 - 2y - 3 = 0$.

$$y^2 - 2y - 3 = (y + 1)(y - 3) = 0, \qquad y = -1 \text{ and } 3$$

Plotting the vertex and the y-intercepts, we have the following graph.

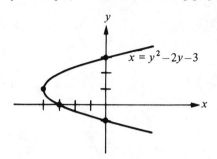

5 Dividing by 144, we have $x^2/9 + y^2/16 = 1$. In the standard form $a^2 = 9$ and $b^2 = 16$. Hence, the x-intercepts are ± 3 and the y-intercepts are ± 4.

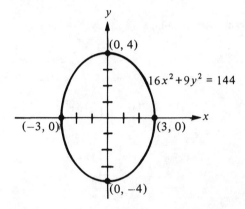

6 Dividing by 16, we have $x^2/16 - y^2/1 = 1$. In the standard form $a^2 = 16$ and $b^2 = 1$. Therefore, the x-intercepts are ± 4 and the asymptotes are $y = \pm(b/a)x$ or $y = \pm(1/4)x$.

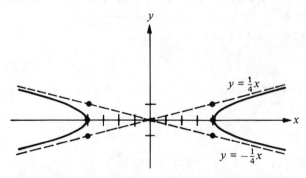

7 The standard form of an ellipse with the center at the origin is $x^2/a^2 + y^2/b^2 = 1$. Since the x-intercepts are ± 6, we have $a^2 = 36$ and hence $x^2/36 + y^2/b^2 = 1$. Now if the ellipse passes through the point $(0, 2)$, we have $0/36 + 4/b^2 = 1$ or $b^2 = 4$. Therefore, the desired equation is $x^2/36 + y^2/4 = 1$ or $x^2 + 9y^2 = 36$.

8 If $4x^2 + 3y^2 = 31$, then $8x + 6yy' = 0$ and thus $y' = -4x/3y$. At the point $P(-1, 3)$, $y' = 4/9$. Now we want the line through $P(-1, 3)$ with slope $m = 4/9$. The point-slope form of the line is

$$y - y_1 = m(x - x_1).$$

Therefore, the desired line has equation

$$y - 3 = \frac{4}{9}(x - (-1))$$
$$9y - 27 = 4x + 4$$
$$9y - 4x - 31 = 0.$$

9

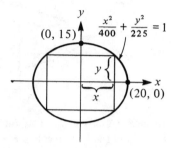

We want the maximum value of xy. We have

$$y^2 = 225\left(1 - \frac{x^2}{400}\right) = \frac{225}{400}(400 - x^2).$$

Thus $y = (3/4)\sqrt{400 - x^2}$. Now we want the value of x such that

$$f(x) = x\left[\frac{3}{4}\sqrt{400 - x^2}\right] = \frac{3}{4}x\sqrt{400 - x^2}$$

is a maximum.

$$f'(x) = \frac{3}{4}\left[x\left(\frac{1}{2}\right)(400 - x^2)^{-1/2}(-2x) + (400 - x^2)^{1/2}\right]$$
$$= \frac{3}{4}\left[\frac{-x^2}{\sqrt{400 - x^2}} + \sqrt{400 - x^2}\right] = \frac{3}{4}\left[\frac{-2x^2 + 400}{\sqrt{400 - x^2}}\right]$$

The maximum occurs when $-2x^2 + 400 = 0$ or when $x = 10\sqrt{2}$. If $x = 10\sqrt{2}$, then $y = (3/4)\sqrt{400 - 200} = (15/2)\sqrt{2}$.

The actual dimensions are $2x$ by $2y$. Therefore, the dimensions of the rectangle are $20\sqrt{2}$ by $15\sqrt{2}$.

10   The standard form of a hyperbola is

$$\frac{x^2}{a^2} - \frac{y^2}{b^2} = 1.$$

We have $a = 2$ and $c = 3$. Since $c^2 = a^2 + b^2$, $9 = 4 + b^2$ and $b^2 = 5$. Therefore, the desired equation is

$$\frac{x^2}{4} - \frac{y^2}{5} = 1.$$

11

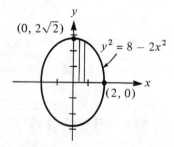

$$V = 2\pi \int_0^2 (8 - 2x^2)\, dx = 2\pi \left[8x - \frac{2}{3}x^3 \right]_0^2$$
$$= 2\pi \left[16 - \frac{16}{3} \right]$$
$$= 2\pi \left(\frac{32}{3} \right) = \frac{64\pi}{3} \text{ cubic units}$$

12 (a) Let $\begin{cases} x' = x + 2 \\ y' = y - 4 \end{cases}$. Then we have

$$\frac{x'^2}{9} + \frac{y'^2}{16} = 1.$$

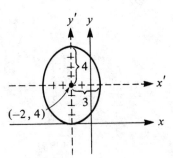

(b)
$$2x^2 - 8x - 4y^2 + 16y = 12$$
$$(2x^2 - 8x \underline{\qquad}) + (-4y^2 + 16y \underline{\qquad}) = 12$$
$$2(x^2 - 4x \underline{\qquad}) - 4(y^2 - 4y \underline{\qquad}) = 12$$
$$2(x^2 - 4x + 4) - 4(y^2 - 4y + 4) = 12 + 8 - 16$$
$$2(x - 2)^2 - 4(y - 2)^2 = 4$$
$$\frac{(x - 2)^2}{2} - \frac{(y - 2)^2}{1} = 1$$

Let $\begin{cases} x' = x - 2 \\ y' = y - 2 \end{cases}$. Then we have

$$\frac{x'^2}{2} - \frac{y'^2}{1} = 1.$$

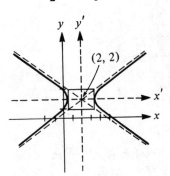

13 (a) We have $2x^2 + 3xy + 2y^2 = 7$.

$$\cot 2\phi = \frac{2 - 2}{3} = 0$$
$$2\phi = 90°$$
$$\phi = 45°$$

(b) $\begin{cases} x = x' \cos \phi - y' \sin \phi \\ y = x' \sin \phi + y' \cos \phi \end{cases}$

$\sin \phi = \cos \phi = \dfrac{\sqrt{2}}{2}$. Therefore,

$$\begin{cases} x = \dfrac{\sqrt{2}}{2}x' - \dfrac{\sqrt{2}}{2}y' \\ y = \dfrac{\sqrt{2}}{2}x' + \dfrac{\sqrt{2}}{2}y' \end{cases}.$$

(c) $2\left(\dfrac{\sqrt{2}}{2}x' - \dfrac{\sqrt{2}}{2}y'\right)^2 + 3\left(\dfrac{\sqrt{2}}{2}x' - \dfrac{\sqrt{2}}{,2}y'\right)\left(\dfrac{\sqrt{2}}{2}x' + \dfrac{\sqrt{2}}{2}y'\right)$

$$+ 2\left(\dfrac{\sqrt{2}}{2}x' + \dfrac{\sqrt{2}}{2}y'\right)^2 = 7$$

$$2\left(\dfrac{1}{2}x'^2 - x'y' + \dfrac{1}{2}y'^2\right) + 3\left(\dfrac{1}{2}x'^2 - \dfrac{1}{2}y'^2\right)$$

$$+ 2\left(\dfrac{1}{2}x'^2 + x'y' + \dfrac{1}{2}y'^2\right) = 7$$

$$\dfrac{7}{2}x'^2 + \dfrac{1}{2}y'^2 = 7$$

$$\dfrac{x'^2}{2} + \dfrac{y'^2}{14} = 1$$

(d)

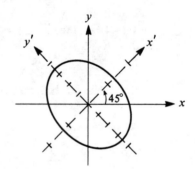

CHAPTER 8

1 $f(x) = \ln(x^3 + 2)$

$f'(x) = \dfrac{1}{x^3 + 2}D_x(x^3 + 2) = \dfrac{3x^2}{x^3 + 2}$

2 $f(x) = \ln(2x^2 + x - 1)$

$f'(x) = \dfrac{1}{2x^2 + x - 1}D_x(2x^2 + x - 1) = \dfrac{4x + 1}{2x^2 + x - 1}$

3 $f(x) = x^2 \ln x$

$f'(x) = x^2D_x(\ln x) + \ln x\, D_x(x^2)$

$= x^2\left(\dfrac{1}{x}\right) + \ln x(2x) = x + 2x \ln x$

4 $f(x) = \ln\left(\dfrac{\sqrt{x+1}}{x^2+3}\right)$

$f'(x) = \dfrac{1}{\dfrac{\sqrt{x+1}}{x^2+3}} D_x\left(\dfrac{\sqrt{x+1}}{x^2+3}\right) = \dfrac{x^2+3}{\sqrt{x+1}}\left[\dfrac{\dfrac{(x^2+3)(1/2)}{\sqrt{x+1}} - \sqrt{x+1}\,(2x)}{(x^2+3)^2}\right]$

$= \dfrac{x^2+3}{\sqrt{x+1}}\left(\dfrac{x^2+3-4x(x+1)}{2\sqrt{x+1}(x^2+3)^2}\right) = \dfrac{x^2+3}{\sqrt{x+1}}\left(\dfrac{-3x^2-4x+3}{2\sqrt{x+1}(x^2+3)^2}\right)$

$= \dfrac{-3x^2-4x+3}{2(x+1)(x^2+3)}$

5 $f(x) = 3e^{-2x}$
$f'(x) = 3e^{-2x}(-2) = -6e^{-2x}$

6 $f(x) = \sqrt{1-e^{3x}} = (1-e^{3x})^{1/2}$
$f'(x) = \dfrac{1}{2}(1-e^{3x})^{-1/2}D_x(1-e^{3x}) = \dfrac{1}{2\sqrt{1-e^{3x}}}D_x(1-e^{3x}) = \dfrac{-3e^{3x}}{2\sqrt{1-e^{3x}}}$

7 $f(x) = x^2e^{-3x}$
$f'(x) = x^2D_x(e^{-3x}) + e^{-3x}D_x(x^2) = x^2(-3e^{-3x}) + e^{-3x}(2x) = -3x^2e^{-3x} + 2xe^{-3x}$

8 $f(x) = 3^{2x-1}$
$f'(x) = 3^{2x-1}(\ln 3)D_x(2x-1) = 3^{2x-1}(\ln 3)(2) = (2\ln 3)3^{2x-1}$

9 $f(x) = \log_{10}(2x^2-3)$
$f'(x) = \dfrac{1}{(2x^2-3)(\ln 10)}D_x(2x^2-3) = \dfrac{4x}{(\ln 10)(2x^2-3)}$

10   If $y = x^2 - \ln x$, then $y' = 2x - (1/x)$. Therefore, if $x = 1$, $y' = m = 1$. The point-slope form of the line is

$$y - y_1 = m(x - x_1).$$

We want an equation of the line through $P(1, 1)$ with $m = 1$. Thus,

$$y - 1 = (1)(x - 1)$$
$$y - 1 = x - 1$$
$$y - x = 0.$$

11 $e^y - x^2 + 2y = 5$
$e^y y' - 2x + 2y' = 0$
$(e^y + 2)y' = 2x$

$$y' = \dfrac{2x}{e^y + 2}$$

12 $f(x) = x^2e^x$
$f'(x) = x^2e^x + 2xe^x$
$f''(x) = (x^2e^x + 2xe^x) + (2xe^x + 2e^x) = x^2e^x + 4xe^x + 2e^x$

Solving $f'(x) = 0$, we have

$$x^2e^x + 2xe^x = 0$$
$$(x + 2)xe^x = 0.$$

Therefore, the critical values are $x = -2$ and $x = 0$. Since

$$f''(-2) = (-2)^2e^{-2} + 4(-2)e^{-2} + 2e^{-2}$$
$$= e^{-2}(4 - 8 + 2) = -2e^{-2} < 0,$$

a local maximum occurs at $x = -2$ or at the point $(-2, 4e^{-2})$. Since

$$f''(0) = (0)^2e^0 + 4(0)e^0 + 2e^0 = 2 > 0,$$

a local minimum occurs at $x = 0$ or at the point $(0, 0)$.

13   If we let $u = x^2 - 3$, then $du = 2x\, dx$ and

$$\int \frac{x}{x^2 - 3}\, dx = \frac{1}{2} \int \frac{du}{u} = \frac{1}{2} \ln |u| + C = \frac{1}{2} \ln |x^2 - 3| + C.$$

14   If we let $u = x^3_. - 1$, $du = 3x^2\, dx$ and

$$\int \frac{5x^2}{x^3 - 1}\, dx = \frac{5}{3} \int \frac{du}{u} = \frac{5}{3} \ln |u| + C = \frac{5}{3} \ln |x^3 - 1| + C.$$

15   If we let $u = 1 + \ln x$, then $du = dx/x$ and

$$\int \frac{(1 + \ln x)^2}{2x}\, dx = \frac{1}{2} \int u^2\, du = \frac{1}{6} u^3 + C = \frac{1}{6}(1 + \ln x)^3 + C.$$

16   If we let $u = 4x$, then $du = 4dx$. If $x = 1$, $u = 4$, and if $x = 2$, $u = 8$. Therefore,

$$\int_1^2 e^{4x}\, dx = \frac{1}{4} \int_4^8 e^u\, du = \frac{1}{4} \Big[e^u \Big]_4^8 = \frac{1}{4}(e^8 - e^4).$$

17   If we let $u = e^x + 3$, then $du = e^x\, dx$ and

$$\int e^x(e^x + 3)^3\, dx = \int u^3\, du = \frac{u^4}{4} + C = \frac{(e^x + 3)^4}{4} + C.$$

18 $\displaystyle \int \frac{x^2 - 2x + 3}{x}\, dx = \int \left(x - 2 + \frac{3}{x} \right) dx = \frac{x^2}{2} - 2x + 3 \ln x + C$

19   If we let $u = x^3$, then $du = 3x^2\, dx$ and

$$\int 3^{x^3} x^2\, dx = \frac{1}{3} \int 3^u\, du = \frac{1}{3} \left(\frac{1}{\ln 3} \right) 3^u + C = \frac{1}{3 \ln 3} 3^{x^3} + C.$$

20

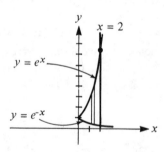

$$A = \int_0^2 (e^x - e^{-x})\, dx = [e^x + e^{-x}]_0^2 = (e^2 + e^{-2}) - (e^0 + e^0) = e^2 + e^{-2} - 2$$

21   Taking the natural logarithims of each side, we obtain

$$y = \frac{(x^2 - 2)^3}{\sqrt{x - 1}}$$

$$\ln y = \ln \left[\frac{(x^2 - 3)^3}{\sqrt{x - 1}} \right] = 3 \ln (x^2 - 2) - \frac{1}{2} \ln (x - 1).$$

Differentiating with respect to x we obtain

$$\frac{1}{y} y' = 3 \left(\frac{2x}{x^2 - 2} \right) - \frac{1}{2} \left(\frac{1}{x - 1} \right) = \frac{6x}{x^2 - 2} - \frac{1}{2(x - 1)}$$

$$= \frac{6x(2)(x - 1) - (x^2 - 2)}{2(x^2 - 2)(x - 1)} = \frac{11x^2 - 12x + 2}{2(x^2 - 2)(x - 1)}.$$

Multiplying both sides by $y = \dfrac{(x^2 - 3)^3}{(x - 1)^{1/2}}$ gives us

$$y' = \frac{(x^2 - 3)^3}{(x - 1)^{1/2}} \left[\frac{11x^2 - 12x + 2}{2(x^2 - 2)(x - 1)} \right] = \frac{(x^2 - 3)^3(11x^2 - 12x + 2)}{2(x - 1)^{3/2}(x^2 - 2)} \ .$$

22 By hypothesis, $q(0) = 2000$ and $q(3) = 6000$.

$$q(t) = q(0)e^{ct}$$
$$q(t) = 2000e^{ct}$$

Letting $t = 3$, we obtain

$$6000 = 2000e^{3c}$$
$$3 = e^{3c}$$
$$3c = \ln 3$$
$$c = \frac{1}{3} \ln 3.$$

Thus the formula for $q(t)$ is

$$q(t) = 2000e^{(1/3)(\ln 3)t}.$$

23 We have

$$f(x) = x^2 + 3 \qquad\qquad g(x) = (x - 3)^{1/2}$$
$$f'(x) = 2x \qquad\qquad g'(x) = \frac{1}{2}(x - 3)^{-1/2} = \frac{1}{2\sqrt{x - 3}} \ .$$

Now $f'(g(x)) = 2(\sqrt{x - 3})$ and thus

$$g'(x) = \frac{1}{2\sqrt{x - 3}} = \frac{1}{f'(g(x))} \ .$$

CHAPTER 9

1 (a) $\displaystyle\lim_{t\to0} \frac{\sin^2 3t}{t^2} = \lim_{t\to0} 9\left(\frac{\sin^2 3t}{9t^2}\right) = 9\lim_{t\to0}\left(\frac{\sin^2 3t}{(3t)^2}\right)$

$$= 9\lim_{t\to0}\left(\frac{\sin 3t}{3t}\right) \cdot \lim_{t\to0}\left(\frac{\sin 3t}{3t}\right) = 9 \cdot 1 \cdot 1 = 9$$

(b) $\displaystyle\lim_{t\to0} \frac{\sin t - \sin t(\cos t)}{t^2} = \lim_{t\to0}\left[\left(\frac{\sin t}{t}\right)\left(\frac{1 - \cos t}{t}\right)\right]$

$$= \left(\lim_{t\to0} \frac{\sin t}{t}\right)\left(\lim_{t\to0} \frac{1 - \cos t}{t}\right) = (1)(0) = 0$$

2 $f(x) = \sin\left(\frac{x}{3}\right)$

$f'(x) = \cos\left(\frac{x}{3}\right)D_x\left(\frac{x}{3}\right) = \frac{1}{3}\cos\left(\frac{x}{3}\right)$

3 $f(x) = \sec(x^2 - 1)$
$f'(x) = \sec(x^2 - 1)\tan(x^2 - 1)D_x(x^2 - 1) = 2x\sec(x^2 - 1)\tan(x^2 - 1)$

4 $f(x) = (\ln x)\cos(\sqrt{x})$
$f'(x) = (\ln x)D_x(\cos\sqrt{x}) + (\cos\sqrt{x})D_x(\ln x)$

$$= (\ln x)(-\sin\sqrt{x})D_x(\sqrt{x}) + (\cos\sqrt{x})\left(\frac{1}{x}\right)$$

$$= (\ln x)(-\sin\sqrt{x})\left(\frac{1}{2\sqrt{x}}\right) + (\cos\sqrt{x})\left(\frac{1}{x}\right)$$

$$= -\frac{(\ln x)\sin\sqrt{x}}{2\sqrt{x}} + \frac{\cos\sqrt{x}}{x} = \frac{-\sqrt{x}(\ln x)\sin\sqrt{x} + 2\cos\sqrt{x}}{2x}$$

5 $f(x) = (x^2 + \tan x)^3$

$f'(x) = 3(x^2 + \tan x)^2 D_x(x^2 + \tan x) = 3(x^2 + \tan x)^2(2x + \sec^2 x)$

6 $f(x) = e^{\sin x^2}$

$f'(x) = e^{\sin x^2} D_x(\sin x^2) = e^{\sin x^2}(\cos x^2)D_x(x^2) = 2xe^{\sin x^2}\cos x^2$

7 $f(x) = \sin^{-1}(3x^2)$

$f'(x) = \dfrac{1}{\sqrt{1 - (3x^2)^2}} \, D_x(3x^2) = \dfrac{6x}{\sqrt{1 - 9x^4}}$

8 $f(x) = e^x \cos^{-1}(x - 1)$

$f'(x) = e^x D_x[\cos^{-1}(x - 1)] + \cos^{-1}(x - 1)D_x(e^x)$

$\quad = e^x\left(-\dfrac{1}{\sqrt{1 - (x - 1)^2}} \, D_x(x - 1)\right) + e^x \cos^{-1}(x - 1)$

$\quad = -\dfrac{e^x}{\sqrt{2x - x^2}} + e^x \cos^{-1}(x - 1)$

9 $f(x) = \dfrac{\arctan x}{\ln x}$

$f'(x) = \dfrac{\ln x \, D_x(\arctan x) - (\arctan x)D_x(\ln x)}{(\ln x)^2}$

$\quad = \dfrac{(\ln x)\left(\dfrac{1}{1 + x^2}\right) - (\arctan x)\left(\dfrac{1}{x}\right)}{(\ln x)^2}$

$\quad = \dfrac{\dfrac{\ln x}{1 + x^2} - \dfrac{\arctan x}{x}}{(\ln x)^2}$

$\quad = \dfrac{x \ln x - (1 + x^2) \arctan x}{x(1 + x^2)(\ln x)^2}$

10 $f(x) = \tan^{-1}\left(\dfrac{e^x}{1 + x^2}\right)$

$f'(x) = \dfrac{1}{1 + \left(\dfrac{e^x}{1 + x^2}\right)^2} \, D_x\left(\dfrac{e^x}{1 + x^2}\right) = \dfrac{1}{1 + \left(\dfrac{e^x}{1 + x^2}\right)^2}\left[\dfrac{(1 + x^2)e^x - e^x(2x)}{(1 + x^2)^2}\right]$

$\quad = \dfrac{(1 + x^2)^2}{(1 + x^2)^2 + e^{2x}}\left[\dfrac{(1 + x^2)e^x - 2xe^x}{(1 + x^2)^2}\right] = \dfrac{(1 + x^2)e^x - 2xe^x}{(1 + x^2)^2 + e^{2x}}$

11 $f(x) = \cosh(x^2 - 1)$

$f'(x) = \sinh(x^2 - 1)D_x(x^2 - 1) = 2x \sinh(x^2 - 1)$

12 $f(x) = \tanh^{-1}(e^x)$

$f'(x) = \dfrac{1}{1 - e^{2x}} \, D_x(e^x) = \dfrac{e^x}{1 - e^{2x}}$

13 $e^{\sin xy} + xy = 6$

$e^{\sin xy}(\cos xy)(xy' + y) + xy' + y = 0$

$(xe^{\sin xy} \cos xy + x)y' = -(y + ye^{\sin xy} \cos xy)$

$\qquad\qquad y' = -\dfrac{y + ye^{\sin xy} \cos xy}{xe^{\sin xy} \cos xy + x}$

14 $f(x) = \cos^2 x - \cos x$

$f'(x) = 2 \cos x(-\sin x) - (-\sin x) = \sin x(1 - 2 \cos x)$

Therefore, the local extrema may occur where

$$\begin{aligned} \sin x = 0 \quad &\text{or} \quad 1 - 2 \cos x = 0 \\ x = 0 \text{ or } \pi \quad & \qquad\qquad \cos x = \frac{1}{2} \\ & \qquad\qquad x = \frac{\pi}{3} \text{ or } \frac{5\pi}{3} \end{aligned}$$

Now

$$f''(x) = \sin x(2 \sin x) + (1 - 2 \cos x) \cos x = 2 \sin^2 x + \cos x - 2 \cos^2 x.$$

$f''(0) = 2(0) + 1 - 2 = -1 < 0$ and thus a maximum occurs when $x = 0$.

$f''(\pi) = 2(0) - 1 - 2(-1)^2 = -3 < 0$ and thus a maximum occurs when $x = \pi$.

$f''(\pi/3) = 2(\sqrt{3}/2)^2 + (1/2) - 2(1/2)^2 = 3/2 > 0$ and thus a minimum occurs when $x = \pi/3$.

$f''(5\pi/3) = 2(-\sqrt{3}/2)^2 + (1/2) - 2(1/2)^2 = 3/2 > 0$ and thus a minimum occurs when $x = 5\pi/3$.

15　If we let $u = 5x$, then $du = 5dx$, and

$$\int \cos 5x \, dx = \frac{1}{5} \int \cos u \, du = \frac{1}{5} \sin u + C = \frac{1}{5} \sin 5x + C.$$

16　If we let $u = 2x^2$, then $du = 4x \, dx$, and

$$\int x \tan 2x^2 \sec 2x^2 \, dx = \frac{1}{4} \int \tan u \sec u \, du$$
$$= \frac{1}{4} \sec u + C = \frac{1}{4} \sec 2x^2 + C.$$

17　If we let $u = \tan 2x$, then $du = 2 \sec^2 2x \, dx$, and

$$\int \tan 2x \sec^2 2x \, dx = \frac{1}{2} \int u \, du = \frac{1}{4} u^2 + C = \frac{1}{4} \tan^2 2x + C.$$

18　$\displaystyle\int_{\pi/6}^{\pi/3} \frac{1 + \cos x}{\sin^2 x} \, dx = \int_{\pi/6}^{\pi/3} (\csc^2 x + \sin^{-2} x \cos x) \, dx$

$$= \left[-\cot x - \frac{1}{\sin x} \right]_{\pi/6}^{\pi/3}$$
$$= \left(-\frac{\sqrt{3}}{3} - \frac{2\sqrt{3}}{3} \right) - (-\sqrt{3} - 2) = 2$$

19　$\displaystyle\int_0^3 \frac{1}{x^2 + (3)^2} \, dx = \left[\frac{1}{3} \tan^{-1} \left(\frac{x}{3} \right) \right]_0^3 = \frac{1}{3} [\tan^{-1}(1) - \tan^{-1}(0)]$

$$= \frac{1}{3} \left(\frac{\pi}{4} - 0 \right) = \frac{\pi}{12}$$

20　If we let $u = x^2$, then $du = 2x \, dx$, and

$$\int \frac{x}{\sqrt{1 - x^4}} \, dx = \frac{1}{2} \int \frac{1}{\sqrt{1 - u^2}} \, du$$
$$= \frac{1}{2} \sin^{-1} u + C = \frac{1}{2} \sin^{-1} x^2 + C.$$

21　If we let $u = 2x$, then $du = 2 \, dx$, and

$$\int \frac{1}{x\sqrt{4x^2 - 9}} \, dx = \int \frac{1}{u\sqrt{u^2 - 3^2}} \, du = \frac{1}{3} \sec^{-1} \left(\frac{u}{3} \right) + C$$
$$= \frac{1}{3} \sec^{-1} \left(\frac{2x}{3} \right) + C.$$

22　If we let $u = \ln x$, then $du = (1/x) \, dx$, and

$$\int \frac{\sinh (\ln x)}{x} \, dx = \int \sinh u \, du = \cosh u + C$$

$$= \cosh (\ln x) + C.$$

23

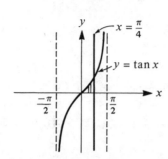

$$A = \int_0^{\pi/4} \tan x \, dx = \left[-\ln |\cos x|\right]_0^{\pi/4}$$

$$= \left(-\ln \left|\cos \frac{\pi}{4}\right|\right) - (-\ln |\cos 0|)$$

$$= -\ln \left(\frac{\sqrt{2}}{2}\right) + \ln (1) = -\ln \left(\frac{\sqrt{2}}{2}\right)$$

$$= -(\ln \sqrt{2} - \ln 2) = -\frac{1}{2} \ln 2 + \ln 2 = \frac{1}{2} \ln 2$$

24

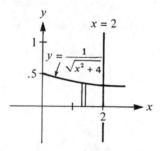

If a typical rectangle is revolved about the *x*-axis, a disc is generated of radius $1/\sqrt{x^2 + 4}$ and hence the volume is

$$V = \pi \int_0^2 \frac{1}{x^2 + 4} \, dx = \frac{\pi}{2} \left[\tan^{-1}\left(\frac{x}{2}\right)\right]_0^2$$

$$= \frac{\pi}{2} [\tan^{-1}(1) - \tan^{-1}(0)] = \frac{\pi}{2}\left(\frac{\pi}{4} - 0\right) = \frac{\pi^2}{8} \text{ cubic units.}$$

25 (a) $\sin^{-1}(1/2) = \pi/6$ because $\sin(\pi/6) = 1/2$ and $-\pi/2 \leqslant \pi/6 \leqslant \pi/2$.

(b) $\cos^{-1}(-\sqrt{2}/2) = 3\pi/4$ because $\cos(3\pi/4) = -\sqrt{2}/2$ and $0 \leqslant 3\pi/4 \leqslant \pi$.

(c) $\tan^{-1}(1) = \pi/4$ because $\tan(\pi/4) = 1$ and $-\pi/2 < \pi/4 < \pi/2$.

(d) $\sin [\arccos(1/2)] = \sin(\pi/3) = \sqrt{3}/2$.

26 Let $y = \arctan(1 - x)$. Now $\tan y = 1 - x$. We want to express $\cos y$ in terms of x.

$$\sec^2 y = \tan^2 y + 1$$

$$\sec y = \sqrt{\tan^2 y + 1}$$

$$\cos y = \frac{1}{\sqrt{\tan^2 y + 1}} = \frac{1}{\sqrt{(1 - x)^2 + 1}} = \frac{1}{\sqrt{x^2 - 2x + 2}}$$

CHAPTER 10

1 Let

$$u = x \qquad\qquad dV = \sin 2x\; dx$$

$$du = dx \qquad\qquad V = -\frac{1}{2}\cos 2x\; dx$$

Integrating by parts,

$$\int x \sin 2x\; dx = -\frac{1}{2}x \cos 2x + \frac{1}{2}\int \cos 2x\; dx$$

$$= -\frac{1}{2}x \cos 2x + \frac{1}{4}\sin 2x + C.$$

2 Let

$$u = x^2 \qquad\qquad dV = e^x\; dx$$

$$du = 2x\; dx \qquad\qquad V = e^x$$

Integrating by parts,

$$\int x^2 e^x\; dx = x^2 e^x - 2\int xe^x\; dx.$$

To evaluate the integral $\int xe^x\; dx$ we must again integrate by parts. Let

$$u = x \qquad\qquad dV = e^x\; dx$$

$$du = dx \qquad\qquad V = e^x$$

Integrating by parts,

$$\int xe^x\; dx = xe^x - \int e^x\; dx = xe^x - e^x + C.$$

Substituting, we now have

$$\int x^2 e^x\; dx = x^2 e^x - 2xe^x + 2e^x + C.$$

3 $\int \cos^3 x\; dx = \int \cos^2 x \cos x\; dx = \int (1 - \sin^2 x) \cos x\; dx$

Now let $u = \sin x,\; du = \cos x\; dx$. Thus

$$\int \cos^3 x\; dx = \int (1 - u^2)\; du$$

$$= u - \frac{1}{3}u^3 + C$$

$$= \sin x - \frac{1}{3}\sin^3 x + C.$$

4 $\int \tan^3 x \sec^3 x\; dx = \int \tan^2 x \sec^2 x(\sec x \tan x)\; dx$
$$= \int (\sec^2 x - 1) \sec^2 x(\sec x \tan x)\; dx$$
$$= \int (\sec^4 x - \sec^2 x)(\sec x \tan x)\; dx$$

Now let $u = \sec x,\; du = \sec x \tan x\; dx$. Thus

$$\int \tan^3 x \sec^3 x\; dx = \int (u^4 - u^2)\; du$$

$$= \frac{1}{5}u^5 - \frac{1}{3}u^3 + C$$

$$= \frac{1}{5}\sec^5 x - \frac{1}{3}\sec^3 x + C.$$

5 Let $x = 4 \sec \theta,\; dx = 4 \sec \theta \tan \theta\; d\theta$. Thus

$$x^2 - 16 = 16 \sec^2 \theta - 16 = 16(\sec^2 \theta - 1) = 16 \tan^2 \theta.$$

Therefore,

$$\int \frac{\sqrt{x^2 - 16}}{x}\; dx = \int \frac{4 \tan \theta}{4 \sec \theta}\;(4 \sec \theta \tan \theta)\; d\theta$$

$$= 4 \int \tan^2 \theta\; d\theta = 4 \int (\sec^2 \theta - 1)\; d\theta$$

$$= 4(\tan \theta - \theta) + C.$$

Now $x = 4 \sec \theta$ or $\sec \theta = x/4$ ($\theta = \sec^{-1}(x/4)$).

Therefore, $\tan \theta = \sqrt{x^2 - 16}/4$ and

$$\int \frac{\sqrt{x^2 - 16}}{x} \, dx = 4(\tan \theta - \theta) + C$$

$$= 4\left[\frac{\sqrt{x^2 - 16}}{4} - \sec^{-1}\left(\frac{x}{4}\right) \right] + C$$

$$= \sqrt{x^2 - 16} - 4 \sec^{-1}\left(\frac{x}{4}\right) + C.$$

6   $\dfrac{x + 1}{x^3 + x^2 - 6x} = \dfrac{x + 1}{x(x - 2)(x + 3)}$

$$= \frac{A}{x} + \frac{B}{x - 2} + \frac{C}{x + 3}$$

$$= \frac{A(x - 2)(x + 3) + Bx(x + 3) + Cx(x - 2)}{x(x - 2)(x + 3)}$$

$$= \frac{Ax^2 + Ax - 6A + Bx^2 + 3Bx + Cx^2 - 2Cx}{x(x - 2)(x + 3)}$$

$$= \frac{(A + B + C)x^2 + (A + 3B - 2C)x - 6A}{x(x - 2)(x + 3)}$$

Therefore,

$$\begin{cases} A + B + C = 0 \\ A + 3B - 2C = 0 \\ \qquad\quad -6A = 1. \end{cases}$$

Solving for A, B, and C we have $A = -1/6$, $B = 1/10$, and $C = 1/15$, and thus

$$\frac{x + 1}{x^3 + x^2 - 6x} = -\frac{1}{6}\left(\frac{1}{x}\right) + \frac{1}{10}\left(\frac{1}{x - 2}\right) + \frac{1}{15}\left(\frac{1}{x + 3}\right).$$

Now

$$\int \frac{x + 1}{x^3 + x^2 - 6x} \, dx = -\frac{1}{6}\int \frac{1}{x} \, dx + \frac{1}{10}\int \frac{1}{x - 2} \, dx + \frac{1}{15}\int \frac{1}{x + 3} \, dx$$

$$= -\frac{1}{6} \ln |x| + \frac{1}{10} \ln |x - 2| + \frac{1}{15} \ln |x + 3| + C$$

$$= \ln \left[\frac{|x - 2|^{1/10}|x + 3|^{1/15}}{|x|^{1/6}} \right] + C.$$

7   $\dfrac{2x^3}{(x^2 + 1)^2} = \dfrac{Ax + B}{x^2 + 1} + \dfrac{Cx + D}{(x^2 + 1)^2}$

$$= \frac{(Ax + B)(x^2 + 1) + Cx + D}{(x^2 + 1)^2}$$

$$= \frac{Ax^3 + Bx^2 + Ax + B + Cx + D}{(x^2 + 1)^2}$$

$$= \frac{Ax^3 + Bx^2 + (A + C)x + (B + D)}{(x^2 + 1)^2}$$

Therefore,

$$\begin{cases} A = 2 \\ B = 0 \\ A + C = 0 \\ B + D = 0. \end{cases}$$

Solving for A, B, C, and D, we have $A = 2$, $B = 0$, $C = -2$, and $D = 0$, and thus

$$\frac{2x^3}{(x^2 + 1)^2} = \frac{2x}{x^2 + 1} - \frac{2x}{(x^2 + 1)^2} .$$

Now

$$\int \frac{2x^3}{(x^2 + 1)^2} \, dx = \int \frac{2x}{x^2 + 1} \, dx - \int \frac{2x}{(x^2 + 1)^2} \, dx$$

$$= \ln |x^2 + 1| + \frac{1}{x^2 + 1} + C.$$

8   Completing the square for the quadratic expression $x^2 - 4x + 20$, we obtain

$$x^2 - 4x \quad + 20$$
$$(x^2 - 4x + 4) + (20 - 4)$$
$$(x - 2)^2 + 16.$$

Now let $u = x - 2$, $du = dx$ and thus

$$\int \frac{1}{x^2 - 4x + 20} \, dx = \int \frac{1}{u^2 + 16} \, du = \frac{1}{4} \tan^{-1} \left(\frac{u}{4}\right) + C$$

$$= \frac{1}{4} \tan^{-1} \left(\frac{x - 2}{4}\right) + C.$$

9   Completing the square for the quadratic expression $x^2 + 6x + 34$, we obtain

$$x^2 + 6x \quad + 34$$
$$(x^2 + 6x + 9) + (34 - 9)$$
$$(x + 3)^2 + 25.$$

Now let $x + 3 = 5 \tan \theta$, $dx = 5 \sec^2 \theta \, d\theta$ and thus $(x + 3)^2 + 25 = 25 \tan^2 \theta + 25 = 25 \sec^2 \theta$ and

$$\int \frac{1}{\sqrt{x^2 + 6x + 34}} \, dx = \int \frac{1}{\sqrt{(x + 3)^2 + 25}} \, dx = \int \frac{1}{5 \sec \theta} \, (5 \sec^2 \theta) \, d\theta$$

$$= \int \sec \theta \, d\theta = \ln |\sec \theta + \tan \theta| + C.$$

We have $x + 3 = 5 \tan \theta$ or $\tan \theta = (x + 3)/5$.

Therefore,

$$\int \frac{1}{\sqrt{x^2 + 6x + 34}} \, dx = \ln \left| \frac{\sqrt{(x + 3)^2 + 25}}{5} + \frac{x + 3}{5} \right| + C$$

$$= \ln |\sqrt{(x + 3)^2 + 25} + x + 3| + D, \text{ where } D = C - \ln 5.$$

10   Let

$$u = (x + 1)^{1/3}$$
$$u^3 = x + 1$$
$$3u^2 \, du = dx.$$

Therefore,

$$\int \frac{x}{(x + 1)^{1/3}} \, dx = \int \frac{u^3 - 1}{u} \, (3u^2 \, du) = 3 \int (u^4 - u) \, du$$

$$= 3\left(\frac{1}{5} u^5 - \frac{1}{2} u^2\right) + C = \frac{3}{5} (x + 1)^{5/3} - \frac{3}{2} (x + 1)^{2/3} + C.$$

11 $\dfrac{x^2 + 1}{(x + 1)(x^2 + 2)} = \dfrac{A}{x + 1} + \dfrac{Bx + C}{x^2 + 2} = \dfrac{A(x^2 + 2) + (Bx + C)(x + 1)}{(x + 1)(x^2 + 2)}$

$$= \frac{Ax^2 + 2A + Bx^2 + Cx + Bx + C}{(x + 1)(x^2 + 2)}$$

$$= \frac{(A + B)x^2 + (C + B)x + (2A + C)}{(x + 1)(x^2 + 2)}$$

Therefore,

$$\begin{cases} A + B = 1 \\ C + B = 0 \\ 2A + C = 1. \end{cases}$$

Solving for A, B, C, we have $A = 2/3$, $B = 1/3$, and $C = -1/3$, and thus

$$\frac{x^2 + 1}{(x + 1)(x^2 + 2)} = \frac{2}{3}\left(\frac{1}{x + 1}\right) + \frac{1}{3}\left(\frac{x - 1}{x^2 + 2}\right).$$

Now

$$\int \frac{x^2 + 1}{(x + 1)(x^2 + 2)} \, dx = \frac{2}{3} \int \frac{1}{x + 1} \, dx + \frac{1}{3} \int \frac{1}{x^2 + 2} \, dx - \frac{1}{3} \int \frac{1}{x^2 + 2} \, dx$$

$$= \frac{2}{3} \ln |x + 1| + \frac{1}{6} \ln |x^2 + 2| - \frac{1}{3\sqrt{2}} \tan^{-1}\left(\frac{x}{\sqrt{2}}\right) + C$$

$$= \ln \left[|x + 1|^{2/3}|x^2 + 2|^{1/6}\right] - \frac{\sqrt{2}}{6} \tan^{-1}\left(\frac{\sqrt{2}x}{2}\right) + C.$$

12   Let $x = 3 \sin \theta$, $dx = 3 \cos \theta \, d\theta$ and thus $9 - x^2 = 9 - 9 \sin^2 \theta = 9(1 - \sin^2 \theta) = 9 \cos^2 \theta$. Therefore,

$$\int \frac{\sqrt{9 - x^2}}{x^2} \, dx = \int \frac{3 \cos \theta}{9 \sin^2 \theta} \, (3 \cos \theta) \, d\theta = \int \frac{\cos^2 \theta}{\sin^2 \theta} \, d\theta$$

$$= \int \cot^2 \theta \, d\theta = \int (\csc^2 \theta - 1) \, d\theta = -\cot \theta - \theta + C.$$

We have $x = 3 \sin \theta$ or $\sin \theta = x/3$.

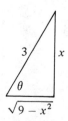

Therefore,

$$\int \frac{\sqrt{9 - x^2}}{x^2} \, dx = -\frac{\sqrt{9 - x^2}}{x} - \sin^{-1}\left(\frac{x}{3}\right) + C.$$

13 $\int \cos^5 x \sin^2 x \, dx = \int \cos^4 x \sin^2 x(\cos x) \, dx$

$\qquad\qquad\qquad = \int (1 - \sin^2 x)^2 \sin^2 x(\cos x) \, dx$

$\qquad\qquad\qquad = \int (1 - 2 \sin^2 x + \sin^4 x)\sin^2 x(\cos x) \, dx$

$\qquad\qquad\qquad = \int (\sin^2 x - 2 \sin^4 x + \sin^6 x) \cos x \, dx$

Let $u = \sin x$, $du = \cos x \, dx$ and thus

$$\int \cos^5 x \sin^2 x \, dx = \int (u^2 - 2u^4 + u^6) \, du$$

$$= \frac{1}{3}u^3 - \frac{2}{5}u^5 + \frac{1}{7}u^7 + C$$

$$= \frac{1}{3} \sin^3 x - \frac{2}{5} \sin^5 x + \frac{1}{7} \sin^7 x + C.$$

14 Let

$$u = \ln x \qquad\qquad dV = x^2 \, dx$$

$$du = \frac{1}{x} \, dx \qquad\qquad V = \frac{1}{3}x^3$$

Therefore,

$$\int x^2 \ln x \, dx = \frac{1}{3}x^3 \ln x - \frac{1}{3} \int x^2 \, dx$$

$$= \frac{1}{3}x^3 \ln x - \frac{1}{9}x^3 + C.$$

15 Completing the square for the quadratic expression $x^2 + 4x + 13$, we obtain

$$x^2 + 4x \qquad + 13$$
$$(x^2 + 4x + 4) + (13 - 4)$$
$$(x + 2)^2 + 9.$$

Now let $u = x + 2$, $du = dx$ and thus

$$\int \frac{x + 3}{x^2 + 4x + 13} \, dx = \int \frac{x + 3}{(x + 2)^2 + 9} \, dx$$

$$= \int \frac{u + 1}{u^2 + 9} \, du$$

$$= \int \frac{u}{u^2 + 9} \, du + \int \frac{1}{u^2 + 9} \, du$$

$$= \frac{1}{2} \ln |u^2 + 9| + \frac{1}{3} \tan^{-1} \left(\frac{u}{3}\right) + C$$

$$= \frac{1}{2} \ln |(x + 2)^2 + 9| + \frac{1}{3} \tan^{-1} \left(\frac{x + 2}{3}\right) + C$$

$$= \ln \sqrt{(x + 2)^2 + 9} + \frac{1}{3} \tan^{-1} \left(\frac{x + 2}{3}\right) + C.$$

16 Let $x = 3 \sec \theta$, $dx = 3 \sec \theta \tan \theta \, d\theta$ and thus $x^2 - 9 = 9 \sec^2 \theta - 9 = 9(\sec^2 \theta - 1) = 9 \tan^2 \theta$. Therefore,

$$\int x\sqrt{x^2 - 9} \, dx = \int 3 \sec \theta (3 \tan \theta)(3 \sec \theta \tan \theta) \, d\theta$$

$$= 27 \int \tan^2 \theta (\sec^2 \theta) \, d\theta = 9 \tan^3 \theta + C.$$

Now $x = 3 \sec \theta$ or $\sec \theta = x/3$.

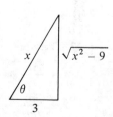

Therefore,

$$\int x\sqrt{x^2 - 9}\, dx = 9\left(\frac{\sqrt{x^2 - 9}}{3}\right)^3 + C = \frac{(x^2 - 9)^{3/2}}{3} + C.$$

17
$$\int \cos^4 x\, dx = \int \left(\frac{1 + \cos 2x}{2}\right)^2 dx$$

$$= \frac{1}{4}\int (1 + 2\cos 2x + \cos^2 2x)\, dx$$

$$= \frac{1}{4}\int \left[1 + 2\cos 2x + \left(\frac{1 + \cos 4x}{2}\right)\right] dx$$

$$= \frac{1}{4}\int \left(\frac{3}{2} + 2\cos 2x + \frac{1}{2}\,' \cos 4x\right) dx$$

$$= \frac{1}{4}\left(\frac{3}{2}x + \sin 2x + \frac{1}{8}\sin 4x\ + C\right)$$

$$= \frac{3}{8}x + \frac{1}{4}\sin 2x + \frac{1}{32}\sin 4x + C$$

18

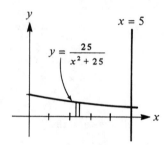

$$V = \pi \int_0^5 \left(\frac{25}{x^2 + 25}\right)^2 dx = 625\pi \int_0^5 \frac{1}{(x^2 + 25)^2}\, dx$$

Let $x = 5\tan\theta$, $dx = 5\sec^2\theta\, d\theta$ and thus $x^2 + 25 = 25\tan^2\theta + 25 = 25(\tan^2\theta + 1) = 25\sec^2\theta$. Therefore,

$$V = 625\pi \int_0^{\pi/4} \frac{1}{625\sec^4\theta}\, (5\sec^2\theta)\, d\theta$$

$$= 5\pi \int_0^{\pi/4} \frac{1}{\sec^2\theta}\, d\theta = 5\pi \int_0^{\pi/4} \cos^2\theta\, d\theta.$$

Now $\cos^2\theta = \frac{1}{2}(1 + \cos 2\theta)$ and thus

$$V = \frac{5\pi}{2} \int_0^{\pi/4} (1 + \cos 2\theta)\, d\theta = \frac{5\pi}{2}\left[\theta + \frac{1}{2}\sin 2\theta\right]_0^{\pi/4}$$

$$= \frac{5\pi}{2}\left(\frac{\pi}{4} + \frac{1}{2}\right) = \frac{5\pi}{4}\left(\frac{\pi}{2} + 1\right) \text{ cubic units.}$$

19 $M_x = (6)(2) + (9)(-4) + (2)(1) = -22$
$M_y = (6)(-1) + (9)(3) + (2)(5) = 31$
We have $m = 6 + 9 + 2 = 17$. Therefore,

$$\bar{x} = \frac{M_y}{m} = \frac{31}{17} \approx 1.8$$

$$\bar{y} = \frac{M_x}{m} = \frac{-22}{17} \approx -1.3.$$

20

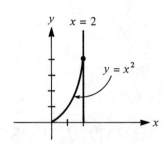

$$\bar{x} = \frac{\int_0^2 xf(x)\,dx}{\int_0^2 f(x)\,dx} = \frac{\int_0^2 x^3\,dx}{\int_0^2 x^2\,dx}$$

$$\bar{y} = \frac{\dfrac{1}{2}\displaystyle\int_0^2 [f(x)]^2\,dx}{\displaystyle\int_0^2 f(x)\,dx} = \frac{\dfrac{1}{2}\displaystyle\int_0^2 x^4\,dx}{\displaystyle\int_0^2 x^2\,dx}$$

We have

$$\int_0^2 x^3\,dx = \left[\frac{1}{4}x^4\right]_0^2 = 4$$

$$\int_0^2 x^4\,dx = \left[\frac{1}{5}x^5\right]_0^2 = \frac{32}{5}$$

$$\int_0^2 x^2\,dx = \left[\frac{1}{3}x^3\right]_0^2 = \frac{8}{3}$$

Therefore,

$$\bar{x} = \frac{4}{\dfrac{8}{3}} = \frac{3}{2}$$

$$\bar{y} = \frac{\dfrac{1}{2}\left(\dfrac{32}{5}\right)}{\dfrac{8}{3}} = \frac{\dfrac{32}{10}}{\dfrac{8}{3}} = \frac{6}{5}.$$

21 $\bar{x} = \dfrac{\int_0^2 x[f(x)]^2\,dx}{\int_0^2 [f(x)]^2\,dx} = \dfrac{\int_0^2 x^5\,dx}{\int_0^2 x^4\,dx}$

We have

$$\int_0^2 x^5\,dx = \left[\frac{1}{6}x^6\right]_0^2 = \frac{32}{3}$$

$$\int_0^2 x^4\,dx = \left[\frac{1}{5}x^5\right]_0^2 = \frac{32}{5}.$$

Therefore,

$$\bar{x} = \frac{\dfrac{32}{3}}{\dfrac{32}{5}} = \frac{5}{3}.$$

Answers
to
Sample Tests

CHAPTER 1

1 (a) $-16 > -20$ (b) $(-5)(-2) > (-5) + (-3)$ (c) $7/3 > 9/4$ (d) $113/3 > 37.2$

2 (a) 3   (b) 3   (c) 2   (d) -1

3 $d(A, B) = 13, d(B, C) = 2, d(A, C) = 11$ **4** $4 - x$

5 (a) $-2 \leqslant x \leqslant 10$ (b) $x > -3$ **6** (a) $x \geqslant -1$ (b) $x < -6$

7 $x < 3$

8 (a) $x < 5$ or $x > 15$. The interval solution is $(-\infty, 5) \cup (15, \infty)$
     (b) $-8/3 \leqslant x \leqslant 4/3$. The interval solution is $[-8/3, 4/3]$.

9 $-2 < x < 3$. The interval solution is $(-2, 3)$.

10 $x - (-1)$ or $x > 4$. The interval solution is $(-\infty, -1) \cup (4, \infty)$.

11   **12** The points in quadrants II and IV.

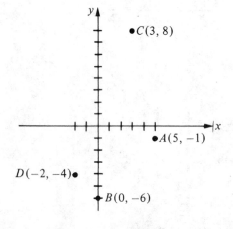

13 (a) $d(A, B) = \sqrt{61}$; the midpoint has coordinates $(1, 11/2)$
     (b) $d(A, B) = \sqrt{106}$; the midpoint has coordinates $(-5/2, -7/2)$

14 $d(A, B) = d(B, C) = 5$. Therefore, the triangle is isosceles.

15 $3x^2 + 18x + 3y^2 + 15 = 0$

16

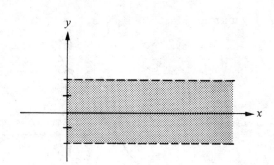

17 (a)

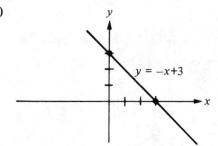

(b)

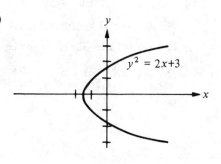

(c)

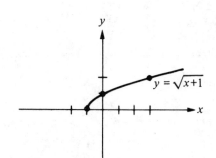

18 (a)

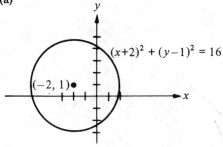

(b)

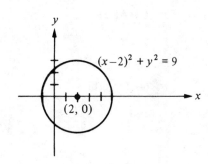

19 (a) $(x + 1)^2 + (y - 4)^2 = 16$ (b) $(x - 1)^2 + (y - 6)^2 = 5$

20 (a) -9 (b) $16/11$ (c) $21/5$

21 (a) $y + 4x - 7 = 0$ (b) $y + 3x + 11 = 0$ (c) $2y - 3x + 6 = 0$

22 slope 4/3; y-intercept 4

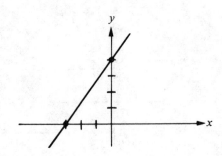

23 (a) 1 (b) 0 (c) -3 (d) $c^3 - 2c + 1$

24 (a) $a^2 - 1$ (b) $a^2 + 2ah + h^2 - 1$ (c) $2a + h$

25 (a) $\{x: x > -3/2\}$ (b) $\{x: x > 1, x \neq 2\}$ **26** All nonnegative real numbers

27 $c(x) = \begin{cases} 1.25x & \text{if } 0 \leqslant x \leqslant 25 \\ 1.5x - (.01)x^2 & \text{if } 25 < x \leqslant 50 \end{cases}$

28

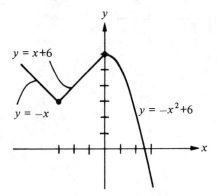

29 (a) $(f \circ g)(x) = 2x$ (b) $(f \circ g)(x) = 6x^2 - 5$ (c) $(f \circ g)(x) = x - 1, x > 1$

30 $f^{-1}(x) = (x + 2)/3$ **31** $f^{-1}(x) = \sqrt{16 - x}$ $x \leqslant 16$

CHAPTER 2

1 5 **2** $y = 3x + 3$

5 (a) 0 (b) 3/19 (c) 2 **6** 4

7 (a) 6 (b) -1 **8** 1

12 1 **14** $c = \sqrt{\dfrac{w + 1}{2}}$

CHAPTER 3

1 (a) $-2x$ (b) $\dfrac{1}{\sqrt{2x - 1}}$ **2** $f'(x) = 16x - 2$

3 $h'(y) = 3y^2 - 2y + 1$ **4** $H'(x) = -\dfrac{7}{(x - 3)^2}$

5 $f'(t) = 5(t^3 + 2t^2 - t + 1)^4(3t^2 + 4t - 1)$

6 $H'(y) = \dfrac{(y + 1)^2(y^2 - 2y + 6)}{(y^2 + 2)^2}$

7 $g'(x) = \dfrac{-3x + 2}{x^3\sqrt{2x - 1}}$

8 $f'(y) = \dfrac{y + 3}{3(y - 1)^{1/3}(y + 1)^{4/3}}$

9 $f'(t) = \dfrac{2t}{\sqrt{2t^2 - 1}}$

10 $H'(z) = \dfrac{-4z}{3(z^2 + 1)^{5/3}}$

11 $g'(x) = \dfrac{(1 - 2x^2)}{3x^{2/3}(2x^2 + 1)^{4/3}}$

12 $h'(x) = \dfrac{-1}{x^2\sqrt{x^2 + 1}}$

13 $y = 4x - 2$

14 $y = -x + 3$

15 $\triangle y \approx -.043$
$dy = -.05$

16 ≈ 9.997

17 $\approx \pm.2512$ cm²

18 $y' = \dfrac{3x^2 - 1}{3y^2 - 2y}$

19 $y + x + 4 = 0$

20 (a) $f'(x) = 4x^3 - 6x$ (b) $g'(t) = \dfrac{t}{\sqrt{t^2 + 1}}$
$\qquad f''(x) = 12x^2 - 6$

$\qquad\qquad\qquad\qquad g''(t) = \dfrac{1}{(t^2 + 1)^{3/2}}$

21 $y'' = \dfrac{-8x + 16}{(x + 1)^4}$

22 $f^{(n)}(t) = (-1)^n n! a t^{-(n+1)}$

CHAPTER 4

1 14, 5

2 (a) 0   (b) 5/6   (c) -1

4 $c = 1$

5 No; not differentiable at 0

6 (a) local minimum of -6 at $x = -1$ (b) local minimum of -1 at $x = 1$
$\qquad$ local maximum of -2 at $x = -3$

7 absolute minimum of -6 at $x = -4$ and $x = -1$
$\qquad$ absolute maximum of -2 at $x = -3$

8 $x < -1/6$

9 Decreasing everywhere, concave upward if $x > -1$, and concave downward if $x < -1$.

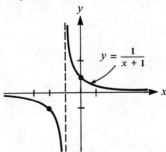

$$y = \frac{1}{x + 1}$$

10 (a) local maximum at $x = 1/3$ (b) local minimum at $x = 2$
$\qquad$ local minimum at $x = 1$ $\qquad\qquad$ inflection point at $x = -\sqrt[3]{16}$
$\qquad$ inflection point at $x = 2/3$

12 (a) $1/2$ (b) 0 (c) $-\infty$ (d) $-\infty$

13 (a)

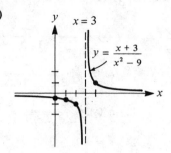

horizontal asymptote: $y = 0$
vertical asymptote: $x = 3$

(b)

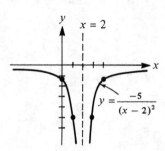

horizontal asymptote: $y = 0$
vertical asymptote: $x = 2$

14 100×150 yards

15 16 beats/min

16 $V = -17\dfrac{5}{6}$ cm/sec

$a = -2\dfrac{1}{108}$ cm/sec^2

17 8/5 ft/sec

18 $4\sqrt{3}/3$ units per second

19 (a) $F(x) = \dfrac{1}{3}x^3 - 2x + C$

(b) $F(x) = \dfrac{1}{4}x^4 + \dfrac{2}{3}x^3 - \dfrac{1}{2}x^2 + x + C$

(c) $F(x) = \dfrac{3}{4}x^{4/3} - \dfrac{5}{8}x^{8/5} + \dfrac{2}{3}x^{3/2} + C$

(d) $F(x) = \dfrac{1}{4}(x - 1)^4 + C$

20 $f(x) = x^3 - x^2 + 3x + 6$

21 45 ft

22 10 units

CHAPTER 5

1 (a) 10   (b) 11   (c) 130

2 $\dfrac{n(n^2 + 2)}{3}$

3 140/3

4 28.635

5 0

6 33/2

9 2.08

10 69/2

11 $\dfrac{4\sqrt{2}}{3} + \dfrac{\sqrt[3]{2}}{2} + 2$

12 0

13 1

14 15/8

15 5/48

16 $(1/21)(3t + 1)^7 + C$

17 $-\sqrt{1 - y^2} + C$

18 $(1/15)(t^3 + 1)^5 + C$

19 $-\dfrac{1}{2(x^2 - 2x + 1)} + C$

20 $-\dfrac{1}{3}\left(2 + \dfrac{1}{x}\right)^3 + C$

21 69/4

22 (a) .6941   (b) .6931

CHAPTER 6

1 64 square units

2 64/3 square units

3 25/3 square units

4 $(128/5)\pi$ cubic units

5 4π cubic units

6 $(320/7)\pi$ cubic units

7 $(1408/15)\pi$ cubic units

8 $(10/3)\pi$ cubic units

9 1875 ft-tons

10 335/27

11 $\int_1^3 \sqrt{1 + 16x^2}\, dx$

12 .14

13 $19,596

CHAPTER 7

1 (a)

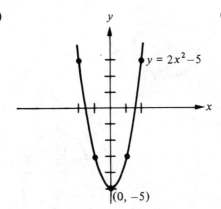

(b)

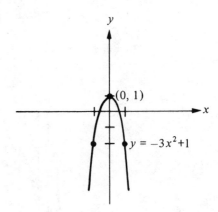

2 (a) $f(x) = 2\left(x - \dfrac{3}{4}\right)^2 - \dfrac{1}{8}$ (b) $f(x) = -4\left(x - \dfrac{1}{4}\right)^2 + \dfrac{13}{4}$

3 (a)

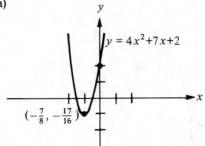

(b)

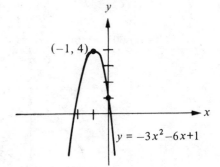

4

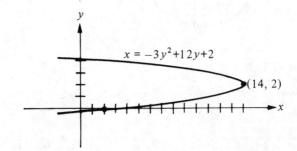

5

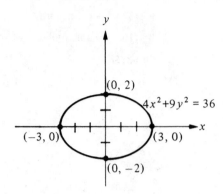

6

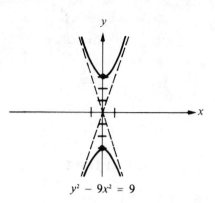

7 $4x^2 - y^2 = 16$

8 $\dfrac{x^2}{4} - \dfrac{y^2}{9} = 1$

9 $y - 2x + 3 = 0$

10 $2\sqrt{2}$

11 $35\pi/12$ cubic units

12 (a)

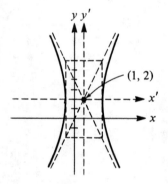

(b)

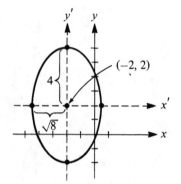

13 (a) $30°$ (b) $\begin{cases} x = \dfrac{\sqrt{3}}{2}x' - \dfrac{1}{2}y' \\ y = \dfrac{1}{2}x' + \dfrac{\sqrt{3}}{2}y' \end{cases}$ (c) $\dfrac{x'^2}{16} + \dfrac{y'^2}{12} = 1$

(d)

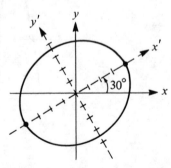

CHAPTER 8

1 $\dfrac{1}{2(x - 3)}$

2 $\dfrac{3x^2 - 2}{x^3 - 2x - 5}$

3 $\dfrac{3x^2 - 4x + 3}{2(x^2 - 3)(x - 1)}$

4 $\dfrac{e^x}{x - 3} + e^x \ln(x - 3)$

5 $4xe^{x^2}$

6 $2x - 2xe^x - 2e^x$

7 $\dfrac{-2e^x}{(1 + e^x)^2}$

8 $(3 \ln 2)2^{3x+1}$

9 $\dfrac{3x^2}{(\ln 10)(x^3 - 1)}$

10   1.102

11 $\dfrac{3x^2y - y^2}{1 + xy}$

12   local maximum at $x = 2$
local minimum at $x = 0$

13 $\dfrac{1}{3} \ln|x^3 + 5| + C$

14 $\dfrac{1}{2} \ln \dfrac{3}{2}$

15 $\dfrac{(2 + \ln \sqrt{x})^3}{3} + C$

16 $\dfrac{1}{3}(1 - e^{-3})$

17 $\dfrac{1}{2}e^{x^2} + C$

18 $\dfrac{3}{2}x^2 + 2x - \ln x + C$

19 $\dfrac{1}{\ln 3} \ln (3^x + 1) + C$

20 $\pi(1 - e^{-1})$ cubic units

21 $(10x^2 - 3x - 22)(x - 1)^2(x - 2)(x + 4)^4$

22 $q(t) = 3000e^{((1/8)\ln 3)t}$

CHAPTER 9

1   (a) 1   (b) 0

2 $-8x \sin (4x^2)$

3 $(xe^x + e^x) \sec^2 (xe^x)$

4 $\dfrac{x^2}{2\sqrt{x + 1}} \cos \sqrt{x + 1} + 2x \sin \sqrt{x + 1}$

5 $2(1 + \sec x)(\sec x \tan x)$

6 $2x \cot (x^2 + 1)$

7 $-\dfrac{2x}{\sqrt{1 - x^4}}$

8 $\dfrac{\ln x}{\sqrt{1 - x^2}} + \dfrac{\sin^{-1} x}{x}$

9 $\dfrac{1}{x^4} \left(\dfrac{x^2}{1 + x^2} - 2x \arctan x \right)$

10 $\cosh (x + 1)$

11 $6x \operatorname{sech}^2 (2x^3 - 1)$

12 $\dfrac{2x}{\sqrt{x^4 + 1}}$

13 $-\dfrac{\sin y + ye^x}{x \cos y + e^x}$

14   maximum at $x = \pi/3$
minimum at $x = 5\pi/3$

15   1/3

16 $\dfrac{(1 + \sec x)^4}{4} + C$

17 $\dfrac{\sin^2 e^x}{2} + C$

18 $\ln|\sec x + \tan x| - \sin x + C$

19 $\dfrac{1}{4} \sin^{-1} \left(\dfrac{4x}{5} \right) + C$

20 $\dfrac{\sqrt{3}}{6} \tan^{-1} \left(\dfrac{\sqrt{3}x^2}{3} \right) + C$

21 $\dfrac{1}{2} \sec^{-1} x^2 + C$

22 $-\dfrac{1}{2} \operatorname{sech} 2x + C$ **23**   2048/105 square units

24 $\pi^2/4$ cubic units

25   (a) $-\pi/2$ (b) $\pi/3$ (c) $-\pi/3$ (d) $\sqrt{3}/3$

26 $\sqrt{1 - x^2}$

CHAPTER 10

1 $-\cos x + \dfrac{1}{3} \cos^3 x + C$

2 $\dfrac{1}{2} x^3 e^{2x} - \dfrac{3}{4} x^2 e^{2x} + \dfrac{3}{4} x e^{2x} - \dfrac{3}{8} e^{2x} + C$

3 $\dfrac{1}{8} \ln \left| \dfrac{2 + x}{2 - x} \right| - \dfrac{1}{4} \arctan\left(\dfrac{x}{2}\right) + C$

4 $\ln|\sqrt{9 + x^2} + x| + C$ **5** $\sin^{-1}\left(\dfrac{2x - 1}{5}\right) + C$

6 $\ln|x - 2| - \dfrac{2}{x - 2} + C$ **7** $-\dfrac{1}{2} e^x \cos x + \dfrac{1}{2} e^x \sin x + C$

8 $x \cos^{-1}(2x) - \dfrac{1}{2}\sqrt{1 - 4x^2} + C$ **9** $\dfrac{1}{3} \tan^3 x - \tan x + x + C$

10 $-\cos x + \dfrac{1}{3} \cos^3 x + C$ **11** $\dfrac{1}{2} x + \dfrac{1}{4} \sin 2x + C$

12 $-\dfrac{\sqrt{9 - x^2}}{9x} + C$ **13** $\dfrac{x}{\sqrt{4 - x^2}} - \sin^{-1}\left(\dfrac{x}{2}\right) + C$

14 $\ln \left| \dfrac{x}{\sqrt{x^2 + 1}} \right| + C$ **15** $\ln|2\sqrt{x^2 - x + 1} + (2x - 1)| + C$

16 $-\dfrac{\sqrt{4 + x^2}}{4x} + C$ **17** $\dfrac{2}{5}(x + 1)^{5/2} - \dfrac{2}{3}(x + 1)^{3/2} + C$

18 $24\pi^2$ cubic units

19 $M_x = 63$ $\bar{x} \approx .8$
        $M_y = 15$ $\bar{y} \approx 3.5$

20 $\bar{x} = e - 1$
        $\bar{y} = \dfrac{1}{2}\left(1 - \dfrac{1}{e}\right)$

21 $\bar{x} = \dfrac{e}{e - 1}$